EVOLUTION'S
BLUNDERS, FRAUDS AND FORGERIES

How efforts to prove Darwinism have led to many blunders, frauds and outright forgeries

Jerry Bergman Ph.D.

ISBN: 978-1-942773-59-7

Cover design & interior layout: Tim Newcombe

First edition: October 2017
Second edition: December 2018

CREATION
BOOK PUBLISHERS

P.O. Box 350, Powder Springs, GA, 30127, USA
Phone: 1-800-616-1264
creationbookpublishers.com

For more information on creation/evolution
and the Christian worldview, go to:

CREATION.com

Acknowledgments

Those I am grateful to for their reviews of this manuscript include Jeff Tomkins, Ph.D., Alex Williams M.S., John Woodmorappe M.A., Bryce Gaudian, Malcolm Bowden, and Wayne Frair Ph.D. These reviewers provided valuable insight and feedback on earlier drafts of this book. I also want to thank Eric Blievernicht B.S., Clifford Lillo, M.A., Ted Siek Ph.D., John UpChurch, Bert Thompson Ph.D., Jody Allen, R.N., George Howe Ph.D., and two anonymous reviewers for their comments on various drafts of this book. The conclusions are mine and not necessarily those of my reviewers. I also wish to thank Dr Wayne Frair for his comments on an earlier draft of chapter 15 and for his excellent article on this topic.[1] Last, I am grateful for the help of Dr Don Batten, Steven Kinna and permission from Creation Research Society, Institute for Creation Research, and *Creation Ministries International* for permission to use sections of my previous publications.

1. Frair, W., Embryology and evolution, *Creation Research Society Quarterly* **36**(2):62–67, 1999.

Foreword by Carl Wieland

Ask the average person about evolution, and 'fraud' is far less likely to be the first association they would make than, say, the word 'science'. A few might know about the widely-publicized Piltdown Man fake, but even then, they would see it as more the exception than the rule; after all, evolution is 'science' and science is about facts, accuracy and truth. It is an ideologically neutral, self-correcting and inexorable march forwards to greater enlightenment (with perhaps the occasional misstep)—or so the story goes.

As always, things get a bit more complicated in the real world of fallible humans; and in any case, evolution has never primarily been about science. Even the leading anti-creationist philosopher (and self-proclaimed "*ardent evolutionist*") Michael Ruse recognized this when he wrote (National Post, May 13, 2000):

> Evolution is promoted by its practitioners as more than mere science. Evolution is promulgated as an ideology, a secular religion—a full-fledged alternative to Christianity, with meaning and morality. … Evolution is a religion. This was true of evolution in the beginning, and it is true of evolution still today. … [it] came into being as a kind of secular ideology, an explicit substitute for Christianity.

This should be no surprise, given that the stakes are so high. The evolution-creation debate deals with some of life's most important issues—such as, were we created and thus have purpose, or are we and all other living things a spontaneous effervescence of nature, destined for nothing nobler than organic manure?

This tour de force by Dr Bergman plunges head-first into this emotion-charged arena. It confirms Ruse's point 'in spades' by dealing with an amazing array of not just frauds and forgeries, but blunders and embarrassments of all types by evolution's practitioners and promoters. And—importantly—it reveals the way in which they were so readily accepted and believed by some of the biggest names in academia. Many of these examples will be unknown to most; a good number of facts were completely new to me, despite decades of familiarity with the literature in the debate.

The book will be a very significant eye-opener for all who read it. It relentlessly exposes things that most evolutionists would probably rather not discuss, or hope stay forgotten. Readers are free to draw their own conclusions as to what could possibly drive and motivate such a sorry parade, but it becomes blatantly obvious that 'science' is no longer a good answer.

Dr Carl Wieland M.B., B.S. is a former medical practitioner who founded *Creation* magazine in 1978, now with subscribers in over 110 countries. He was the Managing Director of *Creation Ministries International* in Australia from 1987 until retiring from this position in early 2015. He is the author of numerous articles and several books, including *One Human Family: The Bible, science, race and culture.*

Endorsements

Talk about a smorgasbord of intriguing revelations—this is it! When I completed reading a chapter, I was already anxious to savor the next one, and not to discontinue reading when other responsibilities beckoned. Each chapter is well documented with scholarly references. Dr Bergman is a prolific writer and speaker and the author of more than 1,000 publications including books and scientific papers. He has been a personal friend of mine for many years, and in an email he sent to me on 14 December 2012 he said: "*I hope this book will be the best one I have written so far.*" It may well be!

Wayne Frair, Ph.D.
Professor Emeritus of Biology, The King's College, New York.

Dr Bergman's earlier books on Darwinism have focused primarily on Darwin himself and the disastrous impact his ideas have had on the world. *Evolution's Blunders, Frauds and Forgeries* examines this pervasive philosophy from a different viewpoint, exploring some of the fakes, failures, falsifications and fictions that have mutilated the history of paleontology and turned countless young people away from their Creator.

Some of these accounts will be familiar to many readers, but the author has provided color and context that make them eye-opening. Others will probably be new to most, including his discussions of a mythical continent where a certain missing link was supposedly born, and truly horrific attempts at human/ape hybridization. In every case, he has done a masterful job of presenting the facts, in the process underscoring the wilful ignorance of this increasingly gullible world.

Major embarrassments to paleontology? You bet. But the truth will out; and with this book, Dr Bergman has given it a tremendous boost.

Kitty Foth-Regner,
Author of *Heaven Without Her.*

If you are a creationist and have a fascination to watch demolition crews implode buildings, this is the book for you. If you loathe the Bible record of creation, you will lose your appetite and your settled stomach only a few pages in. *Evolution's Blunders, Frauds, and Forgeries* is both enlightening and mind-boggling, a much-needed revelation of the shenanigans doctrinaire evolutionists have committed and continue to wield against truth and integrity in the science of origins. Chapter by chapter, we watch repeated head-on train-wreck collisions of the Darwinian fundamentalists, see the mangled pieces fly, then watch with grudging admiration as the Darwinian fraternity 'cleaners' show up and attempt to cleanse the site spic-and-span until the next trains are due. We owe a great debt of gratitude to Jerry Bergman that he has managed to gather enough of the scattered pieces so we can reconstruct much of the 'whos, whats, and hows'. This book needs to be in the hands of captains of scientific progress, encouraging more caution, diligence, and restraint and to know the difference between a red light and a green light. Now I am anxiously awaiting publication so I can reference from this trove of research Dr Bergman has delivered to us. My questions are two: (1) What can be done to get this book onto the required reading list for every history and philosophy of science class in the country? And, (2) Can we all send Jerry enough energy bars to see him through producing a sequel outing the walking-whales fraud and its quiet 'cleaning' and the scandalous acceptance of that fraud even by Christian university scholars and Biologos officials?

Dr Vern Bissell

Ph.D. in civil and hydraulic engineering.

This book will probably be ignored ... by Darwinists. The problem for Darwinists is that they have no coherent answers to the blunders, frauds, and forgeries Bergman describes in exquisite, well-documented detail. So, as is usual when Darwinists are challenged, they will either ignore the challenge or hurl irrelevant *ad hominem* attacks and then attempt to change the subject. If you haven't read Bergman's other books on the topic of Darwinism's problems, you are in for a real awakening—and if you have, then be assured that you will be reading more of Bergman at his best. Like a Ringmaster at the Darwinism Circus, Bergman announces each act and describes the dare-devilry, animal acts, and even the clowns. And be sure to stay for the final act (chapter)—it's definitely a Grand Finale. This would all be Grand Entertainment...if only the effects of Darwinism on humankind weren't so sad.

David Oberpriller

Until retirement a professor of computer science at Arizona Christian University.

Table of Contents

Introduction

The history of efforts to support Darwinism is rife with blunders, frauds, and forgeries. Because Darwin's theory of evolution—including the many attempts to improve it such as neo-Darwinism—is fundamentally wrong, we would expect to find the history of Darwinism littered with blunders, frauds, and forgeries that such a faulty hypothesis would, of necessity, produce. Do we find such a history? Yes we do! This brief review presents some of the more well-known and better documented cases. The cases reviewed in this book are not controversial—the evidence is clear: Darwinists were proven wrong by the evidence.

Selecting cases to review was very difficult because there are so many to select from, but those used here will give the reader a feel for the plethora of blunders, frauds, and forgeries in the history of Darwinism. Darwinism is the theory that simple molecules such as carbon dioxide and hydrogen eventually evolved into people, given enormous amounts of time, chance, the outworking of natural law, the accumulation of mutations, and natural selection. Evolutionists admit that many disagreements exist over many details of evolution, but they claim none exist over the fact of evolution. This book documents otherwise. Because evolution is more history than repeatable science, consequently much disagreement about the theory exists even among evolutionists themselves—though it is only permissible among the evolutionary establishment to question the details of evolution, never its reality.

Disproven ideas serve the evolution establishment

Like many other evolutionary icons, Haeckel's embryos (chapter 10), Piltdown Man (chapter 11), and the facial angle (chapter 6), although long disproven, were all vital in the early years of Darwinism to propagate evolutionism. Unfortunately, their falsification did not result in the demise of evolutionism. One reason is that this worldview had, by that time, gained widespread acceptance and was plastic enough to be able to abandon many of the major 'pillars' that originally established it in the public consciousness. Darwinian evolution was also important in justifying racism for generations, even after this justification was proven to be wrong.

Another key point of this book is to document the fact that the role played by illustrations and simple concepts was crucial in convincing the public and scientists of Darwinism's validity. This is obvious in the chapters on Haeckel's biogenetic law, the progression, and the facial angle. In contrast, the extraordinary complexity that cell biology research is turning up at the molecular level of biological 'evolution' is far too complex for most people to grasp without intensive study.

How science actually works

A scientist insider with a Ph.D. in quantum physics has exposed the less well-known side of scientific discovery, documenting the fact that scientists and the media have purposely obscured how science actually works. The scientific establishment typically paints an image of themselves as logical, level-headed, objective people searching for the truth. The fact is, as Professor Brooks carefully details, many scientists will often do almost anything—follow mystical visions, lie, take drugs, and even cheat—to make a breakthrough or maintain their position in their field. In short, the ends justify the means. In Brooks' words,

> scientists take drugs, they follow crazy dreams, they experiment on themselves and on one another, and occasionally they die in the process. They fight–sometimes physically, but mostly in intellectual battles. They try to entrap one another, standing in their colleagues' way to block progress and maintain the lead. They break all the rules of polite society, trampling on the sacred, showing a total disregard for authority.[2]

Furthermore, some scientists will even "*commit fraud or deceive or manipulate others*" and

> conjure up seemingly ridiculous ideas, then fight tooth and nail to show that the ideas are not only far from ridiculous, but exactly how things really are ... Science is peppered with successes that defy rational explanation, and failures that seem even more illogical. ...
>
> This is not the 'wacky' science, the crazy things that happen on the fringes of research. This is the mainstream. These anarchies are behind many of the Nobel Prizes of the last few decades ... It really does seem that, in science, anything goes.
>
> And this is no modern phenomenon. Science has always been this way.[3]

One of the rare senior scientists to have dared to expose these facts was British biologist and Nobel laureate Peter Medawar. Brooks, quoting Medawar, wrote that it is not rare for scientists to

> 'actively misrepresent' themselves. The famed scientific routine of deductions based on experiments that were themselves based on logical hypotheses 'are simply the postures we choose to be seen ... when the curtain goes up and

2. Brooks, M., *Free Radicals: The Secret Anarchy of Science*, The Overlook Press, New York, p. 6, 2011.
3. Brooks, *Free Radicals*, p. 6.

> the public sees us,' Medawar said, 'The illusion is shattered if we ask what goes on behind the scenes'.[4]

Brooks added that, in the end

> Science is civil war without the bloodshed. There are sieges, and there are bridges to be blown. There are people who must be removed: those who used to be heroes but are now complacent and ineffective must be forced aside for the good of the cause. But … some of this old guard still have arms and ammunition, and will fight to the very end. … many scientific anarchists know what it is to lose everything in the pursuit of discovery.[5]

Furthermore, for over half a century, "*scientists have been involved in a cover-up* [about how science actually works—Ed.] *that is arguably one of the most successful of modern times.*"[6] Both the creation and perpetuation of "*the myth of the rational, logical scientist who follows a clearly understood Scientific Method*" has affected everything in science, including

> the way it is done, the way we teach it, the way we fund it, its presentation in the media, the way its quality control structures—in particular, peer review—work (or don't work), the expectation we have of science's impact on society, and the way the public engages with science (and scientists with the public) and regards scientists' pronouncements as authoritative. We have been engaging with a caricature of science, not the real thing. But science is so vital to our future that it must now be set free from its branding. It is time to reveal science as the anarchic, creative, radical endeavour it has always been.[7]

Brooks then spends over 300 pages documenting what seem outrageous claims. Most of his observations are well known to those who have a good background in the history of science and regularly read biographies of scientists. The problem is: "*Science is a fight to the intellectual death, but not between equal adversaries. It takes place in a gladiatorial arena where the challenger has to overcome not only the established champion, but also his or (more rarely) her supporters. And, whether in attack or defense, the fight is rarely clean.*"[8]

Many scientists argue that, although it may take a millennium, errors in science eventually are corrected. German biologist Ernst Haeckel's fraudulent embryos, even though exposed over a century ago, are still published in many textbooks today

4. Brooks, *Free Radicals*, p. 5.
5. Brooks, *Free Radicals*, p. 193.
6. Brooks, *Free Radicals*, p. 2.
7. Brooks, *Free Radicals*, p. 2.
8. Brooks, *Free Radicals*, p. 214.

to support Darwinism.[9,10,11] Piltdown Man took almost half a century to be exposed, and decades more after that for the forgery to cease being used as proof of evolution. It was used to support Darwinism as late as 2000. And many other examples exist. This fact supports the wisdom of evaluating and criticizing even highly accepted theories, including those postulated years ago and rarely questioned since. Although the truth usually will come out, and the process of science eventually works, it is sometimes far slower than its supporters believe.

As I will document in the following chapters, this is especially true of those ideas promulgated to defend Darwinism. Brooks concludes that success in science is not at all like the common public stereotype, a problem covered in detail in several chapters of this book. This work does not cover many other issues, such as eugenics, nor the problems resulting from attempts to apply Darwinism to society, such as occurred in Nazi Germany, or in many communist countries. That topic will be covered in another work by the author. The chapters are written so that they stand alone, allowing readers to pick and choose chapters to read that interest them.

Charles Darwin's revolution

Charles Darwin's 1859 *Origin of Species* produced a revolution in human thinking more profound than anything before or since in science. The Copernican revolution in the sixteenth century had previously removed the earth from its privileged position at the centre of the universe, but the Darwinian revolution removed God from His privileged position as the Creator of all the different kinds of life, most notably humans. Darwin paid lip service to a Creator as a remote first cause, but once natural selection was widely adopted as being the sculptor of life's details then the question of life's origin became academic. Educated atheists abound today and their reasoning is purely Darwinian.

But Darwin never did displace God with science. His central claim—that all species on Earth are lineal descendants of one or a few originating forms of life—has always lacked a causal mechanism. Causes have been proposed, and then abandoned, right up to the present. The problem has never been the survival of the fittest but the arrival of the fittest. Leading evolutionists have openly admitted that nobody knows the source of genetic variety that natural selection can select from. In essence, as Professor Niles Eldredge implied, evolutionists must 'keep it simple' and 'keep it Darwinian even if it isn't' to convince the public of the validity of

---

9. Assmuth, J. and Hull, E., *Haeckel's Frauds and Forgeries,* P. J. Kenedy & Sons, New York, 1915.
10. Wells, J., *Icons of Evolution: Science or Myth*, Regnery, Washington, DC, Haeckel's Embryos, chapter 5, pp. 102–104, 2000.
11. Judson, H.F., *The Great Betrayal: Fraud in Science*, Harcourt, New York, pp. 82–83, 2004.

Darwinism.[12] The biggest scientific revolution in human history has turned out not to be scientific at all.

It is into this scientific vacuum of Darwin's own making—the lack of a causal mechanism—that true believers have laboured over the years to discover 'proofs' that evolution did occur, even if we don't know how. It is not surprising that a vacuous theory would produce faulty endeavours to find such proofs. And this is exactly what has occurred. In this book I have documented only a few of the many blunders, frauds, and forgeries that have been perpetrated in the name of Darwinian evolution. Individually they should be insignificant—nothing more than the failures which all scientists expect should litter the pathway in discovering genuine truths. But there is a more sinister side to this story. In the ongoing absence of genuine central truths, these blunders, frauds, and forgeries have become the museum pieces of Darwinian history. To the true believers they remain, like dusty idols in their temples of the mind, because there are no genuine truths to replace them. Without a genuine causal explanation, these untruths, like cobwebs moving in the wind, recall a vitality that never was.

12. Mazur, S., *The Altenberg 16: An Exposé of the Evolution Industry,* North Atlantic Books, Berkeley, California, p. 329, 2010.

CHAPTER 1

Darwin's blunder has been falsified: Evolution is true, but going backwards

Introduction

It should not surprise anyone that fraud is common in attempts to prove Darwinism because major problems have always existed, and still exist, in this worldview. The scientific method requires understanding that all scientific theories are provisional, open to modification or rejection by new scientific information and experiments. If the evidence warrants, all theories of science must be updated to reflect current knowledge and understanding. Many major scientific revolutions have resulted from new knowledge. The most famous example was Newtonian physics, which was overturned by Einsteinian physics at the turn of the last century. Darwin, though, displayed exactly the opposite approach to his theory, namely a dogmatic non-scientific attitude. Darwin

> knew that he was right, and that his being right meant that much else people wanted to believe was wrong. Design was just chance plus time, greed not a sin from the devil but an inheritance from the monkeys. "*Our descent, then, is the origin of our evil passions!!*" he had written in his notebook back in … 1838. "*The Devil under form of Baboon is our grandfather!*" Under the beard and beneath the sage wrinkles, he never lost the inner confidence reflected in those words, nor the urge to provocation, and found ways of getting them both expressed in his books.[1]

In other words, Darwin was "*what is now polemically called a Darwinian fundamentalist.*"[2] In addition, far

> from being a child prodigy, Darwin admits, "*I was considered by all my* [school] *masters and by my father as a very ordinary boy, rather below the common standard in intellect.*" He [Darwin] did, however, master the fine art of telling tall tales and spreading false rumors. Though morally disgusted by the failures of amateur con artists, he appreciated the talent of skilled

1. Gopnik, A., *Angels and Ages: A Short Book about Darwin, Lincoln, and Modern Life*, Alfred A. Knopf, New York, pp. 160–161, 2009.
2. Gopnik, *Angels and Ages*, p. 160.

> hoodwinkers—unless he himself was a victim. He takes considerable time in his *Autobiography* to describe several notorious scientific hoaxes, which interested him immensely, and chuckles at some of his own juvenile successes.[3]

Furthermore, "*his was the most fundamental and successful challenge to dogma* [of theism] *that had ever been launched—in a single generation, it caused intelligent people to accept claims about history and man's place in it that had been heretical for thousands of years.*"[4] The reason was that in his most important work, *The Origin of Species,*

> Darwin had said little about the origin of man except to hint that sexual selection might be important in the evolution of racial differences and to recognize that 'light will be thrown on the origin of man and his history'. But it was man's position in the world that interested his readers. The consequences for man—of Darwin's hypothesis—were clear. Man was no longer at the centre of the living world, a created being. He was not the product of a Divine Plan—evolution had no plan. No matter how tactful the author, Darwin's *Origin* shattered nineteenth-century man's belief in his traditional role.[5]

Ironically, in view of how revolutionary Darwin's theory was, "*its reception was … remarkably peaceable.*"[6] This could be partly because there existed only a few arguments to support the doctrine of evolution, and Darwin did what he could to document his view

> that natural selection was a plausible mechanism—not necessarily the best mechanism, but at least a plausible one, because he needed at least some mechanism that was better than Lamarck's theory, in order to have people buy his theory of evolution. His mechanism was natural selection.
>
> Darwin could not prove that the natural selection of random, inborn variations caused evolution. He could and did argue, however, that it could do so; not that it did do so, but that it could. What were his evidences and arguments for this [conclusion]? … his strongest one was artificial selection. Indeed, that is how he starts his book, and he spends much of his book on artificial selection.[7]

---

3. Houston, B., *Natural God: Deism in the Age of Intelligent Design*, New Deism Press, Florida, p. 124, 2012.
4. Gopnik, *Angels and Ages*, p. 161.
5. George, W., *Darwin*, Fontana Paperbacks, Glasgow, p. 65, 1982.
6. Gopnik, *Angels and Ages*, p. 161.
7. Larson, E.J., *The Theory of Evolution: A History of Controversy*, The Teaching Company, Chantilly, Virginia, p. 58, 2002.

Of course, artificial selection no more proves evolution by natural selection than the fact that humans have built computers proves that computers can evolve solely by natural means without intelligence.

Darwin's science substandard

After documenting that Darwin's work was often substandard, Paul Johnson asked, in view of the fact that Darwin was a wealthy man, why did he not hire qualified researchers to improve the quality of his research? Johnson noted that Darwin's income

> was periodically increased by his generous father and, despite a growing family, there were years in which a good half of it was saved and reinvested. It is curious to us that Darwin did not employ a clever young man as an assistant, preferably one with modern language skills who could have combed through the current scientific publications, especially those in German. He could well have afforded such help, and his failure to do so was to prove costly [to the validity of his conclusions—Ed].[8]

Professor Christine Nüsslein-Volhard added that

> Darwin's biggest limitation—as many have pointed out—was that he did not understand genetics; this worried him a great deal, and he tried hard to delineate "*laws of variation*", but he could not explain the origin of variation. He emphasizes, however, that sexual reproduction increases variation and fitness … it sometimes feels as if Darwin got close to Mendel's laws, but all was buried in a big mess of often contradictory reports about all sorts of crosses among wild and domesticated species … [which] clouded Darwin's view and made it impossible for him to see the clear rules that Mendel recognized through his elegant experimental system.[9]

We now know that domesticating animals by interbreeding actually decreases genetic variety in the domestic animal breed. Johnson notes that Darwin flunked out of medical school, and this may be part of the reason why "*he was always stronger on flora and fauna than on people*" when writing to defend his theory.[10]

8. Johnson, P., *Darwin: Portrait of a Genius,* Viking, New York, p. 60, 2012.
9. Nüsslein-Volhard, C., in: (Re)Reading the Origin, *Current Biology* **19**(3):R96–R104, 2009; p. R100.
10. Johnson, *Darwin*, p. 21.

Darwin forced to recant

In spite of Darwin's dogmatism, the problems with his theory were so overwhelming that he realized he had to deal with its many serious scientific flaws. His attempts failed, though, because his theory was factually flawed. Cambridge University professor Peter Vorzimmer wrote that

> the evolutionary writings of Charles Darwin … in the latter part of his life, when contrasted with the *Origin of Species* of 1859, indicate a considerable change in his evolutionary thought over the intervening years. … the overall change effected appears great and the resultant view nearly antithetical to that of the first edition of the *Origin*, … [and] such a radical change could not be looked upon merely as a modification of an earlier view, but as an adoption of a distinctly new one.[11]

Professor Liepman concurred, writing that comparison

> of the six editions of the 'Origin of Species' reveals a definite change in Darwin's propounded theory.

Although the tone of the statements seems to become more positive in later editions, the change of thought indicates a certain inability of the original theory to stand up to criticism.

> … in the last two editions non-selective forces come into play. … although all the factors had been presented in earlier editions the importance of their role had so shifted by the 6th edition that it is difficult not to conclude that the basic axioms of the theory had changed.[12]

In attempting to document his theory, Darwin eventually realized that there existed major "*problems with the theory of natural selection. Indeed, these problems were so profound that even Darwin and Wallace increasingly sought other evolutionary mechanisms to supplant natural selection.*"[13] Most notoriously, Darwin retreated back to the rejected Lamarckian theory of evolution, which postulated that biological

11. Vorzimmer, P., Charles Darwin and blending inheritance, *Isis* **54**(3):371–390, 1963; p. 371.
12. Liepman, H.P., The six editions of the 'Origin of Species', *Acta Biotheoretica* **30**(3):199–214, 1981; p. 199.
13. Larson, *The Theory of Evolution*, p. 83.

characteristics acquired during one's lifetime could be passed onto one's offspring.[14,15] Darwin first published his *Origin of Species* in 1859, but he was forced to keep revising it, thus one must

> look at the particular edition of *Origin of Species* to know what it says. He brought out … [six] editions of *Origin of Species* over the next 20 or so years after the publication of the original; all of them were a little different, and if you look back at the original, it is very Darwinian. It is the account of Darwinian evolution that we know today. If you read the last one, however, you would think that you were reading Lamarck. … It includes so many Lamarckian ideas. He changed his own ideas to meet these scientific objections. He still remains an evolutionist, but the mechanism changes in his own work.[16]

Even the term Darwin used for his theory evolved. Houston wrote that the

> term "*evolve,*" of course, means many things. It means change; it means grow up; it indicates macroevolution, and microevolution, and the current demand to distinguish between the two.

For Darwin, even the term itself evolved: In the first edition of *The Origin of Species* … published in 1859, he uses only forms of the word "*descent*" rather than "*evolution.*" Not until the sixth edition, published in 1872, does he use the word evolution.[17]

Darwin recognized that variation in life was central to the process of natural selection, however,

> Darwin could not explain its sources. Sharp criticism worsened the problem. Darwin, rather than leave his theory incomplete perhaps, ultimately appealed to external forces (use or disuse, or habit, say) in generating favorable variants. That seemed to echo Lamarck's earlier idea (now discredited) of the inheritance of acquired characters. Darwin also claimed that domestication itself increased the rate of variants.[18]

We now know that by domesticating animals, we actually *decrease* genetic variety in the domestic animal. Professor Allchin stated that many admirers of Darwin today are forced to wonder

14. Allchin, D., Celebrating Darwin's errors, *The American Biology Teacher* **71**(2):116–119, 2009; p. 116.
15. Ghiselin, M., *The Triumph of the Darwinian Method*, The University of California Press, Berkeley, pp.162–163, 181–186, 1969.
16. Larson, *The Theory of Evolution*, p. 83.
17. Houston, *Natural God*, p. 124.
18. Allchin, Celebrating Darwin's errors, p. 116.

> How could The Great Darwin have succumbed to such nonsense? Indeed, modern portrayals of Darwin often treat this politely as a blemish or mild embarassment [*sic*]. They tend to "*excuse*" it as a product of the times. (What idea is not a product of its time?)—Or they downplay Darwin's level of commitment, implying that he didn't *really* believe it [his mechanism required for natural selection to select from—Ed].[19]

Furthermore, there is a belief about Darwin that still persists to this day, namely that "*Darwin was a diffident and circumspect observer of animals, not a confident theorist of life.*" Darwin biographer Adam Gopnik responded to this claim by noting that

> Darwin was humble and modest in exactly the way that Lieutenant Columbo is humble and modest. He knows from the beginning who the guilty party is, and what the truth is, and would rather let the bad guys hang themselves from arrogance and overconfidence while he walks around in his raincoat, scratching his head …[20]

The fact is researchers today are "*still not agreed on whether natural selection is the dominant driver of genetic change at the molecular level*" and "*rather than enhancing fitness, natural selection can generate a redundant accumulation of molecular 'defences', such as systems that detect folding problems in proteins. At best, this is burdensome. At worst, it can be catastrophic. In short, the current picture of how and where evolution operates, and how this shapes genomes, is something of a mess.*"[21]

Darwin was also devious in converting the world to his worldview. His "*strategy was one of the greatest successes in the history of rhetoric, so much so that we are scarcely now aware that it was a strategy,*" and it was so successful that "*it immediately inserted him into the Victorian pantheon*" of great scientists and eminent persons.[22] One 'fact' that Darwin observed was influenced by his racist misperception of humans, namely his incorrect belief that "*the gap between savages and civilized men was greater than that between wild and domesticated animals. He* [concluded] … *that evolution had occurred. What he wanted to discover was why it had occurred, as a prelude to finding out how it had occurred.*"[23]

It was not finches, but humans, that were critical in motivating Darwin to develop his theory of evolution. The fact is, Darwinism caught on in spite of its many major and lethal scientific flaws. Today, among scientists it is dogma that is supported by the universities and the courts.

---

19. Allchin, Celebrating Darwin's errors, p. 116.
20. Gopnik, *Angels and Ages*, p. 160.
21. Ball, P., Celebrate the unknowns, *Nature* **496**(7446):419–420, 2013; p. 420.
22. Gopnik, *Angels and Ages*, p. 160.
23. Johnson, *Darwin*, pp. 42–43.

Evolution of man's mind

A central problem that Darwin faced was "*how could the human mind evolve?*" He knew from his theological training at Cambridge University that

> Christianity had attributed these attributes to divinely created souls, in that we all have souls that were created by God, and that the existence of these souls, which only humans have, fundamentally divide [*sic*] humans from other animals. Scientists had generally bought this view. … all the way back to Aristotle … where, in ancient Greece, Aristotle posited that only humans have actual souls, and that they divide humans, fundamentally, from all different animals. Darwin had equivocated on this matter in *Origin of Species*, but he announced his support for, and threw his entire weight behind, origins for humans from simian ancestors in his 1871 book … *The Descent of Man*.[24,25]

In this book Darwin "*looked at the two main differences that scientists and people in general thought divided humans from other animals: the mind, in that humans' minds are fundamentally different than animals' minds, and moral behavior, moral attributes are different.*"[26] Larson added that, for this reason, "*The Descent of Man is pretty tough to read today*" because Darwin

> tried to downplay the differences between the human mind and the animal mind. He did this systematically throughout his book by exaggerating the human-like qualities of animals: their intelligence, their emotions, their ability to communicate … far above what scientists would accept today. He also downplays the mental attributes of some humans. Consequently, he takes the "*lower forms of humans,*" as he describes the Australian aborigines, for instance, and makes them almost apelike, almost like primates in his description. He has a hierarchy of humans.[27]

Houston added that the arguments in his 1871 *The Descent of Man* book were very speculative, thus this book was "*not nearly as credible as Origin of Species*", and if one reads the *Descent of Man* one can think of a million explanations as to why it doesn't work. It's filled with "*just so*" stories that could be, but really seem like idle speculations.

> Even some of Darwin's most loyal supporters could not buy these arguments. Charles Lyell, and even Alfred Russel Wallace, did not buy human

24. Darwin, C., *The Descent of Man*, John Murray, London, 1871.
25. Larson, *The Theory of Evolution*, p. 64.
26. Larson, *The Theory of Evolution*, p. 65
27. Larson, *The Theory of Evolution*, p. 65.

> evolution. They thought that the human mind and moral attributes were simply too different from animals; that they could not have evolved in a step-by-step process.[28]

To make these arguments, Darwin "*appealed heavily to Lamarckian mechanisms.*" In fact

> Darwin became more of a Lamarckian over time. In later editions of even *Origin of Species*, as certainly is true of *Descent of Man*, you almost think you're reading Lamarck … . This is because it's easy to show how some things like love, and moral attributes develop as acquired characteristics. We love our offspring, and so they have more love. Rather than through the "*survival of the fittest*" or a natural selection process of acquired characteristics, we see more of these ideas worked into his book.[29]

Several Darwin scholars have concluded that his evolution theory was less the result of science than a projection of Darwin's own personality into nature. Beth Houston wrote that throughout

> his life, Darwin had a passion for three things: collecting (his obsession being beetles), dissecting, and hunting—especially hunting, or shooting, as the Brits call it.
>
> It should not be surprising that Darwin supported a scientific theory established on the principle of kill or be killed (the phrase itself coined by economist Herbert Spencer), being himself a person who enjoyed the pleasure of killing for its own sake, collecting life forms for the pleasure of displaying conquest and perfecting his own superiority, and dissecting to objectify life for the satisfaction of voyeuristic perusal.[30]

Although lionized today, Darwin's theory has caused much harm and, after 150 years, the evidence is still as problematic now as it was then, actually more so due to the advancement of scientific knowledge, especially cell biology and genetics. Darwin himself recognized that his theory had major problems, and for this reason he kept revising his evolution bible until the last edition ended up being significantly different from his first edition.

The simple fact is, from all we know about physics, chemistry and biology, evolution—defined as the upward progression from simple molecules, such as carbon, oxygen, hydrogen and water, to humans—never could have happened and never did happen.

---

28. Larson, *The Theory of Evolution*, p. 66.
29. Larson, *The Theory of Evolution*, p. 66.
30. Houston, *Natural God*, p. 128.

Survival of the fittest and arrival of the fittest

It is obvious that life more fit to survive will be more likely to survive. The problem with evolution has never been the survival of the fittest, but the arrival of the fittest, and today this is still by far the most serious problem with Darwinism. The main theory of the source of phenotypic variations for natural selection to select from is mutations. Professor Richard Mayer wrote that

> evolution by natural selection … is not predetermined. It is heavily dependent on the variations to be found between members of the species. All variations between species and between individual members of species can ultimately be sourced to random mutations. In effect, whenever a mutation occurs, it is checked for effectiveness with effective mutations leaving more offspring and ineffective mutations leaving fewer or even no offspring.[31]

The late Harvard Professor, Ernest Mayr, wrote that "*Ultimately, all variation is due to mutation.*" [32] Professor Theodosius Dobzhansky wrote "*mutation is the only known source of the raw materials … and hence of evolution*"[33] and much later he wrote with a co-author, Professor Ayala, that mutation is "*the source of the raw materials for evolutionary changes … without mutation all evolution would eventually stop.*"[34]

Evolution true, but going the wrong way

The research has shown that beneficial mutations are exceedingly rare, and near-neutral and deleterious mutations far more common. The best evidence of this is the well-known long-term evolution experiments by Lenski *et al.* They first estimated that only one mutation in a billion was beneficial.[35,36] In a recent *Science* overview article,[37,38] Lenski reports that he has cultured around 10^{14} cells, and in *E.coli* he

31. Mayer, R.E., *The Cambridge Handbook of Multimedia Learning*, Cambridge University Press, New York, p. 23, 2005.
32. Mayr, E., in Moorehead, P.S. and Kaplan, M.M. (Eds), *Mathematical Challenges to the Neo-Darwinian Interpretation of Evolution*, Wistar, Philadelphia, 1967.
33. Dobzhansky, T., On methods of evolutionary biology and anthropology, *American Scientist* **45**(5):381–392, 1957; p. 385.
34. Ayala, F.J. and Dobzhansky, T., *Studies in the Philosophy of Biology: Reduction and Related Problems*, University of California Press, p. 315, 1974.
35. Elena, S., Ekunwe, L., Hajela, N., Oden, S., and Lenski, R., Distribution of fitness effects caused by random insertion mutations in *E.Coli.*, *Genetica* **102/103**:349–358, 1998; p. 356.
36. Gerrish, P.J and Lenski, R., The fate of competing beneficial mutations in an asexual population, *Genetica* 102/103(1–6):127–44, 1998.
37. Pennisi, E., The man who bottled evolution, *Science* **342**:790–793, 2013.
38. Wiser, M. J., Ribeck, N., and Lenski, R. E., Long Term Dynamics of Adaptation in Asexual Populations, *Science* **342**:1364–1367, 2013.

found about one mutation per 1,000 cells, which means that roughly 10^{11} mutations—about 100 billion—are present in his sample. Of these, only a few were measurably beneficial. Being generous, there were 1,000 beneficial mutations in 100 million, and the overwhelming majority of the 'beneficials' were 'loss-of-function' mutations. Thus, the vast majority of mutations, over 99%, are either near-neutral, mildly deleterious, or clearly harmful. Some years ago it was discovered that human DNA has a high mutation rate and is deteriorating at an alarming rate.[39] The result is a steady accumulation of damage to the genome, eventually causing genetic catastrophe, then mutational meltdown and species extinction. As Lynch and Blanchard wrote:

> It is well established on theoretical grounds that the accumulation of mildly deleterious mutations in nonrecombining [This appears to be a correct usage in context—Ed.] genomes is a major extinction risk in obligately asexual populations. Sexual populations can also incur mutational deterioration in genomic regions that experience little or no recombination, i.e., autosomal regions near centromeres, Y chromosomes, and organelle genomes.[40]

In each new generation of humans an estimated 100 to 200 new mutations are added to the average child and eventually, if the child survives to become an adult and has offspring, most of these mutations are added to the human gene pool.[41] Professor Michael Lynch *et al.* wrote that "*a parent … can never produce an offspring with fewer deleterious mutations than it carries itself.*"[42] The number of new harmful mutations varies, but they always increase and never decrease. Darwin was correct when he titled his 1871 book *The Descent of Man* and not *The Ascent of Man,* which, incidentally, was the title of evolutionist Jacob Bronowski's book on human evolution. The fact is, we are descending genetically as the Christian Scriptures teach, a result of the fall of humankind from the original perfection when sin entered the world, and not ascending upward biologically, as evolutionism claims. For this reason evolution is true, but is going the wrong way, as Judaism and Christianity have taught since almost the beginning of humankind's sojourn on Earth.

---

39. Beardsley, T., Mutations galore: humans have high mutation rates. But why worry? *Scientific American* **280**(4):32, 36, 1999.
40. Lynch, M. and Blanchard, J.L., Deleterious mutation accumulation in organelle genomes, *Genetica* **102/103**:29–39, 1998; p. 29.
41. Meisenberg, G. and Simmons, W., *Principles of Medical Biochemistry*, Mosby, Philadelphia, p. 153, 2006.
42. Lynch, M., Conery, J. and Burger, R., Mutational meltdowns in sexual populations, *Evolution* **49**(6):1067–1080, 1995; p. 1067.

A history of macromutation theory failure

Lamarckianism remained strong long after Darwin died, especially among paleontologists. It was strongest around 1900 when Dutch botanist Professor Hugo de Vries (1848–1935) proposed "*mutation theory as a plausible … explanation for the evolution of species.*" The problem was

> Classical Darwinism seemed discredited, because it had no mechanism for preserving variations. … Lamarckianism was discredited by the work of August Weissmann. What was the alternative? Biologists all over Europe and America were scrabbling to try to come up with some answer. If you read scientific papers from this period, you'll just see them struggling with what possibly could be the cause of variation and inheritance, and therefore, evolution. … "*We believe in evolution, but we really don't have a clue of what mechanism is plausible.*"[43]

Therefore de Vries "*came up with a possible solution, and that was 'mutation' theory*" which also had "*its problems*" but in the 1900s every evolution theory had its problems. People were looking for alternatives.

> … De Vries proposed a rather radical solution. He proposed that mutations … would create a big "*jump;*" … not slightly better talons, but dramatically better talons, dramatically changed eyes; dramatic changes.

That was implausible enough, but then he added that they would be widespread enough to happen throughout a population, or at least a significant minority in a population.[44]

The result was that the "*affected population would almost abruptly form a … new variety of species.*" These seem like broad claims, and they were. To him, natural selection still existed, but it really wasn't central. For him, it operated mostly to preserve beneficial mutations. Larson writes:

> Interest soon passed [lapsed—Ed.] among scientists.[45]

De Vries first demonstrated from his research on the evening primrose that dramatic new varieties and traits can arise suddenly and without explanation.[46] He and others believed that the explanation for the new traits was macromutations, which

43. Larson, *The Theory of Evolution*, pp. 108–109.
44. Larson, *The Theory of Evolution*, p. 109.
45. Larson, *The Theory of Evolution*, p. 109.
46. De Vries, H., *The Mutation Theory: Experiments and Observations on the Origin of Species in the Vegetable Kingdom, Vol. 2, The Origin of Varieties by Mutation*, The Open Court Publishing Company, Chicago, 1910.

finally gave evolutionists a mechanism for producing new genetic traits in plants and animals.

Further research revealed that de Vries' results were not due to mutations, but rather were a result of the fact that the evening primrose has an unequal chromosome number that caused hybrid plants to *appear* to produce new varieties. In fact, a rearrangement of existing genetic variation was the cause of the plant's new physical appearance, not mutations as de Vries postulated. Larson noted: "*It created an initial stir in mutation theory, but within half a generation, interest in mutation theory had pretty well passed. It left a legacy and influence, however.*"[47]

An evening white primrose, the plant that de Vries used for his research on mutations.

Early opposition to mutation theory

The opposition to the mutation theory as the origin of variation for natural selection to select from has a long and complex history. As early as 1925, Harvard University Biology Professor Edward Jeffrey recognized that mutations could not be a significant source of new genetic varieties. He wrote that for

> two decades the hypothesis of mutation or the saltatory origin of species has enjoyed a large vogue in American biological laboratories. … first formulated … as the result of the investigations of the Dutch physiologist, De Vries, on Lamarck's evening primrose, *Oenothera lamarckiana*. In this

47. Larson, *The Theory of Evolution*, pp. 109–110.

> species De Vries … observed the appearance of a relatively small number of [new] forms from seed, which differed in marked degree from the parent species.[48]

Jeffrey carefully researched this example, finding that the variety produced was not due to mutations or "*saltatory*" evolutionary jumps as de Vries proposed, but rather it is now "*conceded, even by geneticists and physiologists, that the species of the genus Oenothera often present strong evidence of hybrid origin, and the mutability frequently found in their offspring receives its obvious explanation as the result of previous crossing.*"[49]

Jeffrey added that "*It has since become increasingly obvious … that large numbers of species of plants are of hybrid origin and that these hybrid species, as well as known hybrids, give rise to phenomena … exactly similar to those found in Oenothera and Drosophila.*"[50] Jeffrey concluded from examining several hundred divisions of the *D. melanogaster* spermatocytes that the

> all-important reduction divisions of *D. melanogaster* … present the identical peculiarities of those observed in known hybrids. The cytological investigation of *Drosophila melanogaster* seems accordingly to establish beyond any reasonable doubt that the species is of hybrid origin.[51]

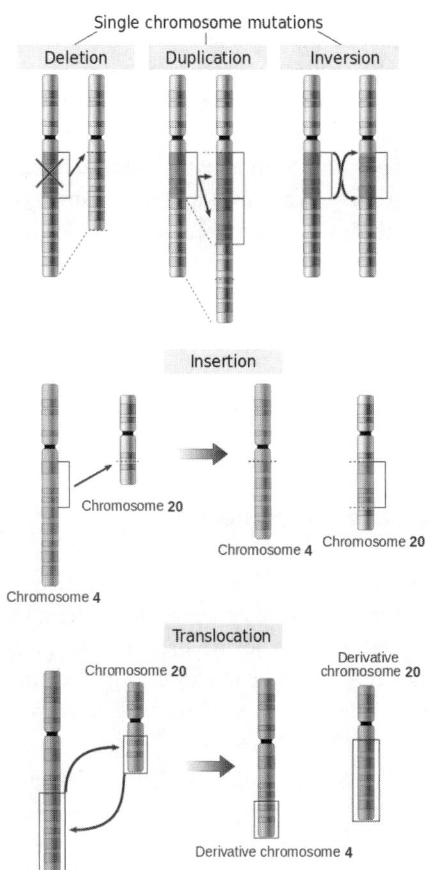

Illustrations of five basic types of chromosomal DNA mutations.

48. Jeffrey, E.C., Drosophila and the mutation hypothesis, *Science* **62**(1592):3–5, 1925; p. 3.
49. Jeffrey, Drosophila and the mutation hypothesis, p. 4.
50. Jeffrey, Drosophila and the mutation hypothesis, pp. 4–5.
51. Jeffrey, Drosophila and the mutation hypothesis, p. 5.

Thus, neither case was an example of new species due to mutations, but simply common hybrids of existing species. Jeffery concluded in 1925 that the mutation theory is dead, and in the future this theory would be an embarrassment to science:

> The Morgan hypothesis of mutation ... runs counter to practically all the inductive conclusions of the biological sciences. ... science appears to warrant no expectation of long life for the mutation hypothesis. It is, moreover, inconceivable that a science ... should itself progress by ... the subversion of the fundamentals of the biological sciences. It is in fact not impossible that before many years have elapsed the doctrine of mutation will appear to the eyes of men a fantastic Fata Morgana.[52]

Unfortunately, Jeffrey's prediction about the demise of the mutation doctrine has not yet come true after almost 100 years of new research has verified that his conclusions were fully valid. This is despite the now overwhelming evidence that mutations did not, and cannot, evolve simple organic compounds into people. Evolution by mutations is accepted in spite of (or perhaps because of?) the fact that no other hypothesis has been able to replace the mutation theory.

Hopeful monsters

The macromutations theory was briefly resurrected in the 1940s by University of California, Berkeley, geneticist Richard Goldschmidt. Goldschmidt concluded that the origin of major new animal and plant types was due to single mutations that caused large and complex changes, which happened to produce more successful lifeforms than those without these new macromutations. Such creatures Goldschmidt called "*hopeful monsters*".

Research has now confirmed that large mutations do not produce hopeful monsters but hopeless monsters as a result of causing major genetic damage. Since then no satisfactory mechanism to produce progressive upward 'molecules to human' evolution by macromutations has been proposed by modern neo-Darwinists.

The fact is, as Darwin's son, Leonard Darwin, wrote, "*how it* [evolution] *came about is still a matter of dispute and is likely to remain so for some time.*"[53] Jeffrey is correct and Leonard Darwin's conclusion still is fully valid today.

The Altenberg Conference

Presentations at the famous Altenberg 16 Conference by 16 of the world's leading evolutionists admitted that "*the theory of evolution which most biologists accept and*

52. Jeffrey, Drosophila and the mutation hypothesis, p. 5.
53. Quoted in Miller, A.M., Evolution and education in the Tennessee trial, *Science* **62**(1594):43–45, 1925; p. 43.

which is taught in the classrooms today, is inadequate in explaining our existence."[54] An Altenberg 16 attendee, evolutionist Dr Jerry Fodor, added, "*I don't think anybody knows how evolution works.*"[55]

Stanford University biophysicist Howard Pattee, referring to natural selection and chemical evolution, wrote that evolution could not have begun from random molecules or DNA sequences because evolution, then and now, teaches that natural selection can only start from "*well-ordered*" sequences. In his words:

> The origin of the degree and type of order found in biological macromolecules is not adequately explained solely as an accumulation of genetic restrictions acquired through natural selection ... since the biological process of replication is itself dependent on the pre-existence of such order, and since the number of sequences that could ever have been tested by selection on the earth is an insignificant fraction of the number of unrestricted sequences which would be possible. Therefore the hypothesis is considered that replication and selection began from well-ordered sequences, rather than random sequences.[56]

The main mechanism for producing genetic variety required for evolution, random mutation, has been falsified, as have all of the other mechanisms postulated to cause macro-evolution.

The more rational evolutionists have known for years that neo-Darwinism cannot work, but have been reluctant to openly say so. It is becoming increasingly difficult for them to suggest a mechanism for evolution that would not imply, or point to, intelligent design. Mutations have failed as a source of genetic variation used to produce phenotypic variation and, as discussed, this fact was known as early as 1925. In 2012 the distinguished Professor of Biological Sciences, Austin Hughes, wrote that of

> all the fads and foibles in the long history of human credulity, scientism in all its varied guises—from fanciful cosmology to evolutionary epistemology and ethics—seems among the more dangerous, both because it pretends to be something very different from what it really is and because it has been accorded widespread and uncritical adherence. Continued insistence on the universal competence of science will serve only to undermine the credibility of science as a whole. The ultimate outcome will be an increase of radical skepticism that questions the ability of science to address even the

54. Quoted in Mazur, *The Altenberg 16*, p. 19.
55. Quoted in Mazur, *The Altenberg 16*, p. 34.
56. Pattee, H.H., On the origin of macromolecular sequences, *Journal of Biophysics* **1**(8):683–710, 1961; p. 683.

> questions legitimately within its sphere of competence. One longs for a new Enlightenment to puncture the pretensions of this latest superstition.[57]

A conversation recounted by Victoria University adjunct biology professor John Ashton summarized the modern state of affairs. He wrote that, while sitting around the lunch table with his colleagues, he

> asked the research scientist in charge of the plant-breeding project a question. "*Do mutations ever give rise to new purposeful genetic information?*"
>
> His answer was immediate. "*Of course—yes!*"
>
> "*Can you give me an example?*" I then asked.
>
> He thought for a moment and replied along the lines of "*Um, I can't think of a specific example right now but ask our geneticist … he will be able to.*"
>
> Later that afternoon I caught up with the senior genetics researcher in the university plant-breeding department and asked him the same question.
>
> His reply was just as quick, but the very opposite! "*Never!*"
>
> Surprised, I pressed him further. He explained that mutations always lead to damaged DNA, which usually results in the *loss* of genetic information. He knew of *no* instances where new purposeful genetic information arose, either by a natural process or through a mutation induced chemically or with radiation.[58]

The problem with extrapolating microevolution to macroevolution

We now know that far more than a few mutations are required to produce the changes required to evolve a new animal order—actually many hundreds or thousands would usually be required. Many evolutionists today postulate that a large number of very small mutations, and not the macromutations that de Vries and Goldschmidt postulated, can account for macroevolution. This conclusion is not based on experimental evidence, but on the assumption that the evidence for microevolution (which creationists call variation within the Genesis kinds) can be extrapolated to macroevolution.

---

57. Hughes, A.L., The folly of scientism, *The New Atlantis; Journal of Technology & Society* **37**:32–50, 2012; p. 50.
58. Ashton, J., *Evolution Impossible: 12 Reasons Why Evolution Cannot Explain the Origin of Life on Earth*, Master Books, Green Forest, Arkansas, pp. 15–16, 2012.

The empirical evidence, however, is clear—neither macromutations nor micromutations can provide a significant source of new genetic information. The fact is: "*Mutation accumulation does not lead to new species or even to new organs or new tissues.*"[59]

What mutations eventually lead to is sickness and death because, as noted, the vast majority, over 99.99%, are near-neutral or harmful. Professor Lynn Margulis, while president of Sigma Xi, the honour society for scientists, added that "*many biologists claim they know for sure that random mutation (purposeless chance) is the source of inherited variation that generates new species of life .... 'No!' I say.*"[60] The question now often asked is, due to "*Contamination of the genome by very slightly deleterious mutations: Why have we not died 100 times over?*"[61]

Both creationists and Intelligent Design advocates conclude that the only plausible source of genetic information is intelligence. Because, of the estimated 100–200 new mutations that are added to the offspring compared to the parents, 99.99% are near-neutral or harmful, Intelligent Design postulates only an intelligent source of genetic information can explain what exists in the natural world. Creationists conclude the source is an Intelligent Creator we call God.

In contrast to the facts, the contemporary evolutionary theory involves primarily the accumulation of genetic mistakes called mutations that are selected by natural selection. They believe that, in essence, the evolution of humans from molecules such as carbon, hydrogen, water, and nitrogen occurred by the accumulation of DNA copying mistakes and mutations. Thus, humans are the result of the accumulation of many billions of mistakes. As noted, the problem has always been that the vast majority of mutations are near-neutral or harmful, even lethal, causing disease, including cancer and about 5,000 other diseases.

One study of 15,336 genes from 6,515 individuals concluded that, given Darwinistic assumptions, 73% of the protein-coding single nucleotide variants and about 86% of those predicted to be deleterious were believed to have arisen in the past 5,000 to 10,000 years.[62] Thus, the human genome is rapidly accumulating deleterious mutations and this has a "*profound effect*" on increasing the burden of deleterious single nucleotide variants in humans.[63]

59. Margulis, L. and Sagan, D., *Acquiring genomes: A theory of the origins of species*, Basic Books, New York, p. 11, 2002.
60. Margulis, L., The phylogenetic tree topples, *American Scientist* **94**(3):194, 2006.
61. Kondrashov, A.S., Contamination of the genome by very slightly deleterious mutations: why have we not died 100 times over? *Journal of Theoretical Biology* **175**:(4):583–594, 1995.
62. Fu, W., *et al.*, NHLBI Exome Sequencing Project, and Akey, J.M., Analysis of 6,515 exomes reveals the recent origin of most human protein-coding variants, *Nature* **493**(7431):216–220, 2013; p. 216.
63. Fu *et al.*, Analysis of 6,515 exomes reveals the recent origin of most human protein-coding variants, p. 216.

Conclusions

Although lionized today, Darwin's theory, as this book documents, has caused much harm and, after 150 years, the evidence for evolution is far more problematic now than it was in Darwin's time due to the advancement of knowledge in science, especially cell biology and genetics. Darwin himself recognized that his theory had major problems and for this reason he kept revising his bible of evolution until the last edition ended up significantly different than his first edition. The blunders, frauds, and forgeries documented in this book are not surprising in view of the fact that Darwin's major thesis is scientifically wrong.

Evolution is 'true', but the clear trend shows it is going the wrong way. The problem is that the vast majority of mutations are near-neutral, i.e. mildly deleterious, and most of the rest are harmful, even lethal. Life is gradually accumulating these deleterious mutations and is facing genetic catastrophe (mutational meltdown), eventually causing extinction. The fact is, never did a

> mutation make a wing, a fruit, a woody stem, or a claw appear. Mutations, in summary, tend to induce sickness, death, or deficiencies. No evidence in the vast literature of heredity change shows unambiguous evidence that random mutation itself, even with geographical isolation of populations, leads to speciation.[64]

Over 5,000 genetic diseases are now known and the number is growing for several reasons, one of which is the accumulation of deleterious mutations. As Ashton wrote, "*What we observe in research laboratories today is DNA slowly deteriorating, not new DNA evolving. This means we actually observe the very opposite of evolution.*"[65] The evidence is clear: evolution is true, but it is going backward.

---

64. Margulis and Sagan, *Acquiring genomes*, p. 29.
65. Ashton, *Evolution Impossible*, p. 132.

CHAPTER 2

The pervasive problem of fraud and forgery in paleoanthropology

Introduction

A review of the history of paleoanthropology, the study of the physical evidence for the evolution of humans, leads to the conclusion that this discipline is far less objective than is the case for most other sciences. In fact, the field is rife with controversy and fraud. Several well-documented examples are cited in some detail to illustrate the types of problems encountered, and also the results of fraud in paleoanthropology.

The interpretation of fossil evidence has been a problem from the beginning of paleoanthropology, as illustrated by these two people arguing over a few scraps of bone.

Extensive historical research has documented the fact that the scientific investigation of human origins is highly subjective—and bias, fraud, and even forgery are common.[1] The best known examples include Piltdown Man, which has been proven to be a composite of a human skull and an ape jaw (see chapter 11) and Nebraska Man (*Hesperopithecus)*, which turned out to be a pig's tooth (see chapter 12), but many other major examples exist.

The scientists involved in these controversies include many of those who have dominated the field of paleoanthropology in the twentieth century. The effects of their fraud can be far reaching and may affect entire disciplines.[2, 3] Even well-known modern paleoanthropology leaders, including the Leakey family (especially Louis, Mary, and Richard Leakey), have been involved in much controversy, including accusations of misrepresentation, sloppy work, and poor documentation.

---

1. Judson, H.F., *The Great Betrayal: Fraud in Science*, Harcourt, New York, pp. 82–83, 2004.
2. Feder, K.L., *Frauds, Myths, and Mysteries: Science and Pseudoscience in Archaeology*, 6th edition, McGraw Hill, 2008.
3. Kohn, A., *False Prophets: Fraud and Error in Science and Medicine*, Basil Blackwell Ltd, New York, 1988.

Sides are taken in these conflicts and, as Morell[4] eloquently documents, the participants sometimes end up in altercations not unlike those fought between nations—where unethical behavior, and almost everything else, is fair game.[5] Only physical aggression is normally ruled out, though even that sometimes occurs.

Craig Childs noted that so high are the personal stakes—prestige, money, honours, and academic awards—that, he claims, not only paleoanthropology but the fields involving human archaeological artifacts as well, are rife with suicide, murder attempts, and hired hit men.[6] He writes that in

> no other field of research have I encountered so many people who have wanted the other party dead. At one point I interviewed an antiquities broker...and a few days later heard a rumor he had put a price on the head of a troublesome foreign journalist. Another man, a pothunter now in prison, explained to an undercover agent that you should always go into the field well-armed—and if law enforcement pays a visit to your digging operation, you "*drop 'em...and never come back.*"[7]

He added that, while

> reporting on a federal raid on looters in the Southwest, a friend sent me a note warning me to watch my back, saying the illicit artifact community was out for blood. You don't get this kind of talk from geologists or stamp collectors.[8]

Childs cites three cases where professional problems motivated suicide, and a "*string of deaths*" (p. 93). He also documents a case where one woman (Roxanna Brown, PhD from UCLA, a prominent authority on Southeast Asian ceramics and director of the Bangkok University's Southeast Asian Ceramics Museum) was jailed for her involvement in the artifact community. The report said she died in jail, under very questionable circumstances, from "*choking on her own fluids*".[9]

Her son sued for wrongful death and settled for $880,000 in July 2009.[10]

---

4. Morell, V., *Ancestral Passions: The Leakey Family and the Quest for Humankind's Beginnings*, Simon and Schuster, New York, 1995. See chapter 15, Murder and Mayhem pp. 210–224 and pp. 477–481.
5. Brooks, M., *Free Radicals: The Secret Anarchy of Science*, The Overlook Press, New York, p. 193, 2011.
6. Childs, C., *Finders Keepers: A Tale of Archaeological Plunder and Obsession*, Little, Brown and Company, New York, 2010; p. 24.
7. Childs, *Finders Keepers*, p. 6.
8. Childs, *Finders Keepers*, p. 6.
9. Childs, *Finders Keepers*, pp. 92–93, 116.
10. Carter, M., U.S. pays $880,000 in death of detained antiquities expert, *The Seattle Times,* July 7, 2009

Paleoanthropology is an especially contentious field for reasons including the strong human interest in our origins. In addition, "*because conclusions of emotional significance … must be drawn from extremely paltry evidence, it is often difficult to separate the personal from the scientific in disputes raging within the field.*"[11] Fix noted that one critical reason for the conflicts is that the human fossil record is still so sparse

> that those who insist on positive declarations can do nothing more than jump from one hazardous surmise to another and hope that the next dramatic discovery does not make them utter fools. … Clearly, some people refuse to learn from this. As we have seen, there are numerous scientists and popularizers today who have the temerity to tell us that there is "*no doubt*" how man originated. If only they had the evidence.[12]

Reminiscent of the issues of personality conflicts in paleoanthropology, Oxford professor Bryan Sykes commented that:

> The whole debate about the timing and origin of the first Americans has the familiar feel of a stagnant intellectual circus, still balanced between entrenched academic foes who will never agree. This, I have realised over the years, is the natural equilibrium that sets in when a field has reached an impasse and where the rigid stance of personalities and their fiefdoms, rather than evidence, has become the deciding factor in an argument. Although this statement is the antipathy of science as a branch of philosophy, where evidence alone is king, it is surprisingly widespread. When a field stagnates like this, the cycle can only be broken by a completely independent kind of evidence.[13]

Another major reason for the numerous controversies in paleoanthropology is that

> paleoanthropology is a field in which the students far outnumber the objects of study. There are lively—and sometimes acrimonious—debates about whether a given fossil is really something new, or merely a variant of an already named species. These arguments about scientific names often mean very little. Whether a humanlike fossil is named as one species or another can turn on matters as small as half a millimeter in the diameter of a tooth, or slight differences in the shape of the thighbone. The problem is that there are simply too few specimens, spread out over too large a geographic area, to

11. Holden, C., The politics of paleoanthropology, *Science* **213**(4509):737–740, 1981; p. 738.
12. Fix, W.R., *The Bone Peddlers: Selling Evolution*, Macmillan, New York, p. 150, 1984.
13. Sykes, B., *DNA USA: A Genetic Portrait of America*, Liveright Publishing Corporation, New York, p. 17, 2012.

> make these decisions with any confidence. New finds and revisions of old conclusions occur constantly.[14]

Yet another reason for the many controversies and forgery allegations is that the anthropological field is divided into 'camps', 'schools', or cliques that are not uncommonly at war with each other. Each school often is dominated by a small group of scientists who are well-known and well-connected charismatic leaders. Each camp tries to 'prove' its own evolution theory, often dogmatically, by using fossils, most of which consist of badly damaged fragments open to multiple interpretations. In the words of evolutionist Henry Gee, the problem is that the "*Fossil evidence of human evolutionary history is fragmentary and open to various interpretations.*"[15]

> Reading various paleoanthropology publications reveals both the extent and the degree of conflicts in a field that, as a whole, has very little relevant hard data, most of which can be construed in several different ways. One reason why much controversy is common is that new fossil discoveries are typically not shared with other scientists for years, if ever, due to factors such as publishing priority concerns. A common complaint is that the people claiming the discovery are far too slow to publish their findings—and are flinging around arguments and interpretations without giving others something solid in print to evaluate. The Leakey and Johanson camps also claim each others' popular books are filled with inaccuracies. White and Johanson in particular complain that while Leakey refuses to accept the designation and placement of *Australopithecus afarensis*, he will not offer an alternative.[16]

To get full credit for a fossil discovery, one normally must publish a scientific article describing the find before anyone else does. To do this, the discovering paleoanthropologists retain exclusive access to their fossils for a decade or more before allowing others to study them. Since these fossils often are fragile and easily broken, working with them tends to damage them. This fact, though, may be used as an excuse by the group that discovered the fossils to not allow others access to them.

For all of these reasons, most researchers have access only to photographs or, at best, casts of the fossils. Most anthropologists must rely on descriptions and interpretations produced by the fossil's discoverer—the very person who has a vested interest in proving his or her own theories. In view of this fact, it is not surprising that major disagreements are common.

14. Coyne, J.A., *Why Evolution is True*, Viking, New York, p. 197, 2009.
15. Gee, H. Return to the planet of the apes, *Nature* **412**:131–132, 2001.
16. Holden, The politics of paleoanthropology, p. 739.

Hoarding important fossil finds

An example of this conflict is when a fossil is discovered, for various reasons the discoverers tend to hoard it to prevent others outside of their clique from exploiting or receiving credit or fame for their discovery, or to prevent others from contradicting their interpretations of the fossils.[17,18] A growing tendency exists for certain paleoanthropologists to refuse access to their finds even after they have published a preliminary description of their fossil discoveries. When published, their artifacts are under the paleontological code that stipulates fossils are to be shared with other researchers. The discoverers may ignore this rule, often arguing they have the right to withhold their fossil finds because of the dubious claim that the

> initial publications, even when prepared in accord with the dictates of the *Code* and published in major vehicles such as *Nature* and *Science*, merely constitute "*announcements*" … "*Publication,*" it is disingenuously contended, occurs only with the appearance of a long interpretive monograph.[19]

Tattersall and Schwartz add that it is common for this monograph publication period to take decades or longer, and may never be completed. Examples they provide include Louis Leakey's *Homo habilis* fossil finds, which were finally written up in the form of a detailed technical monograph by Professor Phillip V. Tobias "*some 30 years after their discovery, while the important fossil crania from Forbes' Quarry and Steinheim*" sites have yet to be written up in any detail 150 and 69 years respectively since their recoveries. More recently, several new hominid species

> published as early as 1994 still remain off-limits to researchers not belonging to the describing cliques. This has potentially harmful consequences, for, if not rapidly subjected to informed scrutiny, the initial describers' interpretation of the specimens' significance tends automatically to become established wisdom in the field. In this way, untested notions readily become incorporated into textbooks, the secondary literature, and the vast reaches of the popular media, without any consideration of alternative interpretations. As things too often are, alternative interpretations are difficult or impossible to formulate, because even casts (poor substitutes for the originals in any event) are rarely available and … photographs of specimens published in *Nature* or

---

17. Tattersall, I. and Schwartz, J.H., Is paleoanthropology science? Naming new fossils and control of access to them, *The Anatomical Record* **269**(6):239–241, 2002.
18. One reviewer of this book noted that this is a serious problem in archaeology as well; with finds often published years after they were found, dig reports delayed for decades, and announcements to the media being made before publication. He suggests this may well indicate a prevalent attitude in archaeology generally, and in other historical sciences.
19. Tattersall and Schwartz, Is paleoanthropology science? p. 240.

> *Science* tend to be so small and lacking in contrast that much useful information is obscured.[20]

A more recent example is Professor Teuku Jacob who stalled in returning the *Homo floriensis* fossils to the original researchers in Jakarta. One researcher commented that he is "*not optimistic about the bones' return to Jakarta*" and even though the "*conflict continues*" the Jakarta researchers plan to continue their research and publication. Fortunately, in this case several qualified researchers were later allowed access to the fossils.[21] The problem is "*science is a system of provisional knowledge that constantly requires re-examination and testing. It cannot function as a system in which assertions have to be left unchallenged for want of free access to the primary data.*"[22] This goal is hindered by restricting access to fossils by other scientists, especially creationists.

Blocking access to creationists

The difficulty that creationists and others have in obtaining access to fossils is another problem. Museums and other human fossil remains repositories commonly refuse access requests made by creationists. The difficulties that confront creationists, such as Dr Jack Cuozzo when he attempted to access fossil humans, illustrate the problems in challenging existing interpretations. His experience is detailed in his 1998 book *Buried Alive: The Startling Truth About Neanderthal Man.*

Cuozzo discusses in detail what he claims was a "*violent reaction*" that his research into Neandertal Man caused, providing another illustration of the extreme reaction that Darwin doubters can provoke. In this case, there were seven witnesses to the events—two adults and five children.[23]

It all began in the late 1970s when Cuozzo began to question the evolutionary interpretation of the fossil record.[24] The antagonism resulted from his attempt to study the original Neandertal skeletal material housed in several Paris museums.

Cuozzo had taken numerous radiographs of the Neandertals with a portable cephalometric X-ray machine developed by General Electric Corporation for use in fossil research. At the time there were only two portable cephalometric X-ray machines in the world. He believed that the radiographs provided evidence against the orthodox evolutionary view of the Neandertals. Fortunately, as Cuozzo details in his book, he was able to arrive in the United States with his radiographs intact. The X-ray photographs, it turned out, produced important new information about

---

20. Tattersall and Schwartz, Is paleoanthropology science? p. 240.
21. Culotta, E., Battle erupts over the 'hobbit' bones, *Science* **307**(5713):1179, 2005.
22. Tattersall and Schwartz, Is paleoanthropology science?, p. 239.
23. Cuozzo, J., *Buried Alive: The Startling Truth About Neanderthal Man,* Master Books, Green Forest, Arkansas, p. 13, 1998.
24. Cuozzo, *Buried Alive*, p. 17.

Neandertals that was detrimental to Darwinism, including evidence showing that many textbook measurements were incorrect.[25]

Arrogance in paleoanthropology

A major issue in dealing with the problem is that no small amount of arrogance exists within the scientific community. Hooper concluded that some scientists dogmatically believe not only that they have the answer, but also that only they have the right to ask the questions—and if they don't, no-one else should.[26] A review of history vividly shows that an 'other side' to the dominant views of scientists exists. The dominant side is the views of scientists who control publication in *Nature, Science, PNAS, Cell,* and other leading scientific journals.

This fact illustrates a common problem in paleoanthropology related to the difficulties leading scientists have in evaluating the data fairly and objectively. An example is Tim White, a professor at the University of California, Berkeley, who had a falling out with Dr Donald Johanson to the extent that "*White and Johanson now barely speak to each other because of earlier bitter disagreements over research style and conduct.*"[27] Tim White's former University of Michigan professor, Dr Milford Wolpoff, supported this negative assessment:

> Tim knows the "*right*" way ... and that's with a capital "*R*" .... I used to think that once he got a job and was treated with professional respect, he'd calm down a bit. But I was wrong.[28]

Morell noted that "*White's self-righteous stance surfaced* [in the field] ... *leading him to be 'unspeakably rude and arrogant to others.'*"[29]

She concluded that, like Wolpoff, Richard Leakey also "*assumed that White would eventually outgrow this behavior. Instead, Richard himself became a target*" of White's arrogance.[30] For example, when Richard Leakey, the leader of the fossil expedition, explained his objections to White's writing a scientific paper about his (White's) interpretations of some fossils, including some unpublished hominid fossils, without Leakey's awareness until the final draft was completed, Leakey wrote: White "*started shouting at me, called me a dictator, said it was a disgrace that I should be in charge—all this rubbish ... he wanted to have nothing more to do with me, and finally walked out of my office and slammed the door.*"[31]

25. Cuozzo, *Buried Alive*, p. 17.
26. Hooper, J., *Of Moths and Men: An Evolutionary Tale—The Untold Story of Science and the Peppered Moth*, Norton, New York, 2002.
27. Dalton, R., The history man, *Nature* **443**(7109):268–269, 2006; p. 269.
28. Morell, *Ancestral Passions*, p. 477.
29. Morell, *Ancestral Passions*, p. 477.
30. Morell, *Ancestral Passions*, p. 477.
31. Morell, *Ancestral Passions*, p. 478.

Similar conflicts are not uncommon in this field: "*Squabbles over credit for discoveries and permits to work at key sites are common.*"[32] An example Dalton cites is that paleoanthropologists Donald Johanson and Maurice Taieb's competitors used a potentially inflammatory passage in a book that Johanson published to upset the Ethiopian authorities and cause Johanson and Taieb to be banned from research in Ethiopia. The ploy was successful—they were banned for a decade.

Many anthropologists have concluded that we should not be surprised by this behaviour because humans are "*bloody aggressors*" as a result of the evolutionary survival of the fittest battle. Leakey's critics view him as the leader of a small clique of researchers that are trying to build their

> own scientific empire in East Africa; a clique of what Tim White terms "*academic loyalists*" devoted to Louis Leakey's stubborn adherence to unfounded theories about man's origins. Critics also say that a favorite Leakey theme—that man is innately a cooperative and food-sharing creature rather than a bloody aggressor—is at best only thinly supported by available evidence.[33]

The Leakeys have been at the centre of this war for the last half-century. And unfortunately, for several reasons "*paleoanthropology has a history of being dominated by individualists, and the late Louis Leakey, perhaps the most colorful of them all, bore major responsibility for enlarging the endeavor by drawing in the public's interest—and along with that, money.*"[34]

Johanson versus the Leakeys

One of the most well-known missing link wars was between the two giants of paleoanthropology, Richard Leakey and Donald Johanson. The early human evolutionary theory postulated that humans descended "*from the apes.*"[35] When no convincing evidence was uncovered for this view, Leakey and others came up with an alternative view—that humans and apes "*evolved from some other, unknown creature that was antecedent to both humans and apes.*"[36] This theory postulated that humans did not evolve from apes but humans and apes evolved from some distant long-extinct common ancestor, the so-called missing link. A major problem with this idea was there existed

> a big hole in the fossil evidence for the human line of descent. We had ourselves at one end of the scale, and we had our cousins the modern apes at the

32. Dalton, The history man, p. 269.
33. Holden, The politics of paleoanthropology, p. 739.
34. Holden, The politics of paleoanthropology, p. 737.
35. Hellman, H., *Great Feuds in Science*, Wiley, New York, p. 160, 1998.
36. Hellman, *Great Feuds in Science*, p. 160.

same end. We also had some fossil evidence for ancient apes, thought to date way back to an estimated 10 million years ago and more.

But how about the intermediary stages? Where was the "*missing link*"? Next to the Holy Grail, the missing link may be the most sought-after prize in human history. Every civilization, every recorded society has myths and legends attempting to explain where we came from. It was about this link, basically, that Leakey and Johanson were wrangling.[37]

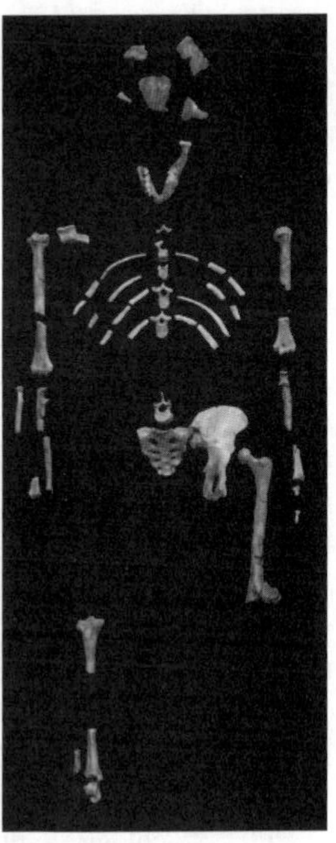

The skull pieces and other bone fragments of *Australopithecus afarensis* commonly referred to as Lucy.

After 30 years of fruitless searching, the Leakeys finally found some skull fragments and simple tools near the skull that they argued was the missing link. Now named *Australopithecus boisei*, the find changed their lives forever—fame and fortune soon followed. Human evolution now had its Holy Grail.

A few years later Johanson's team found some badly damaged skull pieces and other bone fragments they named Lucy, which they claimed was 40% complete, when actually it was closer to 30% or less complete. The find soon rocketed him to worldwide fame. Johanson gave the scientific name *Australopithecus afarensis* to his find, claiming that the creature was a new species. Johanson also claimed she (some claim Lucy was a male, a controversy still being debated) was the oldest human ever found, thus she would be the mother of mankind, and further maintained that she was bipedal.[38] Hellman explained that

> *A. afarensis* sits at the base of a neat Y-shaped tree. Lucy, the Mother of Mankind, forms the stem, which branches off in one direction to *Homo habilis*, which in turn leads eventually to *Homo sapiens*, modern man. The other branch of the Y leads to Louis Leakey's *A. boisei* and thence to extinction. This directly contradicted the Leakeys' belief that the human line began much earlier. Thus were several lifetimes of work put on the line, and with some Leakey fossils used as ammunition against their own position. Also, Johanson thereby claimed the title to being finder of *the* missing link.[39]

37. Hellman, *Great Feuds in Science*, p. 160.
38. Hellman, *Great Feuds in Science*, p. 168.
39. Hellman, *Great Feuds in Science*, p. 170.

Mary Leakey disputed most of his claims, even calling the Johanson team's work "*slovenly.*"[40]

Their argument is over the central facts of human evolution, and this controversy illustrates the fact that theories of human evolution are mostly speculation. The evidence available is scant, fragmentary and equivocal.

For this reason, a fundamental problem in anthropology is naming, and thereby creating, a new species. It "*is always a traumatic event. In this case, Johanson's introduction of* Australopithecus afarensis *created a storm on several fronts ... Mary* [Leakey] *had probably known of his intention,* [but] *the public announcement was particularly galling because his classification ran exactly counter to the position long held by the Leakeys.*"[41]

A good example of the many major naming disagreements among evolutionists was provided by Oxford Professor Richard Dawkins. Dawkins writes that taxonomists, those scientists who name different life-forms, often dispute names, which indicates the level of controversy about origins and evolution. For example, he writes that many taxonomists

> speak of *Homo neanderthalensis* not *Homo sapiens neanderthalensis*, elevating Neanderthal man from sub-species to species status. Generic names and specific names are also often disputed, and often change with successive revisions in the scientific literature. *Paranthropus boisei* has been, in its time, *Zinjanthropus boisei* and *Australopithecus boisei*, and is still often referred to, informally, as a robust australopithecine—as opposed to the two 'gracile' (slender) species of *Australopithecus* mentioned above. One of the main messages ... concerns the somewhat arbitrary nature of zoological classification.[42]

Dawkins added that the accepted

> rules of zoological nomenclature are strict to the point of pedantry. Priority of naming takes precedence over sense and suitability. 'Southern ape' might be a lousy name but no matter: it predates the much more sensible *Plesianthropus* and we seem to be stuck with it, unless ... somebody will uncover, ... a long-forgotten fossil, clearly the same kind as Mrs. Ples and the Taung Child, but bearing the scrawled label, '*Hemianthropus* type specimen, 1920'. At a stroke, all the museums in the world would immediately have to relabel their *Australopithecus* specimens and casts, and all books and articles on hominid prehistory would have to follow suit. Word-processing programs across the world would work overtime sniffing out any occurrences of *Australopithecus* and replacing them with *Hemianthropus*. I can't think

40. Hellman, *Great Feuds in Science*, p. 171.
41. Hellman, *Great Feuds in Science*, p. 170.
42. Dawkins, R., *The Greatest Show on Earth: The Evidence for Evolution*, Free Press, New York, p. 190, 2009.

> of any other case where international rules are potent enough to dictate a worldwide and backdated change of language overnight.[43]

An example of the identification problem that Dawkins cites is the following three fossils. The museum number is followed by the various names in italics given to the fossil by the experts, as shown:

> KNM ER 1813: *Australopithecus habilis, Homo habilis*
>
> KNM ER 1470: *Australopithecus habilis, Homo habilis, Australopithecus rudolfensis, Homo rudolfensis*
>
> OH 24 ('Twiggy'): *Australopithecus habilis, Homo habilis*[44]

Why is terminology such a problem? Dawkins explains a major reason is because of the sparse fossil evidence, which obviously allows much room for interpretation:

> I wish we really did have a complete and unbroken trail of fossils, a cinematic record of all evolutionary change as it happened. *I wish it, not least because I'd love to see the egg all over the faces of those zoologists and anthropologists who engage in lifelong feuds with each other over whether such and such a fossil belongs to this species or that, this genus or that* [emphasis added].[45]

The conflict worsens

When Louis Leakey's son, Richard, was invited on Walter Cronkite's television program to discuss evolution and creationism as an ardent evolutionist, Richard agreed to appear.[46] This ploy to get him on the show turned out to be a ruse—Cronkite actually did not want Richard to rail against creationism, but rather to pit him and Johanson against each other to debate their radically different opinions about *Australopithecus afarensis* and other putative hominids.

It turned out as the show progressed that Johanson was less interested in an intellectual exchange to achieve a better understanding of human evolution than he was in attacking those with whom he disagreed. Some people, such as Milford Wolpoff, felt Richard Leakey came out better in this acrimonious exchange. Shortly after the Cronkite show, the National Geographic Society—the Leakeys' main source of financial support—presumably in part as a consequence of the bad publicity it generated, turned down Richard's grant application for funds to support his

43. Dawkins, *The Greatest Show on Earth*, pp. 191–192.
44. Dawkins, *The Greatest Show on Earth*, p. 194.
45. Dawkins, *The Greatest Show on Earth*, p. 196.
46. Morell, *Ancestral Passions*, p. 520.

Koobi Fora fossil exploration research and for new explorations in the areas north and west of Lake Turkana.[47]

The endless, vicious, and sometimes physical confrontations between the Leakeys and other leading anthropologists, such as Donald Johanson and Timothy White, are very illuminating as to how critically important preconceptions are in interpreting and understanding the fossil evidence. Because fossil evidence usually accounts for less than 10% of the animal by volume (rarely are organs, muscles, skin, hair or other parts preserved), this evidence can be interpreted in several ways, even in the very rare situation in which a skeleton is fairly complete.

Lucy (*Australopithecus afarensis*) is the most complete putative human ancestor skeleton discovered so far.[48,49,50] As noted, less than 40% of the skeletal remains were eventually recovered at Hadar, and debate still exists whether the bones recovered all belong to the same individual. Most other fossil finds consist of, at best, a few bone fragments, sometimes only teeth. As Lewontin noted, when we study the

> remote past, before the origin of the actual species *Homo sapiens*, we are faced with a fragmentary and disconnected fossil record. Despite the excited and optimistic claims that have been made by some paleontologists, no fossil hominid species can be established as our direct ancestor.[51]

A problem noted above is that cliques develop, and the leader of one of these cliques justified excluding others from examining the fossils by implying "*that he had assembled the best possible team to study one set of fossils concerned (and thus by implication that it was unnecessary for others to see them).*"[52] The author of a *Science* report on the fossils asked "*if it 'really mattered' whether only the describers and their cronies saw the type specimens of new species at first-hand.*"[53]

Tattersall and Schwartz conclude that it is "*absurd to act as if the finders of particular fossils are alone qualified to study them*", and that it is "*one thing for high priests in temples to reserve access to religious relics; science is an entirely different case. Science is not a matter of faith (or of power); it is a matter of the free flow of information.*"[54]

---

47. Morell, *Ancestral Passions*, p. 523.
48. Dalton, The history man, p. 268.
49. Regal, B., *Human Evolution: A Guide to the Debates (Controversies in Science), ABC-CLIO,* Santa Barbara, California, p. 109, 2004.
50. Kimbel, W. and Delezene, L., Lucy Redux: A Review of Research on *Australopithecus afarensis*, American Journal of Physical Anthropology, Volume 140, Issue S49, pp. 1–163. Supplement: Yearbook of Physical Anthropology 2009. pp. 2–48.
51. Lewontin, R.C., *Human Diversity*, Scientific American Library, New York, p. 163, 1995.
52. Tattersall and Schwartz, Is paleoanthropology science? p. 240.
53. Tattersall and Schwartz, Is paleoanthropology science? p. 240.
54. Tattersall and Schwartz, Is paleoanthropology science?, p. 241.

Debates part of science

Debates are also required to make progress in science—but the viciousness that Morell eloquently documents is hardly what we would expect of paleoanthropologists who are interested in truth and desire to rationally evaluate their ideas. Nor is this behavior rare. Gardner notes that mainline anthropologists reacted to one fellow anthropologist, Dr William Arens, who disagreed with the orthodox view, "*with the same kind of fury they displayed toward Derek Freeman's* Margaret Mead and Samoa, *a book exposing Mead's gullibility in taking at face value the myths told to her by Samoan pranksters.*" Gardner adds that

> Anthropologists have yelled insults at Arens in meetings. They have pounded him relentlessly in their writings. Reviewers called his book "*dangerous*" and "*malicious.*"[55]

The extent of the outrageous behavior shown by these individuals was so extreme that it could not be discussed in a family publication. In addition, the morals of some leading paleoanthropologists leave much to be desired. Some people have claimed that Louis Leakey took advantage of women by using his position to exploit them for sexual favours. He had several affairs, which earned him a reputation as a ladies' man.[56] Some also condemn Louis's son, Richard, as not only wrong but also ignorant. Holden wrote that some authorities actually view him "*as a nonscientist who parades his lack of credentials in the many speeches he delivers.*"[57]

For example, University of Michigan paleontologist C. Loring Brace, in a scathing review of Richard Leakey's two books *Origins* and *People of the Lake,* wrote that Richard Leakey's "*deficiencies in his education*" (he does not have a university degree in paleontology or any other subject) show up in "*sheer ignorance of basic evolutionary principles and the non-African aspects of this field*" and also "*in his inability to appraise the nature of the facts that have been discovered as a result of his fieldwork.*" He adds that these two books by Richard Leakey "*present an amalgam of recent discoveries, sweeping generalizations, and gross errors in fact that is guaranteed to produce intellectual indigestion in those who really know the field—at the same time that the nonspecialist regards it all as the authoritative voice of 'science'.*"[58]

Professor Brace also contends that Leakey held very antiquated incorrect views of human evolution. The major 1980s and 1990s war between the Leakey and

55. Gardner, M., *Did Adam and Eve Have Navels? Discourses on Reflexology, Numerology, Urine Therapy, and Other Dubious Subjects,* Norton, New York, pp. 139–140, 2000.
56. Morell, *Ancestral Passions,* pp. 242–244.
57. Holden, The Politics of Paleoanthropology, p. 739.
58. Loring Brace, C., Review of What New Discoveries Reveal About the Emergence of Our Species and Its Possible Future and People of the Lake, *American Anthropologist* **81**(3):702, 704, 1979.

Johanson camps involved not only differing interpretations, but also strident claims that the other side was ignorant of the field.

Professor von Zieten's key research finds falsified

A more recent case is the work of German anthropologist Professor Reiner Protsch von Zieten. Research has confirmed that what the British *Guardian* called "*one of archaeology's most sensational finds*"—what they claimed was a 36,000-year-old skull fragment discovered in a peat bog near Hamburg—has now been falsified. Until falsified, this fragment was believed to be a "*vital missing link between modern humans and Neanderthals.*"[59] The 30-year academic career of the distinguished Protsch "*has now ended in disgrace after the revelation that he systematically falsified the dates on this and numerous other 'stone age' relics.*"[60]

Furthermore the crucial skull fragment once believed to have come from the world's oldest Neandertal has, according to Oxford University's radiocarbon dating unit, now been determined to be closer to a mere 7,500 years old. Other skulls were incorrectly dated by Protsch as well. After redating the evidence, it was concluded that Protsch had methodically falsified the dates on numerous artifacts: he had simply made up the dates to fit his theories. Testing revealed all of the skulls dated by Protsch were, in fact, far younger than he had claimed.

Thomas Terberger, the scientist who discovered the fraud, stated that as a result of the hoax, "*anthropology is going to have to completely revise its picture of modern man.*"[61] A committee also found that Protsch committed numerous other "*falsehoods and manipulations.*" His deceptions were so serious that it "*may mean an entire tranche of the history of man's development will have to be rewritten.*"[62]

Yet another of Protsch's finds, the Binshof-Speyer woman, was determined to have lived in 1,300 BC, not 21,000 years ago as Protsch claimed, and the Paderborn-Sande man, which was dated by the professor at 27,400 BC, died only "*a couple of hundred years ago, in 1750.*"[63] Further research determined that Protsch had passed off fake fossils as real, and had also plagiarized other scientists' work. The scandal was finally exposed when Protsch was caught trying to sell his university department's entire chimpanzee fossil collection to a museum in the United States.

The committee that investigated him required ten different meetings with 12 witnesses, documenting that Protsch's actions "*were increasingly bizarre. After a while it was hard to take it seriously. … It was just unbelievable. … what he did was incredible.*"[64] It was also determined that the professor, who had a fondness for

59. Harding, L., History of modern man unravels as German scholar is exposed as fraud, *The Guardian*, February 19, 2005.
60. Harding, History of modern man unravels … , p. 1.
61. Quoted in Harding, History of modern man unravels … , p. 1.
62. Harding, History of modern man unravels … , p. 1.
63. Harding, History of modern man unravels … , p. 1.
64. Harding, History of modern man unravels … , p. 2.

Porsches and Cuban cigars, could not even operate the carbon dating equipment that he had claimed to have used to produce his now discredited dates! This claim should have aroused suspicion because carbon-14 dating is almost always done by highly trained specialists in well-equipped labs, rarely by paleontologists.

Protsch was forced to end his career after the confirmation of his many "*falsehoods and manipulations*" came to light. This scandal is critically important in physical anthropology because his 30-year academic career yielded many sensational finds that were important evidence for modern evolution theory. He evidently found that he could get away with the frauds, and continued to make outrageous claims until they became so ludicrous that his peers were forced to investigate. The university administrators admitted that they should have discovered the professor's bizarre fabrications much earlier, but the "*high-profile anthropologist … proved difficult to pin down.*"[65]

The hobbit bone war

One of the latest paleoanthropology conflicts was over the so-called hobbit fossil man bones believed to be those of eight individuals, discovered in 2003 in the Liang Bua cave on the Indonesian island of Flores. The bones are from a creature now given the scientific name *Homo floresiensis.*

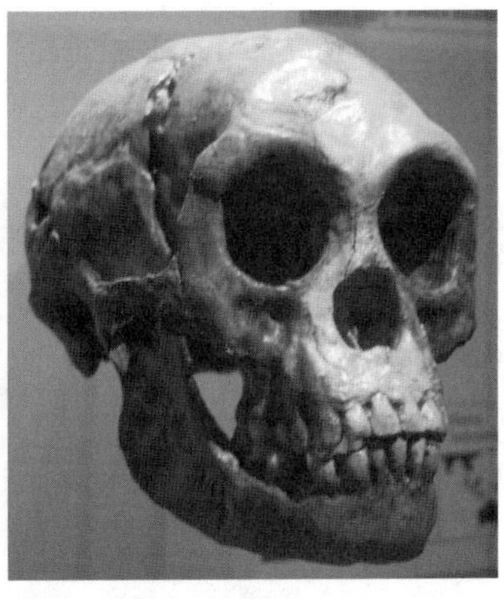

A cast of the fossil hobbit (*Homo floresiensis*) skull.

Source Wikimedia Commons

The bones' discoverer believed that they represented a new branch of human evolution. A major problem in this interpretation is that the bones were dated at only 18,000 years old. Although discovered by a team led by Mike Morwood, a rival team soon had taken possession of the skeleton. The conflict was exacerbated when Indonesian paleoanthropologist Dr Teuku Jacob, noting that pygmies still live nearby, concluded that the bones are not from a missing link, but rather are a "*modern human pygmy with microcephaly.*"[66] Morwood judged this conclusion mind-bogglingly wrong.[67]

Tensions built when Jacob made public his conclusion that *H. floresiensis* is *not* a new human species but a *Homo sapiens*. The bones were later returned to the

65. Harding, History of modern man unravels … , p. 2.
66. Culotta, Battle erupts over the 'hobbit' bones.
67. Culotta, Battle erupts over the 'hobbit' bones.

scientists that discovered them "*after months of dispute with a competing scientist* [i.e. Teuku Jacob] *who had taken them away.*"[68]

Tim White and Chris Stringer both rejected Jacob's conclusions.[69] To help settle the dispute, Jacob sent rib bone pieces to be DNA-analyzed, but those who advocated the new species theory demanded that they be returned immediately.[70] Soon after the bones were returned, Morwood reported that they were "*seriously damaged*" but Jacob insisted that the bones were intact when they left his lab.[71]

Morwood also claimed that the bones were not only damaged, but a "*still-unpublished jawbone 'broke in half … and was badly glued back together, misaligned'*" and "*the left side of the pelvis—which he calls one of the hominid's most distinctive features … was 'smashed'*",[72] making it much more difficult to determine what kind of human or animal the fossil was from. The jaw was broken in half between the front teeth, obliterating structures that were critical to determining its proper identification, and the pelvis was broken into two large and four smaller pieces.[73]

Jacob's critics also alleged that, in the process of making a mould to produce copies of the bones, "*breakage and loss of anatomic detail*" occurred and the cranial base of the skull and jawbone were seriously damaged.[74] Jacob denied doing any damage, noting that his lab was the only one in Indonesia equipped for paleoanthropological study having both highly trained staff and up-to-date testing equipment. In fact, Jacob noted that "*his team reconstructed some of the remains, putting pieces together in order to study them.*"[75] A number of paleoanthropologists have sided with Jacob, one noting that when he saw the bones, including the left side of the pelvis, they were all undamaged. Another researcher doubted if making moulds could damage the bones.[76]

In October 2005, details of a new find were published in the scientific literature, including another new jawbone that was virtually identical to a previous find. Morwood claimed the newest discovery supported the 'new species' interpretation. Examples he cited in support of his interpretation include the jaws' lack of a chin structure. The researchers argued this was important because chins are a distinguishing feature of *H. sapiens*. They also found spectacularly long arm bones

---

68. Dalton, R., Fossil finders in tug of war over analysis of hobbit bones, *Nature* **434**(7029):5, 2005.
69. Dalton, Fossil finders in tug of war over analysis of hobbit bones.
70. Dalton, Fossil finders in tug of war over analysis of hobbit bones.
71. Culotta, E., Discoverers charge damage to 'hobbit' specimens, *Science* **307**(5717):1848, 2005.
72. Culotta, Discoverers charge damage to 'hobbit' specimens.
73. Dalton, R., More evidence for hobbit unearthed as diggers are refused access to cave, *Nature* **437**(7061):934–935, 2005.
74. Culotta, Discoverers charge damage to 'hobbit' specimens.
75. Culotta, Discoverers charge damage to 'hobbit' specimens.
76. Culotta, Discoverers charge damage to 'hobbit' specimens.

identified as being from two individuals.[77] These finds raised more questions than they answered.

Dalton wrote that disputes such as the Liang Bua Cave controversy were not rare, but this one was unprecedented. Another problem was, as noted by Morwood, that the conflicts which developed between the different paleoanthropologists resulted in his team not being allowed to work at the hobbit work site, the Liang Bua Cave. As this case illustrates, conflicts

> over paleoanthropology dig sites are not uncommon—there has been considerable squabbling over the control of hominid sites in Africa. But it is unprecedented to close down such a spectacular site. "*Liang Bua is the crown jewel of the caves,*" says Brown, adding that only a small percentage of it has been excavated so far. "*This is where the team should be focusing.*"[78]

Research that continued at other sites on Flores and nearby islands has found some

> promising hints about the origin of *H. floresiensis,* but no new hominid bones. Work in the Soa Basin, for example, suggests that hominids were present on Flores significantly earlier than 840,000 years ago, the earliest date previously reported … But without access to Liang Bua, the mysteries of the ancient 'hobbit' people will probably remain secret for the foreseeable future.[79]

Nonetheless, the quarrel over whether the find really represents a new species continues to the extent that paleoanthropologist Peter Brown concluded it proved "*a complete circus.*"[80] The latest finds include fragments of six or more individuals, producing the observation that "*Overall,* H. floresiensis *presents a fascinating conundrum, and prompts some tantalizing predictions that will continue to strain credulity without more fossil evidence.*"[81]

One reason for this conundrum is that a "*minuscule brain in a species so recent that also made stone tools, has strained credulity*", at least in the eyes of some paleontologists.[82] The new view is problematic for the evolutionist because "*if proponents of the new view of hobbits are right, the first intercontinental migrations were undertaken hundreds of thousands of years earlier*" than previously believed

> by a fundamentally different kind of human, one that arguably had more in common with primitive little Lucy than the colonizer paleoanthropologists

77. Dalton, More evidence for hobbit unearthed … , p. 935.
78. Dalton, More evidence for hobbit unearthed … , p. 935.
79. Dalton, More evidence for hobbit unearthed … , p. 935.
80. Dalton, Fossil finders in tug of war over analysis of hobbit bones.
81. Lieberman, D.E., *Homo floresiensis* from head to toe, *Nature* **459**(7243):41–42, 2009; p. 42.
82. Lieberman, *Homo floresiensis* from head to toe, p. 41.

> had envisioned. This scenario implies that scientists could conceivably locate a long-lost chapter of human prehistory in the form of a two-million-year record of this primitive pioneer stretching between Africa and Southeast Asia if they look in the right places.[83]

Needless to say, this conclusion "*does not sit well with some researchers*" for many reasons, including the concern that the "*further back we try to push the divergence of the Flores* [hominin], *the more difficult it becomes to explain why a* [hominin] *lineage that must have originated in Africa has left only one trace on the tiny island of Flores*" [Editorial inserts in original].[84]

The view that *H. floresiensis* is a legitimate new species has been challenged by a number of other scientists, including Field Museum of Chicago primate evolution expert Dr Robert Martin.[85] He has opined that the first find, called LB1—the only example whose brain size can be estimated—could have been a modern human with some yet unidentified medical disorder, which others claim may be microcephaly. As of this date, the conflict continues, but meanwhile

> many scientists are welcoming the shake-up. LB1 is "*a hominin that no one would be saying anything about if we found it in Africa two million years ago,*" asserts Matthew W. Tocheri of the Smithsonian Institution, who has analyzed the wrist bones of the hobbits. "*The problem is that we're finding it in Indonesia in essentially modern times.*"[86]

Tocheri added that "*If we don't find something in the next 15 years or so in that part of the world, I might start wondering whether we got this wrong ... The predictions are that we should find a whole bunch more*" new *floresiensis* fossils.[87] After over ten years since the Hobbit was uncovered, and scores of scholarly papers on the Hobbit, many questions about its identity still remain unsolved.

Conclusions

In a field based on little empirical evidence, many assumptions, and strong personalities, the so-called 'bone wars' illustrate the conflicts common among scientists in this academic discipline. The unprofessional, and at times even fraudulent behaviour, of the leading participants is far from what one would expect from highly

83. Wong, K., Rethinking the hobbits of Indonesia, *Scientific American* **301**(5):66–73, November 2009.
84. Martin, R., quoted in Wong, Rethinking the hobbits of Indonesia, p. 72.
85. Wong, Rethinking the hobbits of Indonesia, p. 72.
86. Wong, Rethinking the hobbits of Indonesia, p. 73.
87. Wong, Rethinking the hobbits of Indonesia, p. 73.

trained professionals.[88] Holden wrote that the problem in paleoanthropology is the fact that this field

> naturally excites interest because of our own interest in our origins. And, because conclusions of emotional significance to many must be drawn from extremely paltry evidence, it is often difficult to separate the personal from the scientific in disputes raging within the field.

He added that

> The very nature of paleoanthropology encourages divisiveness. The primary scientific evidence is a pitifully small array of bones from which to construct man's evolutionary history. One anthropologist has compared the task to that of reconstructing the plot of *War and Peace* with 13 randomly selected pages. Conflicts tend to last longer [than in other fields—Ed.] because it is so difficult to find conclusive evidence to send a theory packing.[89]

Archaeologist Craig Childs has documented the epidemic of fraud and forgeries in not only ancient bones but also in the whole field of human artifacts. He documented three suicides—Dr James Redd, Ted Gardiner, and Steven Shrader—which resulted over conflicts in this pursuit, adding that "*In no other field of research have I encountered so many people who have wanted the other party dead. … Another man … explained to an undercover agent that you should always go into the field well-armed.*"[90]

As we have documented, the fact is paleoanthropology is an "*unexacting kind of science.*"[91] This fact is compounded by the problem of researchers refusing outside access to their fossil finds, even though, as Tattersall and Schwartz argued, published fossils have to be freely available for research if science is to work as it should.[92] And, partly for this reason, although the field is more sophisticated today, "*it continues to be riddled with controversies and dominated by personalities.*"[93] This brief survey supports Holden's conclusion that the "*very nature of paleoanthropology encourages divisiveness. … Louis Leakey's personal ideas about the extreme antiquity of the* Homo *line … continue to divide the field years after his death.*"[94]

Fraud and new discoveries are forcing so much revision in the paleoanthropology field that *Time* magazine's senior science editor, a former science teacher, Charles Alexander, stated that so many of the facts he once believed to be true in evolution

88. Grant, J., *Corrupted Science: Fraud, Ideology and Politics in Science*, Facts, Figures and Fun, Surrey, UK, 2007.
89. Holden, The Politics of Paleoanthropology, p. 737.
90. Childs, *Finders Keepers*, pp. 6, 89–93.
91. Medawar, P., quoted in Hill, A., The gift of Taungs, *Nature* **323**(6085):209, 1986.
92. Tattersall and Schwartz, Is paleoanthropology science?, p. 239.
93. Holden, The politics of paleoanthropology, p. 737.
94. Holden, The politics of paleoanthropology, p. 737.

have been found to be false that he was forced to concede "*just about everything I taught them* [his students—Ed.]" he said "*was wrong.*"[95]

95. Quoted in Headland, T.N., Revisionism in ecological anthropology, *Current Anthropology* **38**(4):605–630, 1997, p. 605; and Long, E.V., "To our readers", *Time* **143**(11):4, 14 March 1994.

CHAPTER 3

The rise and fall of two putative first life-forms: *Bathybius haeckelii* and *Eozoön*

Introduction

Two important well-known historical examples of putative transitional forms between non-life and pre-cellular life are *Bathybius haeckelii* and *Eozoön*. Although widely accepted by many leading scientists for over a decade, the opinion of critics that they were nothing more than unusual rock formations or precipitates eventually became the scientific consensus. Both examples were eventually determined to be simply that—unusual mineral or chemical formations.[1,2] Growing doubt about *Eozoön* caused other geologists and paleontologists to become interested enough to investigate for themselves. The result was that by the end of the nineteenth century many researchers began to agree with King and Rowney, and to believe that *Eozoön* was merely an unusual rock. As a result supporters for *Eozoön* soon dropped away. When Dawson published *The Dawn Life* in 1875, which claimed *Eozoön* as the starting point for creation, King's lengthy and scathing review was published in the highly respectable *Annals and Magazine of Natural History* and followed by another refutation of *Eozoön* by the German naturalist Otto Hahn.[3]

Both *Eozoön* and *Bathybius haeckelii* are two more examples of the long string of failed attempts to prove Darwinism as defined in the introduction.

A major problem for macroevolution has always been gaps in the putative fossil record, especially the unbridgeable chasm between non-life and the first simple life-forms. This chapter reviews two attempts to fill in this gap with two alleged extremely ancient life-forms which at first appeared to evolutionists to be significant evidence of evolution from non-life into 'simple' life-forms.

They were just two of many examples that Darwinists naively used to support evolution. As Professor Nicolaas Rupke concluded, soon

> after the publication of Darwin's *The Origin of Species* (1859), the conceptual need was felt by a number of Darwin's supporters to link the … hypothesis of planetary evolution with the hypothesis of organic evolution and establish

1. Adelman, J., Eozoön: debunking the dawn animal, *Endeavour* **31**(3):94–98, 2007.
2. Rupke, N.A., *Bathybius haeckelii* and the psychology of scientific discovery, *Studies In History and Philosophy of Science Part A*, 7(1):53–62, 1976; pp. 53–54.
3. Adelman, Eozoön, p. 97.

> by that the philosophy of "*universal transformism.*" The link was thought to consist of factual evidence for the origin of life out of inorganic matter, i.e. *abiogenesis.* However, at about the same time, Pasteur conducted his classic experiments on fermentation (1860–1866) and made a cogent case ... against *abiogenesis.*[4]

About the same time as when Pasteur was completing his decisive experiments disproving abiogenesis, the leading German zoologist Ernst

> Haeckel reported in his *Generelle Morphologie der Organismen* (1866) on the existence of a group of very primitive microbes, which he called *Monera.* A *Moneron* was defined as a primitive form of life consisting of undifferentiated protoplasm and lacking a nucleus. In a separate monograph on this group, Haeckel described in some detail a number of different *Monera,* among which the most primitive of all ... he called *Protamoeba primitiva.* It was described as being entirely homogeneous and reproducing itself by process of binary fission. The primitive level of organization of the *Monera* was interpreted to indicate that the group represented life *in statu nascendi*, and as such it made *abiogenesis* conceivable.[5]

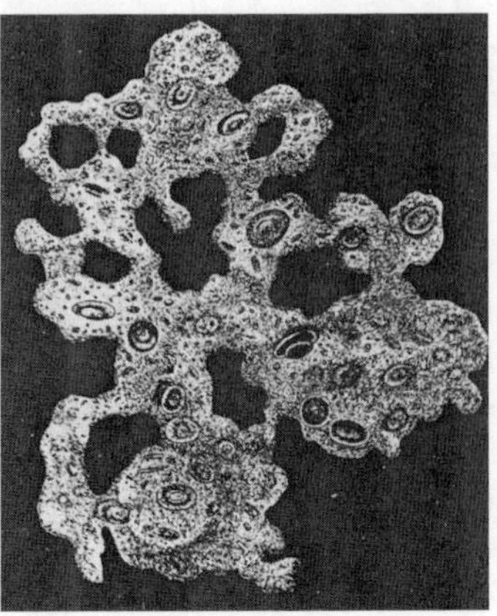

An illustration of *Bathybius* showing the detailed structure of this supposed primitive life form that turned out to be a chemical precipitate.

From: C. Wyville Thomson. *The Depths of the Sea*, Macmillan, London, p. 412, 1873.

This first primitive Monera organism was a find later named *Bathybius haeckelii* in honor of Haeckel.

The *Bathybius haeckelii* story

At the 1868 Norwich meeting of the British Association for the Advancement of Science, Thomas Henry Huxley announced the discovery of a new class of organisms that he concluded were transitional between non-life and living cells, which

4. Rupke, *Bathybius haeckelii* and the psychology of scientific discovery, p. 53.
5. Rupke, *Bathybius haeckelii* and the psychology of scientific discovery, p. 54.

was interpreted by some scholars as proving abiogenesis.[6] He found the putative organisms in mud samples that were dredged up north-west of Ireland in 1857.[7]

The samples were placed in alcohol by those on the dredging ship(s) who collected them, in an attempt to preserve them. This procedure could have caused chemical changes in the purported life-forms found. Huxley examined the samples with a microscope that achieved up to 1200 times magnification.[8]

Under the microscope, he observed a gelatinous substance that he at this time interpreted as living protoplasm (He eventually admitted his mistake when the putative primitive life forms were revealed to be merely simple non-living chemical compounds).

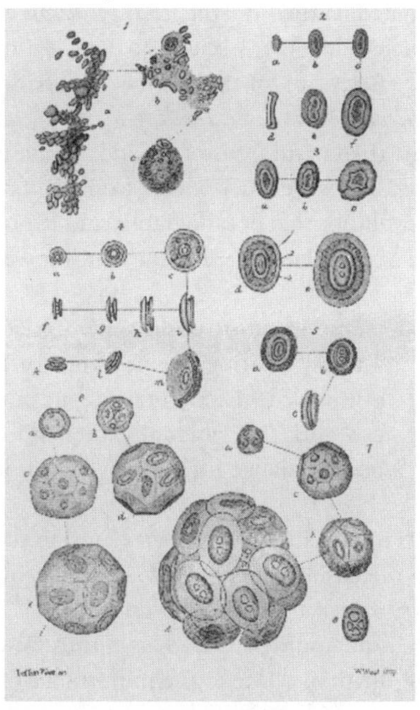

An illustration of the *Bathybius haeckelii* discovery shown in the upper left hand corner which is in vivid contrast to the other actual living creatures.

From aleph0.clarku.edu/huxley/SM3/bathy.html

The genus name of the new life-form was *Bathybius* after its deep oceanic habitat, and its species name was *haeckelii,* after the German biologist, Huxley's fellow champion of Darwinism.[9]

Haeckel considered it *"an important member of his new class of unicellular organisms."*[10]

Haeckel, as cited in Packard, concluded the Moneron was *"in a fully developed and freely moving condition, consists of an entirely homogeneous and structureless substance, a living particle of albumen, capable of nourishment and reproduction"*, thus a living primitive animal.[11]

Huxley also identified two types of coccoliths—microscopic calcite structures created by some marine phytoplankton for protection, often forming enormous chalk and limestone deposits—inside the gelatinous substance, that he called *Cyatholithi*

6. Report of the British Association for the Advancement of Science, 38th Meeting, p. 102.
7. Rupke, *Bathybius haeckelii* and the psychology of scientific discovery, pp. 54–55.
8. Rupke, *Bathybius haeckelii* and the psychology of scientific discovery, p. 55.
9. Rehbock, P.F., "Huxley, Haeckel, and the oceanographers: the case of *Bathybius haeckelii*", *Isis* **66**(4):504–533, 1975; p. 504.
10. Rehbock, "Huxley, Haeckel, and the oceanographers", p. 504.
11. Quoted in Packard, A.C., *Life Histories of Animals, Including Man or Outlines of Comparative Embryology*, Henry Holt and Company, New York, p. 1, 1876.

and *Discolithi*. Huxley interpreted these structures to be the skeletal components of *Bathybius haeckelii*, comparable to the spicules in sponges.

The find Haeckel identified as "*undifferentiated protoplasm*" soon was interpreted as fulfilling a critical evolutionary link in the enormous gap between non-living organic matter and life. Haeckel enthusiastically stated that the discovery of this *Bathybius 'urschleim'* (primordial slime), this protoplasm from which all life had originated, turned the theory into "*a complete truth.*"[12,13] For this reason, *Bathybius* was believed by many scientists to be critical evidence for Darwin's theory of evolution.

After careful examination, "*Huxley confidently maintained that Bathybius formed a living scum … extending over thousands of square miles*" on the ocean bottom.[14] Scottish natural historian and marine zoologist Prof. Sir Charles Wyville Thomson served as the chief scientist on the Challenger expedition from 1830 to 1832 that revolutionized oceanography and led to his knighthood. He described the discovery as very interesting, adding that if it were

> placed in a drop of sea water under the microscope, we can usually see, after a time, an irregular net-work of matter resembling white of eggs, distinguishable by its maintaining its outline and not mixing with the water. This net-work may gradually alter in form, and entangled granules and foreign bodies change their relative positions.[15]

Its importance lay in the conclusion that *Bathybius* was the first proof of a primitive non-cell "*organic life-form*" in the record of life. It was soon judged as "*the evolutionary precursor of all higher organisms.*"[16]

The finding received an enthusiastic welcome by scientists and certain segments of the public, due to the importance of finding a critical "*missing link*" necessary to prove Darwinism: "*the primordial pabulum out of which all things had come.*" The

> ultra-Darwinian enthusiasts were enchanted. Haeckel clapped his hands and shouted out Eureka loudly. Even the cautious and discriminating mind of Professor Huxley was caught by this new and grand generalisation of the 'physical basis of life.' It was announced by him to the British Association [for the Advancement of Science] in 1868. Dr. Will[iam] Carpenter took up the chorus. He spoke of 'a living expanse of protoplasmic substance,' penetrating with its living substance the 'whole mass' of the oceanic mud. A fine new Greek name [was] devised for this mother slime, and it was christened 'Bathybius,' from the consecrated deeps in which it lay. The conception ran

---

12. Rupke, *Bathybius haeckelii* and the psychology of scientific discovery, p. 56.
13. *Urschleim* is a term Haeckel used to refer to Monera, not an actual species name.
14. Eiseley, L., *The Immense Journey*, Random House, New York, p. 35, 1957.
15. Quoted in Packard, *Life Histories of Animals, Including Man …* , p. 3. Note, Thomson's name is incorrectly spelt "Thompson" in this source.
16. Rehbock, "Huxley, Haeckel, and the oceanographers", p. 505.

> like wildfire through the popular literature of science, and … there was something like a coming plebiscite in its favour.[17]

The gelatinous ooze that clung around particles gave the appearance that the life-form was ingesting food particles. From this finding the evolutionary scientists concluded that *Bathybius* consisted of an amorphous lump of protein, confirmed to be one of the 'Monera' capable of assimilating the nutrients required to live. They also determined that it was a more evolved life-form than organic molecules below the level of the cell.[18]

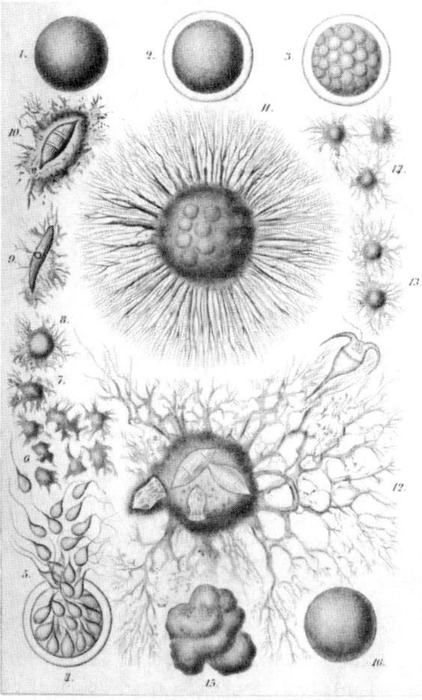

Haeckel's theory of the reproductive cycle of a Moneron (the term later became Moneran) from an egg to a fully developed animal. This represents his theory that simple homogeneous matter consisting of mucus or slime of albuminous carbon evolved into complex life forms.

From: Haeckel, E., *The History of Creation*, Appleton, New York, 5th ed., inset facing p. 188, 1911.

These evolutionists postulated that these Monera organisms could evolve from non-living matter by physical-chemical forces alone. At first hailed as critical support of evolution, *Bathybius* triggered many reports and much scientific research. Rupke reported that the "discovery of *Bathybius haeckelii* generated a great deal of excitement in the life and earth sciences and a number of biologists and geologists continued the investigation of this 'Moneron' for years after its discovery.[19]

The research involved many of the leading evolutionists of the mid-nineteenth-century and produced acrimony for almost a decade. The result was that the status of the 'living scum' as a primitive life-form was 'confirmed' by scientists in many scientific disciplines, including biology, chemistry and geology. One such scientist was Sir Charles Wyville Thomson, who later became the chief researcher on another expedition looking for more 'Moneron' samples.

Thomson examined an ooze sample taken from the Atlantic Ocean floor and published an 1869 paper titled "*On the depths of the sea*"[20] which detailed his scientific reasons for supporting the *Bathybius* theory. Thomson also described

17. Campbell, G.D., A great lesson, *The Nineteenth Century*, No. 707, pp. 293–309, September 1887; pp. 307–308.
18. Eiseley, *The Immense Journey*, p. 35.
19. Rupke, *Bathybius haeckelii* and the psychology of scientific discovery, p. 57.
20. See *The Journal of the Royal Dublin Society*, Vol. V, pp. 316–326, which includes the paper read at the society in April 1869.

Bathybius in his classic oceanography textbook titled *The Depths of the Sea*.[21] In his 1870 *Beiträge zur Plastidentheorie (Contributions to plastid theory)*, Ernst Haeckel advanced the theory that plastids (e.g. chloroplasts), and possibly other organelles, became part of eukaryote cells by the formerly free-living bacteria entering another cell as an endosymbiont,[22] and incorrectly concluded from Huxley's report "*that the sea floor of the open ocean at greater depths (below 5000 ft) is covered with enormous masses of free living protoplasm.*"[23]

Soon after Huxley's discovery, another *Bathybius* specimen was identified by the English geologist Dr William B. Carpenter. Haeckel obtained a sample of the deep-sea mud

> dredged by Wyville Thompson [*sic*] and W. B. Carpenter off the south-west coast of Ireland. The sample had been sent to him preserved in alcohol. Haeckel also observed the gelatinous substance with its granular texture which he coloured with a carmine solution and interpreted as real protoplasm. He thought it likely, though not entirely certain, that the coccoliths were skeletal components of *Bathybius*.[24]

Haeckel's discovery prompted further exaggeration by Huxley, who

> accepted Haeckel's exaggeration of his 1868 report and he added to this an exaggerated account of Haeckel's description of *Bathybius* in a speech before the Royal Geographical Society in 1870. He said with respect to his by now reputed discovery: "*Evidence of its existence had been found throughout the whole North and South Atlantic, and wherever the Indian Ocean had been surveyed, so that it probably forms one continuous scum of living matter girding the whole surface of the earth. This opinion has been confirmed in all its essential details by Prof. Haeckel, who had published an admirable account of specimens obtained by him.*"[25]

Haeckel also described a number of different *Monera,* such as one named *Protamoeba primitiva* that he concluded made abiogenesis conceivable.[26] In a speech given in 1870

---

21. Thomson, C.W., *The Depths of the Sea*, Macmillan, London, pp. 411–415, 1873.
22. Haeckel, E., Beiträge zur plastidentheorie, *Jenaische Zeitschrift für Medizin und Naturwissenschaften* **5**:492–547, 1870.
23. Rupke, *Bathybius haeckelii* and the psychology of scientific discovery, p. 56.
24. Rupke, *Bathybius haeckelii* and the psychology of scientific discovery, p. 56.
25. Rupke, *Bathybius haeckelii* and the psychology of scientific discovery, pp. 56–57; T. H. Huxley, *Proceedings of the Royal Geographical Society.* 15, 37 (1871).
26. Rupke, *Bathybius haeckelii* and the psychology of scientific discovery, p. 54.

> Haeckel expressed the belief that it was virtually certain that *Bathybius* originated by process of *abiogenesis*. … he argued that the question of the origin of life could not be solved by experiment (an apparent reference to Pasteur), but only through a philosophical approach.[27]

The evolution of the hypothetical simple-celled life forms into humans as postulated by Haeckel and other evolutionists. Drawing by G. Avery.
Source: *Scientific American* **34**(11): 167, March 11, 1876. Colour version on Wikimedia Commons.

Furthermore, German biologist Dr O. Schmidt reported that during

> an oceanographic expedition in the Adriatic Sea he had found evidence of the existence of *Bathybius* there as well. In addition, he reported that he had observed *Bathybius* in ooze samples that had no alcohol added to them … In

27. Rupke, *Bathybius haeckelii* and the psychology of scientific discovery, pp. 56–57.

> addition to the coccoliths, he observed more rod-shaped particles which he called rhabdoliths.[28]

In the same year, the German geologist C.W. von Gümbel published a study of numerous deep-sea mud samples that were also preserved in alcohol, concluding, in support of Huxley and Haeckel, that

> Bathybius with its coccoliths formed a living substance. In addition, he reported that its occurrence was not confined to the bathyal environment, but that it existed also in shallower marine environments and all around the world.[29]

In his paper Professor Gümbel also emphasized the lithogenetic importance of *Bathybius* in the geologic record.[30] Soon English geologist H.C. Sorby documented scientifically that coccoliths occur in many limestones. Many leading scientists of the time now believed that they had firmly proved life could evolve from non-life by purely natural means.

Protobathybius

What was judged as a more primitive example of the Monera than *Bathybius* was discovered in 1874 along the Grinnell Land coast by the US Arctic expedition aboard the ship *Polaris*. The discovery, by German surgeon and naturalist E. Bessels "*was characterized by the absence of coccoliths, and its movement ability was described as due to amoeboid action. Bessels called his discovery Protobathybius Robesonii,*" reporting it in *The Popular Science Monthly*.[31,32] Bessels reported that the new life-form was

> mainly distinguished from Bathybius by the absence of both the Discolithes and Cyatholithes. For this reason I take it to be an older form than Bathybius … . It consists of nearly pure protoplasm, tinged most intensely by a solution of carmine in ammonia. It contains fine gray granules of considerable refracting power, and besides the latter a great number of oleaginous drops, soluble in ether. It manifests very marked amoeboid motions and takes up particles of carmine or other foreign substances suspended in the water in which it is kept.[33]

---

28. Rupke, *Bathybius haeckelii* and the psychology of scientific discovery, p. 57.
29. Rupke, *Bathybius haeckelii* and the psychology of scientific discovery, p. 57.
30. Rupke, *Bathybius haeckelii* and the psychology of scientific discovery, p. 58.
31. Bessels, E., *The Popular Science Monthly* **5**:382, 1874.
32. The modern convention when formulating a binominal name is to use lower case for the species, as in *Protobathybius robesonii*. However, the original naming has been retained here for accuracy.
33. Packard, *Life Histories of Animals, Including Man* … , pp. 3–4.

Soon a zoo of other life-forms in this family was discovered including *Protogenes primordialis,* a simple, shapeless mass of protoplasm lacking vacuoles, containing what the finders claimed were over 1,000 very fine pseudopodia (the temporary projections of unicellular cells that extend and contract by the reversible assembly of microfilaments) and numerous anastomoses (a connection created between two tubular structures such as blood vessels). The largest specimens had a diameter of 1 mm (0.04 in) and they concluded that the marine form reproduced by fission.

Another example, *Myxodictyum*, consisted of several individuals, each one similar to *Protogenes* but with fewer pseudopods. This find was discovered in the Straits of Gibraltar.[34] The single specimen was observed to form a mass with a diameter of about 38 mm (1.5 in).

Protomonas amyli, a freshwater monad-like form discovered by Professor Cienkowski had a diameter of 2 to 5 mm (0.08 to 0.20 in). Yet another, *Protomyxa aurantiaca*, had a simple, shapeless, orange-red body, and in the encysted condition forms a globular jelly-like mass with a diameter of over 12 mm (0.5 in). It was found on empty shells of *Spirula peronii* floating on the open sea off the coast of the Canary Islands.

The 'most evolved' form of the Monera was *Myxastrum radians,* which formed a radiating jelly ball with a diameter of from 3 to 5 mm, and had very tough, stiff pseudopods. In the encysted condition, it had a diameter of nearly 13 mm (over 0.5 in) and was found on a beach of one of the Canary Islands.[35]

Eozoön: the dawn animal

Yet another well-known example of Monera was *Eozoön canadense* or the "*dawn animal of Canada.*" Its supporters claimed that it was the first life-form on Earth.[36] The eminent geologist, Sir John William Dawson, examined a large set of specimens[37] to find scientific evidence to vindicate the view that these finds were fossils of primitive life forms.

The 'animal' was first discovered in Canada in 1858 by Sir William Logan,[38] who had spent years looking for evidence of the earliest form of life. *Eozoön* was determined to be a life-form that was found in a rock formation "*unquestionably …*

34. Packard, *Life Histories of Animals, Including Man …* , p. 4.
35. Packard, *Life Histories of Animals, Including Man …* , p. 4.
36. Adelman, Eozoön, p. 94.
37. Dawson, J.W., New facts relating to Eozoön canadense, *The Canadian Naturalist* **8**:282–285, 1878; p. 285.
38. O'Brien, C.F., The dawn animal of Canada, *Isis* **61**(2):206–223, 1970.

more ancient than the oldest fossiliferous Cambrian rocks."[39] The "*remarkable discovery*" was "*zealously followed up*" by some of the leading scientists of the day.[40]

Fig. 17. Structure of the oldest known Fossil (*Eozoön Canadense*). A thin section magnified. From a Photograph by Dr. Carpenter, London.

An illustration of *Eozoön*; the geology text containing it described it as the oldest known fossil. Winchell was Professor of Geology at the University of Michigan.

Source: Alexander Winchell, *Sketches of Creation*, Harper & Brothers, New York, p. 68, 1898.

The *Eozoön* life-form was examined by numerous experts, including eminent authorities in London, and their report was published in the *Proceedings of the Geological Society* in 1865.[41] Their conclusion was that the *Eozoön* was a fossil of a primitive primordial organism that its supporters concluded scientifically linked life with non-life.

This discovery, which created a sensation in the scientific community, was challenged by very few scientists. Most agreed that it was a link between non-life and life. The doubters that existed, Dawson argued, were uninformed. The criticism against the discovery was partly "*due to the fact that so few scientific men are in a position fully to appreciate the evidence*" that *Eozoön* is a fossil life form.[42]

The find also was considered significant evidence for evolution by many of the leading geologists of the day.[43]

39. Dawson, J.W., *Relics of Primeval Life*, Fleming H. Revell Co., New York, p. 125, 1897.
40. Silliman, B. and Dana, J.W., (Eds), Möbius on Eozoön canadense, *The American Journal of Science and Arts (Second Series)* **40**(90):344–362, 1865; p. 344.
41. Silliman and Dana, Möbius on *Eozoön canadense*, p. 138.
42. Dawson, J.W., Möbius on *Eozoon Canadense, The American Journal of Science and Arts,* Third Series, 17(99):196–202, 1879; p. 196.
43. Adelman, Eozoön, p. 94.

Dawson's confidence was such that he considered any skepticism about *Eozoön's* animal status to be "*unreasonable.*"[44]

Dr Carpenter wrote that he believed "*Eozoon* [sic], *as well as Bathybius, may have maintained its existence through the whole duration of Geological Time, from its first appearance to the present Epoch.*"[45]

This claim soon found its way into the textbooks and popular treatises.[46] Sir John William Dawson, in his book on *Eozoön* (first published in 1875 titled *The Dawn of Life*), claimed that *Eozoön* was the starting point of the origin of life. He did, though, allow that some form of "*vegetable life may have preceded it*", because some plants were then seen as even more primitive than *Eozoön.*[47]

The lifestyle and behaviour of this primitive life-form was worked out in detail by several scientists. They concluded that it grew on the ocean floor and survived by throwing out "*from its whole surface its pseudopods to seize whatever floating particles of food the waters carried over it.*"[48] It "*grew upward in inverted, conical, or club-shaped forms,*" and its tubes, or oscula, admitted the life-giving seawater deep into its bowels, allowing this primitive life-form to grow and reproduce.

They also concluded that *Eozoön's* lifespan had definite limits—and when they reached these limits they died, causing an entirely new colony to begin growing.[49] Its evolutionary relationship to modern animals was also worked out in detail.

The confidence of scientists about this claim was illustrated by Sir W. Logan's boast that there is "*no one that I know who has seen the specimens and does not believe them to be fossils, so … Eozoön is pretty well established.*"[50] As late as 1897, Dawson published a book largely devoted to *Eozoön* and similar very primitive putative life-forms. In this book he presented evidence of *Eozoön's* biological structures, including turbinates, acervuline cells, tubuli, and flocculi.[51]

Darwin was especially intrigued by *Eozoön* because "*its age and simplicity of structure seemed compatible with the theory of evolution by natural selection.*"[52]

Darwin first discussed *Eozoön* only a year after the find was published in the *Proceedings*. In the 1866 edition of his *Origin of Species,* he wrote:

---

44. Dawson, J.W., *Dawn of Life: Being the History of the Oldest Known Fossil Remains, and Their Relation to Geological Time and to the Development of the Animal Kingdom*, Hodder & Stoughton, London, p. 223, 1875.
45. Carpenter, W.B., Preliminary report of dredging operations in the seas to the north of the British Islands, carried on in Her Majesty's steam-vessel Lightning, *Proceedings of the Royal Society of London* **17**:168–200, 1868; p. 191.
46. Dawson, J.W., *Nature and the Bible: A Course of Lectures Delivered in New York,* Robert Carter and Brothers, New York, p. 223, 1875.
47. Dawson, *Relics of Primeval Life*, p. 194.
48. Dawson, *Relics of Primeval Life*, p. 181.
49. Dawson, *Relics of Primeval Life*, p. 182.
50. Quoted in Adelman, Eozoön, p. 94.
51. Dawson, *Relics of Primeval Life*, pp. 147–190.
52. Adelman, Eozoön, p. 94.

> within the last year the great discovery of the Eozoon in the Laurentian formation of Canada has been made; and after reading Dr. Carpenter's description of this remarkable fossil, it is impossible to feel any doubt regarding its organic nature. There are three great series of strata beneath the Silurian system in Canada, in the lowest of which the Eozoon was found ... We are thus carried back to a period so far remote, that the appearance of the so-called Primordial fauna (of Barrande) may by some be considered a comparatively modern event."[53]

In the sixth and last edition of the *Origin,* Darwin wrote that *Eozoön*

> belongs to the most lowly organised of all classes of animals, but is highly organised for its class; it existed in countless numbers, and ... preyed on other minute organic beings, which must have lived in great numbers. Thus the words, which I wrote in 1859, about the existence of living beings long before the Cambrian period, and which are almost the same with those since used by Sir W. Logan, have proved true.[54]

The non-cellular evolutionary link life-form refuted

Not everyone, though, was fully convinced of the validity of these putative non-cellular early life-forms. One example was Mr John Murray who carefully evaluated the evidence and was never able to

> find or see any trace of this pelagic protoplasm when the dredges of the 'Challenger' came fresh from bathysmal bottoms. Again and again he looked for it, but never could he discover it.[55]

53. Darwin, C., *On the Origin of Species by Means of Natural Selection*, 4th edition, John Murray, London, p. 371, 1866.
54. Darwin, C., *On the Origin of Species by Means of Natural Selection*, 6th edition, D. Appleton and Company, New York, p. 287, 1883.
55. Campbell, A great lesson, p. 308.

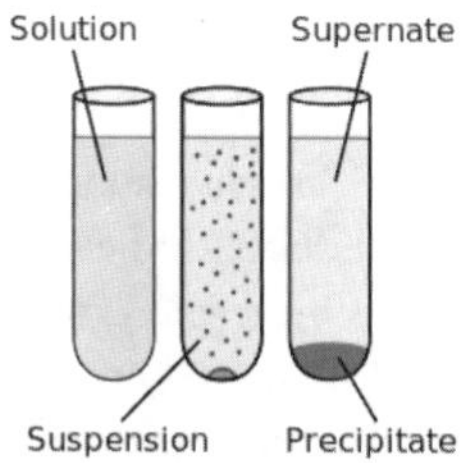

A diagram showing a precipitate, which can be formed by a chemical reaction of two compounds that dissolve in water and then forms one or more new compounds that are not water soluble. The new compounds then precipitate out of the water and in the illustration sink to the bottom of the test tube.

Source: Zab Milenko on Wikimedia Commons.

In the end, all of the Monera turned out to be nothing more than a chemical precipitate of lime sulphate, a compound commonly called gypsum, or similar compounds. This "*beautiful theory wistfully remembered ... as 'explaining so much'*" failed miserably to explain the origin of life.[56]

Eiseley concluded that the fiasco resulted from the "*projective dream*" of "*scientists striving to build an evolutionary family tree upon existing organisms*" in an effort to support Darwin.[57]

Campbell explained that one important discovery which eventually led to the theory's demise occurred on board a ship called the *Challenger*. On this ship one

> of Mr. Murray's assistants poured a large quantity of spirits of wine into a bottle containing some pure sea-water, when lo! the wonderful protoplasm Bathybius appeared. It was the chemical precipitate of sulphate of lime produced by the mixture of alcohol and sea-water. This was bathos indeed. On this announcement 'Bathybius' disappeared from science, reading us, in more senses than one, a great lesson on 'precipitation.'[58]

A major problem with the find was that the

> original discovery of *Bathybius* was based on only a few samples of ooze dredged in the same general locality in the North Atlantic Ocean. The early reports that *Bathybius* had a near universal deep-sea distribution were based on the belief that it represented primordial slime. Later reports of its wide distribution in both present-day oceans and in the geologic record were based on the misinterpretation of coccoliths as tests of *Bathybius*.[59]

After the *Bathybius haeckelii* and *Eozoön* claims were thoroughly refuted by analytical chemistry, most scientists accepted the compelling evidence against it. Haeckel and a few others, though, continued for years to argue that *Bathybius* was "*both an*

56. Eiseley, *The Immense Journey*, p. 36.
57. Eiseley, *The Immense Journey*, pp. 36–37.
58. Campbell, A great lesson, p. 308.
59. Rupke, *Bathybius haeckelii* and the psychology of scientific discovery, p. 62.

important member of his new class of unicellular organisms, the Monera, and a keystone in his mechanistic philosophy of life."[60]

After almost two decades, Haeckel was finally forced to reject Huxley's blunder.[61] Nonetheless, he continued to allow this falsified example to be used in his textbooks for decades after its exposure as a fraud.[62] In an 1891 article responding to Campbell, Huxley never mentioned the *Bathybius*, evidently because he could not refute the evidence against claims it was a living protoplast. One tragic aspect of the blunder was the enormous amount of money, time, and talent wasted on ocean dredging, laboratory investigations, books, and erroneous publications in leading scientific journals. Eiseley wrote that many leading scientists of the day "*participated in what was, and remains, one of the most curious cases of self-delusion ever indulged in by scholars.*"[63]

Bathybius was a "*product of an overconfident materialism, a vainglorious assumption that the secrets of life were about to be revealed*".[64] Other reasons for its acceptance were summarized by Campbell as follows:

> Expectant imagination soon played its part. Wonderful movements were seen in this mysterious slime. It became an 'irregular network,' and it could be seen gradually 'altering its form,' so that 'entangled granules gradually changed their relative positions.' The naturalists of the 'Challenger' began their voyage in the full Bathybian faith. …
>
> This is a case in which a ridiculous error and a ridiculous credulity were the direct results of theoretical preconceptions. Bathybius was accepted because of its supposed harmony with Darwin's speculations.[65]

Bathybius is now known to be one of the "*most peculiar and fantastic errors ever committed in the name of science.*"[66]

Research disproves *Eozoön's* status as a life-form

The *Eozoön* controversy lasted for almost fifty years. Not long after its discovery it "*developed into one of the most contentious issues in nineteenth-century geology.*"[67]

60. Rehbock, "Huxley, Haeckel, and the oceanographers", p. 504.
61. Rehbock, "Huxley, Haeckel, and the oceanographers", p. 504–505.
62. Sibley, A., *Bathybius haeckelii* and a 'reign of terror', *J. Creation* **23**(1):123–127, 2009; p. 123; creation.com/bathybius.
63. Eiseley, *The Immense Journey*, p. 35.
64. Eiseley, *The Immense Journey*, p. 35.
65. Campbell, A great lesson, p. 308.
66. Eiseley, *The Immense Journey*, p. 34.
67. O'Brien, The dawn animal of Canada, p. 206.

A major reason for the long dispute was its critical significance as evidence for evolutionary theory. However, even if *Eozoön* were proven to be one of the first forms of life, it would still require filling the enormous gaps between this very simple putative life-form and the simplest life forms known today which are a million times more complex than *Eozoön*.[68]

However, if *Eozoön* were proven valid, "*evolutionists could rejoice in having found, at the earliest date of known animal life, the simplest form of life, a form reasonably akin to the 'one primordial form' of Darwin's speculation.*"[69]

So strongly had the scientific community clung to *Eozoön* that, although little "*doubt remains of the inorganic origin of Eozoön … encyclopedia and textbook accounts seldom declare its inorganic nature unequivocally; phrases such as 'probably of inorganic origin' or 'most scientists believe' recur over and over.*"[70]

As the evidence piled up against *Eozoön*, Dawson dug in his heels. In defence of his *Eozoön* life-form, he claimed that "*much unreasonable scepticism has been expressed … with reference to the animal nature of Eozoön Canadense.*"[71] Fortunately for science, not every scientist was convinced that the fossils were genuine pre-cell life-forms, and their doubts were eventually proven by careful chemical analysis. *Eozoön* was nothing more than an unusual mineral formation altered by the effects of crystallization and segregation.[72]

Summary

The *Bathybius* and *Eozoön* were both attempts to bridge the gap between inorganic compounds and life. Scientists were so confident in both, that they were scientifically classified as "*Gymnomonera, comprising the genera Bathybius, Protobathybius, Protamoeba, Protogenes, and Myxodictyum, which do not become encysted and consequently protected.*"[73] In Short, the *Bathybius* conclusion was

> based on a misinterpretation of the mineral calcium sulphate occurring in colloidal dispersion by the addition of alcohol to deep-sea ooze samples. A misinterpretation of such enormity by several of the foremost contemporary scientists, the quick and wide acceptance of *Bathybius* in the life and earth sciences, the re-confirmation of its existence on several occasions, and the additional discovery of *Protobathybius Robesonii,* all could occur

68. O'Brien, The dawn animal of Canada, p. 206.
69. O'Brien, The dawn animal of Canada, p. 206.
70. O'Brien, The dawn animal of Canada, p. 223.
71. Dawson, *Dawn of Life*, p. 223.
72. King and Rowney, cited in Mitchell, M.E., On Eozoön canadense, *Isis* **62**(3):381–383, 1971; p. 381.
73. Packard, *Life Histories of Animals, Including Man…* , p. 1.

> because the discovery was a corollary to the respected superstructure of evolutionary theory.[74]

Both *Bathybius* and *Eozoön* were ultimately proven to be nothing more than inanimate matter, as has every other attempt since then as part of the 150-year-long quest to validate the earliest stages of evolution. As Rupke concluded,

> confidence in the heuristic value of evolutionary theory in the second half of the 19th century produced the discovery of a fictitious primitive form of life, called *Bathybius*, its sub-division into two *genera*, its reported occurrence over vast regions of the ocean floor, its identification in the geologic record, and its wide acceptance in the life and earth sciences for the period of almost a decade.[75]

This "*fictitious primitive form of life*" is today an enormous embarrassment for Darwinists. Ironically, we are further away from a solution to both the origin of life and the very earliest purported stages of evolution today than ever before in history. One reason is because of our rapidly increasing level of knowledge about the specified complexity required for even the simplest life-forms possible.

Seton, in a summary of the *Bathybius* story, wrote that from the mud of the bottom of the sea "*in the early days of deep-sea study, Haeckel imagined he had derived his famous Monera—a creature presenting the phenomena of life, irritability and nutrition, without any trace of differentiation of organs. Huxley christened this marvellous being—which fitted in so well with Haeckel's godless theory of creation—'Bathybius Haeckelii'.*"[76,77]

It is now well documented that an unbridgeable gap exists between life and non-life, a fact widely recognized by scientists today.[78]

The origin of life problem is so great that many eminent scientists claim it is not even part of evolution theory![79,80]

---

74. Rupke, *Bathybius haeckelii* and the psychology of scientific discovery, p. 62.
75. Rupke, *Bathybius haeckelii* and the psychology of scientific discovery, p. 53.
76. Seton, W., Physiology of the sea, *The Catholic World*, pp. 162–169, November 1888; p. 167.
77. The modern convention when formulating a binominal name is to use lower case for the species, as in *Bathybius haeckelii.* However, the original naming has been retained here for accuracy.
78. Shapiro, R., *Origins: A Skeptic's Guide to the Creation of Life on Earth*, Summit Books, New York, 1986.
79. Calvin, M., *Chemical Evolution: Molecular Evolution Towards the Origin of Living Systems on the Earth and Elsewhere,* Oxford University Press, New York, 1969.
80. See Darwiniana, Abiogenesis—Origins of Life Research; or TalkOrigins archive, Index to Creationist Claims, Claim CB090, for typical evolutionist arguments on the topic. Searching for Abiogenesis or Origin of Life on creation.com will return a list of articles refuting such statements.

The fact is, abiogenesis, or life from non-life, is chemical evolution, thus is a key part of the General Theory of Evolution. Explaining away the origin of life problem, as attempted by scientists today, is ultimately futile because the theory of evolution requires abiogenesis to get started, even though known physical and chemical laws absolutely forbid it.

CHAPTER 4

More paleoanthropology fraud: The cases of Aimé Rutot, Charles Dawson and Viswat Jit Gupta

Paleoanthropologist Aimé Rutot and the eolith controversy

Belgian Museum conservator Aimé Rutot (1847–1933) was a leading European paleoanthropologist widely respected by many in the scientific community for decades. As a prominent scientist with an international reputation, he published in the leading scientific journals not only in geology, but also in paleoanthropology.[1] Rutot specialised in early human artifacts, especially stone flints.[2]

Rutot is most well-known for his work on eoliths, artifacts believed to be the "*crude evolutionary precursors of Paleolithic*" tools that were claimed to be able to document human brain evolution. Eolith is from the Greek *eos* meaning dawn and *lithos* meaning stone. Eoliths were first named and collected by Gabril de Mortillet in about 1881.[3] The many "*dawn stone*" finds were a major scholarly topic for decades.

By evaluating the eoliths, Rutot and his many disciples argued they were the products of the evolving human brain. Rutot and his supporters concluded that the eoliths were physical evidence that proved a very primitive human brain once existed, thus in their minds proving evolution. They reasoned the eoliths were evidence that primitive brains produced primitive tools and more advanced, evolved brains produced more advanced tools.

Natural stones or human-reworked stones?

These pre-Paleolithic tools were judged by many leading paleoanthropologists to be earlier and simpler than those tools fashioned by more evolved humans. They were actually so simple that it was difficult to determine if they were, in fact, stones reworked by humans or just common naturally formed rocks. One of Rutot's many highly respected converts included Professor Hermann Klaatsch (1863–1916) who discussed in some detail Rutot's work and its importance as evidence for human

1. De Bont, R., The creation of prehistoric man: Aime Rutot and the eolith controversy, 1900–1920, *Isis* **94**(4):604–630, 2003; p. 606.
2. De Bont, The creation of prehistoric man, p. 604.
3. O'Connor, A., Geology, archaeology, and the 'raging vortex of the "eolith" controversy', *Proceedings of the Geologists' Association* **114**(3):255–262, 2003; p. 255.

evolution.[4] Another supporter of the eolith theory was Charles Dawson of the Piltdown forgery fame, who presented papers at conferences, such as the Royal Anthropological Institute in 1915, on the importance of eoliths in human evolution.[5]

Around 1900 more discoveries strengthened Rutot's belief in the human origins of eoliths.[6] A problem was that many of the marks on the stones did not appear intentional, such as is obvious in Indian arrowheads. Ironically, Rutot concluded the marks documented "*a primitive idea of utilization*" of stones.[7] His ideas were then spread throughout the world by the sale of artifacts, statues, and pictures, all of which served to sell human evolution to the public. These stones were even involved in the famous Piltdown forgery.[8]

A formal picture of barrister Charles Dawson (1864–1916) who is widely regarded as the perpetuator of not only the Piltdown fraud but other frauds as well.

Rutot's most ambitious museum project was the "*three-dimensional reconstruction of human evolution*" display, based on his ideas that humans evolved from a "*bestial precursor*" to modern mankind and this accordingly could be documented by the eolith stones. In this and other displays, the 'Negro' was often represented as a less evolved evolutionary stage compared to the 'white race'.[9] The human statues were all crafted to depict some combination of simian and human (often Negro) traits, assembled according to his eolith theory, not fact.

In true Darwinian fashion, his view was that the "*white Europeans were the vanguard of progress*" and that war was actually necessary for progress, both ideas that were woven into his eolith theory.[10] He also relied heavily on racism, concluding that the "*three human races had only a very distant common ancestor.*" As a result, Rutot did not speak

> of "*the origin*" of humanity but of plural "*origins.*" In his view, the superficial similarities between the different races were based on resemblances in lifestyle, not on a common origin. Rutot would even go on to connect every human race with a type of anthropoid ape, stating that the former were the evolved and the latter the degenerate forms of a common stock.[11]

---

4. Klaatsch, H., *The Evolution and Progress of Mankind* (edited and enlarged by Adolf Heilborn and translated by Joseph McCabe), Frederick A. Stokes Company Publishers, New York, p. 265, 1923.
5. Weiner, J.S., *The Piltdown Forgery*, Oxford University Press, New York, p. 135, 2003.
6. De Bont, The creation of prehistoric man, p. 608.
7. De Bont, The creation of prehistoric man, p. 608.
8. Weiner, *The Piltdown Forgery*, p. 116.
9. De Bont, The creation of prehistoric man, p. 622.
10. De Bont, The creation of prehistoric man, p. 628.
11. De Bont, The creation of prehistoric man, p. 628.

His success in spreading his Eolithic theory and his

> views of prehistoric races was due in part to the fact that they met accepted scientific standards. Furthermore, they were the bearers of ideas that were shared by at least some European scientists. … His ideas spread because he was able to involve lots of people in his expanding networks, at the center of which was his own museum. These networks helped him to be omnipresent. He published his articles in leading periodicals; he received archaeological finds from all over the world; his categories were used in important museums; his theories were taught by respected scholars; and his reconstructions of the past were widely known and accepted as authoritative. He skillfully used … different channels to spread his ideas—in popular magazines as well as in universities.[12]

Rutot concluded that the evolution from Eolithic to Paleolithic man was not Darwinian, slow and gradual. Instead, based on the archaeological record and de Vries' mutation theory, it occurred rapidly by leaps.[13] From this evidence Rutot concluded that "*evolution occurred by leaps and that small individual variations were of no importance in a long-term perspective.*"[14]

Based on the archaeological record, Rutot determined that a "*clear dividing line*" existed between "*eoliths and paleoliths*"[15] which we know today was actually a division between naturally made and human-constructed artifacts.

Rutot cooperated with other scientists and other researchers by sending them reports, photographs and even sample eoliths from his extensive collection for their study and evaluation. This enabled him to gain international support for his ideas. At the peak of this debate, in 1906, Rutot's work was widely accepted and he received numerous scientific rewards, recognition, and honours.

As more research on Rutot's findings was completed, the doubts about both his theory and his evidence mounted. Although Rutot claimed that he could distinguish "*real eoliths*" from "*pseudo-eoliths*",[16] the main problem he, like everyone else, faced was in differentiating between the two. The struggle between the supporters of his eolith theory and the detractors became fierce, with each side accusing the other of retouching their photographs, or even outright forgery, and even some claiming that their critics were mentally ill.[17]

Most of Rutot's examples of the putative oldest known human tools that he labelled eoliths have now been shown to be misidentified—careful examination has concluded that they showed no evidence of human workmanship, debunking

12. De Bont, The creation of prehistoric man, p. 629.
13. De Bont, The creation of prehistoric man, p. 616.
14. De Bont, The creation of prehistoric man, p. 616.
15. De Bont, The creation of prehistoric man, p. 616.
16. De Bont, The creation of prehistoric man, p. 610.
17. De Bont, The creation of prehistoric man, p. 614, especially footnote 28.

Rutot's whole eolith theory and, concurrently, his attempt to construct a prehistoric race of primitive humans.[18] Rutot's "*extensive collection of stone implements*" has now been "*discredited as an assemblage of forgeries and misinterpretations.*"[19]

From his eolith collection Rutot attempted to extrapolate the habits and mental capacities of the makers—now recognized as a foolish exercise given the fact that his eoliths were all natural, and not man-made. In his writings, Rutot went into enormous detail speculating about the character, motivations, goals, mentality, intelligence, attitudes, and logic of the race of people that he believed shaped his large rock collection, all based on his eolith stone theory! He concluded, among other things, that the eolith makers were passive, peaceful, and imitative creatures.[20] The eoliths also, he argued, indicated that their creators strove for a "*certain degree of perfection*" but lacked evidence that they were progressive or active creators. All of this uncritical speculation was unfounded and proved to be embarrassing when the true identity of the rocks was determined.

He even discussed in detail the relationships between the eolith and the Paleolithic people, which he determined were two different races. He concluded that the inferior race, the eolith creators, became extinct, though some few descendants survived in isolated groups. He considered the Tasmanian Aborigines, who were systematically exterminated a mere sixty years previously, the last of that inferior race. In later work Rutot stated that other "*races,*" lacking the "*progressive mutations*" of the whites, would eventually follow the Tasmanian example.

> Pygmies, Bushmen, Fuegians, and North American Indians were next on Rutot's list, and he made it clear that racial competition would eliminate many other groups as well. Like many other nineteenth-century anthropologists, Rutot stated that their extinction was a corollary of their social and biological primitivity. This was the "*natural game of the laws of limitation, combined with the ever-extending development of the so-called civilized peoples.*" Violent colonialism was just part of natural progress. … Time served only as a function of natural selection in which the mentally superior eventually massacred the inferior. … In Rutot's world there existed two options, "*to evolve or to perish,*" and both outcomes were direct results of biological determinism.[21]

18. De Bont, The creation of prehistoric man, p. 604.
19. De Bont, The creation of prehistoric man, p. 604.
20. De Bont, The creation of prehistoric man, p. 616.
21. De Bont, The creation of prehistoric man, p. 619.

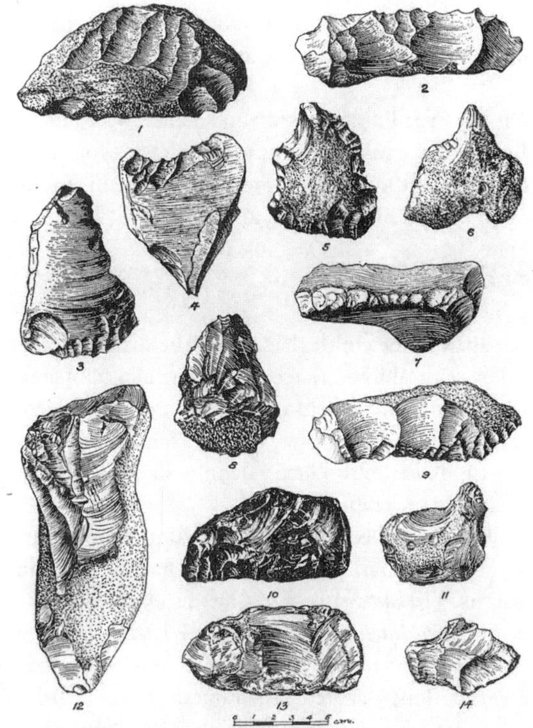

Eoliths from Europe. 1, Puy Boudieu (France); 2, Puy Courny (France); 3, Saint Prest (France); 4, Boncelles (Belgium); 5, 6, Kent Plateau (England); 7, Salisbury (England); 8, 9, 11, 12, 13, 14, Pre-Crag Ipswich (England) after J. R. Moir; 10, Pre-Crag Norwich (England) after Sir E. Ray Lankester.

A set of what were thought to be eoliths, stones that look like they were modified by primitive humans. The source of this sample is from several European countries. It is now known that most claimed eolith samples are either broken rocks, or paleoliths, stones that were modified by humans for use as tools.

Source: Wikimedia Commons. The original is likely from an old textbook produced by Wellcome Images.

A major confirmation of the existence of the eolith race, in Rutot's mind, was Piltdown Man, which proved his theory because "*Piltdown was not only the old human fossil that the éolithophiles had been waiting for; it was even 'excavated'*" in immediate association with Eolithic tools. Furthermore,

> most scientists interpreted the relatively developed skull as an argument in favor of parallel evolution, making Neanderthal a primitive dead-end side branch—a hypothesis Rutot had favoured for some years. With regard to the dating, Rutot initially endorsed the claim of the influential Scottish anatomist Arthur Keith (1866–1955) that the cranium pieces were the remains of

> "*Tertiary man*." Woodward and Dawson had more cautiously presented it as a Lower Quaternary find, but Rutot eagerly agreed with the English *éolithophiles* that the producer of the Pliocene Sussex tools had been discovered.[22]

De Bont notes that both the Piltdown Man and eoliths were "*inextricably bound up with*" efforts to find putative missing links to document evolution by the "*believers … to prove their views*."[23] Rutot was later forced to change his mind about Piltdown Man as new research proved his ideas wrong.

Rutot's theory debunked

The main evidence against the eolith theory was the discovery that perfect eoliths could be produced by natural forces, such as pressure and temperature changes that caused rock flaking. Water movement could also produce the eolith pattern that resembled a stone tool that had one or two chips, as opposed to a human-made stone tool that had 20 to 100 flakes to produce a definite shape, such as a sharp edge that could be used for cutting or scraping.

Warren extensively researched the fracture of flint for five years to evaluate the Eolithic theory, concluding that no clear evidence had been produced that proved the existence of eoliths.[24] In his words, referring to the conclusions of his critics that the eoliths "*must be due to intelligent design on the part of man*", the argument for this conclusion, "*though attractive on the surface, is unscientific to the core*", a fitting end to the three-decade-long debate.[25] The famous paleoanthropologist Professor Marcellin Boule also came to the same conclusion.[26] Rutot once remarked that, even though "*everything has been discredited*" by his peers, he was still going to cling to his conclusions.[27]

Charles Dawson's many forgeries

Although most well-known for his connection to the Piltdown fraud, Charles Dawson was also involved in numerous other questionable paleoanthropology finds

22. De Bont, The creation of prehistoric man, pp. 621.
23. De Bont, The creation of prehistoric man, pp. 621–622.
24. Warren, S.H., On the origin of 'eolithic' flints by natural causes, especially by the foundering of drifts, *The Journal of the Anthropological Institute of Great Britain and Ireland* **35**:337–364, 1905; p. 337.
25. Warren, On the origin of 'eolithic' flints … , p. 338.
26. O'Connor, A., Geology, archaeology, and the 'raging vortex of the "eolith" controversy'.
27. De Bont, The creation of prehistoric man, p. 605.

that relate to human evolution.[28,29,30] Dawson *"achieved recognition as a great, if not the greatest,"* British antiquarian and paleaontologist of his day.[31] Although Dawson earned a living as a solicitor, since his youth he spent much time in search of, and collecting, fossils. He even worked with the distinguished geologist Samuel Beckles.[32]

So great were his achievements that, in 1885, he was elected a fellow of the Geological Society at the young age of 21![33] Russell documented Dawson's enormous productivity, enabling him to sell his many fossil discoveries to the British Museum's 'Dawson Collection' throughout the late 1880s to the early 1900s for large sums of money. His many important finds included three new dinosaur species,

> one of which was named *Iguanodon dawsoni* by the paleontologist Richard Lydekker. Later discoveries included the finding, in 1891, of teeth from a previously unknown species of Wealden mammal, later named *Plagiaulax dawsoni.* Dawson periodically continued his fossil-hunting activities up until 1911, at times working with Marie-Joseph Pierre Teilhard de Chardin, a young Jesuit priest and keen amateur geologist, discovering more unique remains, including a new species of mammal named *Dipriodon valdensis,* and two new forms of fossil plant, *Lycopidites teilhardi* and *Selaginella dawsoni.*[34]

Another problem arose with Dawson's *Plagiaulax dawsoni*, a new mammal species that was considered by many experts an important missing link in the purported evolutionary tree leading to humans. The find, a single tooth discovered in 1891, was submitted and evaluated by the curator of the British Museum of Natural History, Arthur Smith Woodward.[35] Woodward's conclusion, based on the single tooth, was that the tooth was of a "*transitional form between reptile and mammal.*"[36]

Then, 20 years later, Dawson discovered two more teeth and, soon after, Teilhard de Chardin found another tooth, all which they concluded confirmed their original conclusions. Since then, no new evidence of *Plagiaulax dawsoni* has ever come to light.[37]

---

28. Bergman, G., A history of the Piltdown hoax, *Rivista di Biologia/Biology Forum* **96**(3):457–484, 2003.
29. Russell, M., *Piltdown Man: The Secret Life of Charles Dawson & the World's Greatest Archaeological Hoax*, Tempus Publishing, Gloucestershire, UK, 2003.
30. Walsh, J.E., *Unraveling Piltdown: the Science Fraud of the Century and its Solution*, Random House, New York, 1996.
31. Russell, *Piltdown Man*, p. 10.
32. Russell, *Piltdown Man*, p. 13.
33. Walsh, *Unraveling Piltdown*, p. 16.
34. Russell, *Piltdown Man*, p. 14.
35. Walsh, *Unraveling Piltdown*, p. 16.
36. Walsh, *Unraveling Piltdown*, p. 182.
37. Russell, *Piltdown Man*, pp. 29.

As was true of Dawson's later finds, the "*date and location of the discovery are both vague.*"[38] Research has now conclusively shown that *Plagiaulax dawsoni* was a fake.[39] Dawson, an avid collector of fossils, likely modified some of the teeth in his large collection to make them look more like those of what he pictured as the hypothetical missing link. All of the major people involved in the *Plagiaulax dawsoni* fake were also involved in the Piltdown affair, and Dawson was the likely hoaxer of this fake as well. Dawson also used some of the same deception techniques used in the Piltdown hoax. All of his fossils and other finds eventually came under suspicion, causing a careful re-evaluation that proved many, if not most, of his discoveries were questionable, if not outright forgeries.

The field work that brought Dawson to the notice of paleontologists, from his first discovery, *Plagiaulax*, to his last, *Piltdown,* was all connected to the search for putative human evolutionary links.[40]

The problem, as this chapter illustrates, is that the scientific method is an ideal method for gaining knowledge, but it is an especially difficult way to 'prove' certain scientific hypotheses, such as those involving human origins. An evidentialist approach is not suitable for "*the theory of evolution* [which] *is ... a theory highly valued by scientists ... but which lies in a sense too deep to be directly proved or disproved.*"[41]

Professor Viswat Jit Gupta

A more recent case, and one of the "*most pungent*" cases of fraud (though not involving human fossils), involved paleontologist Viswat Jit Gupta.[42] Professor Gupta claimed to have discovered a treasure trove of fossils that added "*astonishing additions to the faunal lists*" of species in the area in which he worked.[43,44] His claims were widely accepted for years. After extensive investigation, researchers concluded that he salted the region with fossils that evidently had been stolen from teaching collections. In his last 25 years he published close to 300 papers on his finds—all of which are now in doubt, as also are all of the numerous papers based, in part, on Gupta's research.[45] Talent concluded that as a result of Gupta forgeries, the scientific data for the Paleozoic and Mesozoic periods of the Himalayas has

38. Walsh, *Unraveling Piltdown*, p. 183.
39. Russell, *Piltdown Man*, p. 30.
40. Russell, *Piltdown Man*, p. 167.
41. Broad, W. and Wade, N., *Betrayers of the Truth: Fraud and Deceit in the Halls of Science*, Simon and Schuster, New York, p. 17, 1982.
42. Talent, J., The case of the peripatetic fossils, *Nature* **338**(6217):613–615, 1989.
43. Talent, The case of the peripatetic fossils, p. 613.
44. Talent, J., The peripatetic fossils: Part 5, *Nature* **343**(6257):405–406, 1990.
45. Grant, J., *Corrupted Science: Fraud, Ideology and Politics in Science*, Facts, Figures and Fun, Surrey, UK, p. 78, 2007.

> become so marred by inconsistency as to throw grave doubts on the scientific validity of any conclusions that might be drawn from it. Because the biostratigraphical underpinning of so much Himalayan stratigraphy is in question, the credibility of many years of labor by numerous geologists is at stake.[46]

The tragedy is: "*The difficulty, labor, and time that have been required to clear up the mess are incalculable. A residue of doubt will long shadow later work*" in paleozoogeography due to Gupta.[47] Talent adds that "*similar cases of carelessness over data or confusion over concepts are rife.*"[48]

A colleague of Gupta who was on several expeditions with Gupta wrote that "*most of the doubts expressed by Talent are well-founded.*"[49] An example he gave was that a sample he provided to Gupta to examine was found to contain "*numerous conodonts*" but the remainder of the sample that Ahluwalia kept for analysis was "*completely barren*" of conodonts—clear evidence that Gupta seeded the sample. He also cites numerous examples of scientific misconduct, such as planting fossil specimens taken from museums or other storage locations to document new discoveries, and finding middle or lower Permian index fossils in Upper Carboniferous sequences.[50]

Another colleague of Gupta, Dr Bhatia, found evidence of remarkable similarities between samples Gupta claimed that he found and those determined by field research to be from very different strata, raising suspicions that Gupta was again planting fossils or lying as to where they were found.[51]

Yet another colleague of Gupta claimed to have obtained samples from the area where Gupta did his fieldwork, then listed several reasons why Gupta's conclusions, as published in several papers, were invalid, or at least very questionable.[52] He concluded from this evidence that he had no choice but to withdraw one of the three papers that he co-authored with Gupta.[53]

In his defence, Gupta wrote that he has offered his critics an opportunity to visit him to examine his relevant fossil collections to disprove the claim that he salted rocks with specimens brought from elsewhere.[54] He argues that dozens of co-workers had worked with him when the controversial finds were made, and that fraud by so many people is very unlikely. He also argues that the government would not allow him to make detailed maps for security reasons, preventing him from obtaining

46. Talent, The case of the peripatetic fossils, p. 614.
47. Judson, H.F., *The Great Betrayal: Fraud in Science*, Harcourt, New York, p. 134, 2004.
48. Talent, The case of the peripatetic fossils, p. 614.
49. Ahluwalia, A.D., The peripatetic fossils: Part 3, *Nature* **341**(6237):13–15, 1989; p. 13.
50. Ahluwalia, The peripatetic fossils: Part 3.
51. Bhatia, S.B., Early Devonian ostracodes, *Nature* **341**(6237):15, 1989.
52. Bassi, U.K., The Kinnaur region, *Nature* **341**(6237):15–16, 1989; p. 15.
53. Bassi, The Kinnaur region, pp. 15–16.
54. Gupta, V. J., The peripatetic fossils: Part 2, *Nature* **341**(6237) 11–12, 1989; p. 11.

precise location data. The claimed "*anomalies*", Gupta argues, call for explanations, and more research, not accusations.[55] His detractors were not convinced.

Evidence now exists that he began "*inventing things*" at the very start of his more than 30-year career. After returning to Germany from America, where he did his doctorate and later accepted a professorship, he "*simply made things up.*" An example of this was a supposedly 50-million-year old "*half-ape*" that he claimed was from Switzerland but was actually found in France. Continued investigation will likely reveal much more about this case, which has reminded many people of the infamous Piltdown affair. Holden concludes that one problem in paleoanthropology is the "*small, elite field*" of professionals in the field, which continues

> to grow as hyper-specialization sets in and additional advances take place in the lab rather than in the field. It tends to be dominated by particular personalities and no matter what new technologies come to the service of the profession, it is the individual who finds the hominid bone who is going to be in the limelight—also in the money. The element of luck adds a piquance to an undertaking that by its nature is of intense public interest. As one observer says, "*you can have equally fascinating scientific squabbles about aphids—the difference is, no one outside the field cares.*"[56]

Professor M.M. Imam

One last example of fraud in paleontology, albeit again not paleoanthropology, is Professor M.M. Imam who "*illustrated material he supposedly collected in remote areas of both Egypt and Libya*" using plagiarized photomicrographs as proof of his research findings.[57] He is accused of stealing at least 19 photomicrographs of fossil algae, which he, in turn, used to support his research findings and conclusions. As a result of the valid concerns about his plagiarism and forgery, all of his research, especially that in paleomicrobiology, is now disputed.[58]

Honest paleoanthropologists

Evolutionists are at times very candid about the state of human evolution, such as Johanson's admission in his book that "*nobody really places a great deal of faith in any human family tree*" now.[59] Yet, many of their arguments are over this tree,

55. Gupta, The peripatetic fossils: Part 2, p. 11.
56. Holden, C., The politics of paleoanthropology, *Science* **213**(4509):737–740, 1981; p. 740.
57. Granier, B., A micropalaeontological fraud that affected the JAES, *Journal of African Earth Sciences* **50**(1):1–5 2008; p. 4.
58. Granier, A micropalaeontological fraud that affected the JAES, p. 4.
59. Johanson, D. C., *Lucy's child: the discovery of a human ancestor,* William Morrow and Company, Inc., New York, p. 131, 1989.

which seems to change with each new fossil find. The reason is that these trees are based on evidence so fragmentary that a variety of plausible interpretations are possible—which is a major reason for the many heated conflicts that the various participants in paleoanthropology have been involved in since the field originated over a century ago.

Conclusions

These few cases reviewed in this chapter illustrate how common the problem of fraud is, and the enormous damage done to science that results from fraud, forgery, and blunders to prove evolution. The Piltdown case is the most well-known, but only the tip of the iceberg, and so many cases exist that we can only cover a few of the better-documented cases in this book. A number of plans designed to reduce the fraud problem have been proposed, such as more rigorous peer review, but how successful these solutions will be only time will tell.[60]

60. Chang, K., On scientific fakery and the systems to catch it, *The New York Times Science Times*, pp. 1, 4, 15 October 2002.

CHAPTER 5

Pithecanthropus alalus, the missing link that never existed: The story of a failed attempt to prove evolution

Introduction

The main evidence used to document human evolution is old bone fragments. The problem is:

> Human bones are common in cemeteries, but remains of our more ancient ancestors and relatives are fewer. … and notoriously difficult to recover. This is particularly true for fossils that are [claimed to be] millions of years old. Biomolecules are geologically short-lived and thus unavailable for parsing truly ancient species lineages.[1]

Furthermore, when old bones are found "*Disagreements are common, and the configuration of the hominid twig on the tree of life remains a matter of particular contention.*"[2] This chapter is about one of the most interesting cases of a human ancestor that lacked not only bones, but teeth, and was created totally in the imagination of one of the most famous evolutionists that ever lived.

Figure 1
Pithecanthropus alalus. This 1894 drawing of an imaginary creature described by Haeckel was a present from the artist for Haeckel's 60th birthday. It was reproduced in 1898 in Haeckel's book *Natürliche Schöpfungsgeschichte* (first ed. 1868; in English *The History of Creation*, first ed. 1876).

The story of the missing link created in the mind of Darwin's leading German disciple, Professor Ernst Haeckel, documents the importance of illustrations and authority in influencing the public's acceptance of evolutionary speculation. The *Pithecanthropus alalus* story is

1. White, T., Paleoanthropology: five's a crowd in our family tree, *Current Biology* **23**(3):R112–R115, 2013; p. R112.
2. White, Paleoanthropology.

one of many events causing major embarrassment to paleoanthropologists today in the long history of the many failed attempts to prove human evolution from a primitive primate ancestor. Winchester is one of several references that spoke of *Pithecanthropus alalus* as "*short, squat creatures* [that] *were definitely human beings, but with such a low mentality that they could not live in the complex society of today.*"[3]

This statement is ironic in view of the fact that *Pithecanthropus alalus* (meaning speechless ape-man) was a putative missing link that never existed.[4] Haeckel, the "*great German apostle of Darwinism*" believed that man evolved "*from the apes and postulated as an annectant form a creature physically halfway between the two.*"[5] The traits of the ape-man evolutionary link originated in Haeckel's mind based on his idiosyncratic, and now largely disproven, ideas about human evolution. The problem was:

> Professor Haeckel insisted a creature intermediate between men and apes must have existed and gave it the Latin name *Pithecanthropus alalus*, meaning "*ape-man without speech.*" In Haeckel's enthusiasm for his subject, he ignored a cardinal rule of scientific classification, or taxonomy: You cannot name a creature before you know whether it exists![6]

This putative creature lived where Haeckel believed humans first evolved, a mythical land called Lemuria. Lemuria was believed to be an enormous, now-sunken continent that once existed all the way from the coast of Africa to the Philippines.[7] Haeckel believed his ape-man spread out from Lemuria to eventually populate the rest of the world.

Supposedly, after many of the ape-men left Lemuria, most of the continent sank into the ocean, cutting the expatriates off from their less evolved brethren, which Haeckel concluded allowed them to evolve into modern humans and acquire speech.[8]

P. alalus also eventually diversified into the twelve different species of humans that Haeckel believed made up the modern human races.[9]

Haeckel described this "*true missing link*" as follows:

---

3. Winchester, A.M., *Biology and its Relation to Mankind*, D. Van Nostrand, Princeton, New Jersey, p. 853, 1962.
4. Moser, S., *Ancestral Images: The Iconography of Human Origins*, Cornell University Press, Ithaca, New York, p. 138, 1998.
5. Boas, F. (Ed.), *General Anthropology*, Heath and Company, Boston, Massachusetts, p. 44, 1938.
6. Milner, R., *The Encyclopedia of Evolution: Humanity's Search for Its Origins*, Facts on File, New York, p. 147, 1990.
7. Theunissen, B, *Eugene Dubois and the Ape-Man From Java*, Kluwer Academic, Dordrecht, The Netherlands, p. 6, 1989.
8. Ramaswamy, S., *The Lost Land of Lemuria*, The University of California Press, Berkeley, California, p. 40, 2004.
9. Ramaswamy, *The Lost Land of Lemuria*; p. 40.

> The form of their skull was probably very long, with slanting teeth; their hair woolly; the colour of their skin dark, of brownish tint. The hair covering the whole body was probably thicker than in any of the still living human species; their arms comparatively longer and stronger; their legs, on the other hand, knock-kneed, shorter and thinner, with entirely undeveloped calves; their walk but half erect.[10]

Flesh and bones soon were added to this somewhat detailed description in the form of an engraving published in artist Henri du Cleuziou's 1887 work titled *The creation of man and the first ages of humanity.* Cleuziou added much artistic licence to the image that he produced. His picture of *P. alalus* shows a tall, thin, hairy male figure walking towards his cave home holding a large stick with a simple axe-head attached to one end (see figure 2 above right). He was pictured as a man with modern physical anatomy modified by adding several ape-like features, including ape-like hairiness and woolly-coated ape-like feet.

Figure 2
Pithecanthropus alalus according to the conclusions of Haeckel.
Source: illustration in Henri du Cleuziou's *La création de l'homme et les premiers âges de humanité* [The creation of man and the first ages of humanity], C. Marpon et Flammarion, Paris, 1887.

These traits of *P. alalus,* such as his hairy covering, dark skin, and thick lips were inspired primarily by certain ape and negroid racial features. A problem was "*Ernst Haeckel, the influential German evolutionist, went so far as to include this hypothetical 'missing link' in his books and even gave it a Latin species name*" implying that it was a real link that was no longer missing.[11]

The most famous picture of *P. alalus* (figure 1) was by the prominent artist Gabriel von Max (1840–1915) in 1894. From 1898 onwards it was reproduced in the last three editions of Haeckel's book.[12] When he introduced the painting to the world, Haeckel received a great deal of public acclaim for his 'discovery'. Moser wrote that von Max

> brought Haeckel's "*missing link*" to life in a painting which he gave to Haeckel on his birthday and which Haeckel reproduced in later editions of

10. Haeckel, E., *The History of Creation,* Vol. 2, Kegan Paul, Trench, Trübners, London, p. 438, 1889; [same page in 1911 edition].
11. Milner, *The Encyclopedia of Evolution,* p. 308.
12. Haeckel, E., *Natürliche Schöpfungsgeschichte,* Georg Reimer, p. 105, 1902.

> his major work *Natürliche Schöpfungsgeschichte* (The History of Creation). This dramatic picture features a docile couple with an infant.[13]

Von Max's depiction was very different from Cleuziou's, as is obvious by comparing the two pictures shown in figures 1 and 2. Von Max's drawing showed a short, hairy ape-faced male clinging to a tree, indicating that he could not stand up unassisted. In front of him was a short, less ape-like female, sitting cross-legged on the ground while breast-feeding her baby. Moser describes the obese nude male staring "*vacantly into space, perhaps contemplating his miserable situation*" as the nude hairy "*female gazes at the viewer, perhaps demanding sympathy for their plight.*"[14]

Furthermore, although clearly human, both of the figures in this painting had "*many ape-like qualities, including their feet, their hairiness and their ape-like posture. Without clothes and a material culture of any form, they appeared very vulnerable.*"[15]

Also, both depictions of *P. alalus* have many negroid features because it was widely believed that "*the lower races … are relics of human ancestors, 'living fossils' who would provide clues as to what ancestral man might have looked like.*"[16]

In short, Haeckel used 'scientific racism' to create his *P. alalus* in order to link apes to modern humans. Although Haeckel rejected certain putative ape-man fossil finds, he did support

> the authenticity of the reconstruction produced by Gabriel von Max … . He emphasized Max's thorough knowledge of primate anatomy, stating that this and his extensive collection of skeletal remains enabled him to present a highly plausible interpretation. Later, Haeckel referred to the genius of the artist in creating such an accurate representation. The dramatic appeal of this painting, like Boitard's portrait, resulted in it being reproduced in many other texts on human evolution.[17]

Pictures are easily grasped and, to the uninformed, can be very convincing evidence of evolution. As Haeckel's biographer commented, when the von Max picture was published "*who could doubt the existence of that contented-looking burgher family?*"[18] Theunissen noted that "*Haeckel regarded human descent from the apes as a proven fact and, in his opinion, the process was sufficiently documented through comparative anatomy and embryology, rendering unnecessary the search for fossil transitional forms.*"[19]

---

13. Moser, *Ancestral Images*, p. 140.
14. Moser, *Ancestral Images*, p. 141.
15. Moser, *Ancestral Images*, p. 141.
16. Ramaswamy, *The Lost Land of Lemuria*, p. 41.
17. Moser, *Ancestral Images*, p. 141.
18. Richards, R.J., *Ernst Haeckel: The Tragic Sense of Life*, University of Chicago Press, Chicago, p. 255, 2008.
19. Theunissen, *Eugene Dubois and the Ape-Man From Java*, p. 74.

Haeckel postulated that only 22 separate steps were required to evolve the earliest lumps of matter, which he called Monera, into modern humans. His *P. alalus* was link number 21. Ramaswamy noted that the idea "*that a submerged continent like Lemuria was the original cradle of mankind solved the problem of producing material proof in the form of fossil remains.*"[20] Thus, the reason there was no evidence of *P. alalus* was because all of the fossil remains were destroyed when the mythical land of Lemuria sank into the ocean.

Was Haeckel's vision vindicated?

Some claim that Haeckel's hypothetical ape-man was vindicated by Eugene Dubois' discovery of a fossil commonly referred to as Java Man. Regarding this claim, Milner wrote:

> In one of his bolder public pronouncements, Haeckel stated that the "*missing link*" between men and apes must have lived in Java or Borneo. Although there was no known fossil evidence for such a creature, he gave it a Linnaean name anyway—*Pithecanthropus alalus* … and encouraged his students to go out and find it. It is one of the amazing stories of science that a young doctor who attended Haeckel's lectures, a Dutchman named Eugene Dubois, became so infused with this confident enthusiasm he went to Java and dug up what he called *Pithecanthropus erectus* (later renamed *Homo erectus*).[21]

Haeckel's reason for selecting this location was because he thought Java was once part of the mythical continent of Lemuria where he believed that humans first evolved from apes. A major problem with the claim that Dubois discovered Haeckel's *P. alalus* is the fact that Dubois' Java Man was very different from Haeckel's hypothetical missing link.

Another myth in the story of Eugene Dubois' discovery was that, having discovered a "*missing link that Ernst Haeckel predicted must exist,*" Dubois named it *Pithecanthropus erectus,* using the genus name that Haeckel coined, *Pithecanthropus,* for his hypothetical human ancestor. Although Dubois did give the fossils the genus name *Pithecanthropus,* meaning 'ape-man', his initial choice was *Anthropithecus,* meaning, 'man-ape'. As Theunissen convincingly argued, Dubois ended up using the term *Pithecanthropus* for reasons other than to recognize Haeckel's ideas.[22] It turned out that many of Haeckel's ideas were proven wrong.[23]

---

20. Ramaswamy, *The Lost Land of Lemuria*, p. 40.
21. Milner, *The Encyclopedia of Evolution*, p. 206.
22. Theunissen, *Eugene Dubois and the Ape-Man From Java*, p. 206.
23. Swisher, C.C. III, Curtis, G.H, and Lewin, R., *Java Man: How Two Geologists' Dramatic Discoveries Changed our Understanding of the Evolutionary Path to Modern Humans*, Scribner, New York, pp. 31, 52–57, 79, 181, 2000.

Actually, Haeckel should have suggested to his students that, instead of going to Java, they should journey to the northeast part of Africa, which turned out to be a far more fruitful region for finding putative hominoid fossils. Haeckel did influence Dubois, and Theunissen cited as evidence of his influence the fact that "*Dubois belonged to the school of morphology founded by Haeckel and Gegenbaur*" and was "*no more averse than Haeckel to speculative reconstructions of possible lines of descent or to the insertion of hypothetical intermediate forms, as we can clearly see from Dubois' phylogenetic tree for* Pithecanthropus."[24]

Conclusions

In the end, *Pithecanthropus alalus* became a major embarrassment to paleoanthropologists, an event that most evolutionists today would rather forget, not least because of its racist implications. As Milner wrote, "*Haeckel was often reckless in his methods, as if he had some kind of direct line to the source of evolutionary truth.*"[25]

Theunissen opined, "*Haeckel was not lacking in imagination; even his contemporaries felt that he sometimes indulged too freely in speculation.*"[26]

In the end, although Haeckel was tentative in his advocacy of Lemuria, keeping open the possibility that it might be in Asia or Africa where the first humans evolved, "*to the end of his scholarly life he continued to invoke Lemuria as the cradle of mankind.*"[27]

The *P. alalus* story was the beginning of a series of guesses, speculations, blunders, and forgeries involving an ideological blindness that still exists today, and still adversely affects science, especially paleoanthropology.

---

24. Theunissen, *Eugene Dubois and the Ape-Man From Java*, p. 74–75.
25. Milner, *The Encyclopedia of Evolution*, p. 206.
26. Theunissen, *Eugene Dubois and the Ape-Man From Java*, p. 6.
27. Ramaswamy, *The Lost Land of Lemuria*, p. 38.

CHAPTER 6

The human facial angle blunder to prove evolution and the human race hierarchy

Introduction

The use of the facial angle, a method of measuring the forehead-to-jaw relationship, has a long history. It was often used to make judgments about the inferiority or superiority of certain human races. University of Chicago Professor of Zoology Ransom Dexter wrote, the "*subject of the facial angle has occupied the attention of philosophers from earliest antiquity.*"[1]

Even in Aristotle's day the facial angle was used to help determine a person's intelligence and to rank human races from inferior to superior.[2,3] It was first used in modern times for the purpose of comparing human races by Petrus Camper (1722–1789).[4] The facial angle theory then became widely popular until it was disproved in the early part of the twentieth century.[5]

The theory proposed that evolutionary history involved a progression from a nearly horizontal facial angle in fish to a vertical one in humans, a transition that also was used to support the evolution of ape-like creatures to humans (see figure 1). Facial angle was also commonly used in classifying other animals from primitive to highly evolved life-forms.[6]

Proponents of the facial angle theory hypothesized that facial angle not only showed a trend from fish to humans, but also could be used to *rank* human racial groups from inferior to superior.[7] It soon became a "*primary instrument of scientific racism.*"[8]

---

1. Dexter, R., The facial angle, *Popular Science Monthly* **4**:588, 1874.
2. Haller, J., *Outcasts from Evolution*, University of Illinois Press, Chicago, p. 9, 1971.
3. Colander, D., Prasch, R. E. and Sheth, F. A., *Race, Liberalism, and Economics*, University of Michigan Press, Ann Arbor, Michigan, p. 45, 2006.
4. Camper, P., *Dissertation on the Natural Varieties Which Characterize the Human Physiognomy*, 1792 (published posthumously).
5. Nederveen Pieterse, J., *White on Black: Images of Africa and Blacks in Western Popular Culture,* Yale University Press, New Haven, Connecticut, p. 47, 1992.
6. Lawrence, W., *Lectures on Physiology, Zoology, and the Natural History of Man*, Foote and Brown, Salem, Massachucetts, pp. 115, 146–147, 289–291, 1828.
7. Jeffries, J.P., *The Natural History of the Human Races,* Edward O. Jenkins, New York, pp. 346–348, 1869.
8. Gould, S.J., Petrus Camper's angle, *Natural History* **96**(7):12–18, 1987; p. 14.

The facial angle was widely cited as 'scientific' evidence by racists, such as Arthur de Gobineau, to justify racism on what they believed were solid scientific grounds.[9]

It was also influenced by the now discredited pseudoscience of phrenology, the 'science' of determining mental traits by evaluating various skull traits such as bumps and valleys (See Figure 4 on page 95). As an example, which was also used in phrenology, the ancients believed a 90 degree facial line was a sign of a great level of

> knowledge and reflection, and a corresponding contraction of the mouth, jaws, tongue, nose, indicated a noble and generous nature. Hence they have extended the facial angle to 90° in the representation of legislators, sages, poets, and others, on whom they wished to bestow the most august character. In the statues of their heroes and gods they have still further exaggerated the human, and reduced the animal characteristics; extending the forehead over the face, so as to push the facial line beyond the perpendicular, and to make the angle 100°.[10]

Thus, facial angle was believed by scientists to have effectively quantified not only the "*very striking difference between man and all other animals,*" but also the difference between the various human 'races'.[11] Science historian John Haller concluded that the "*facial angle was the most extensively elaborated and artlessly abused criterion for racial somatology*" in the late 1800s.[12]

Supporters of this theory cited, as convincing proof, very distorted drawings of an obvious Negro or Australian Aboriginal as being the lowest type of human and a Caucasian as the highest racial type (see figure 2). The slanting Negro forehead shown in the pictures indicated a smaller frontal cortex, such as is typical of apes, demonstrating to naïve observers their alleged inferiority. This observation was important because the frontal cortex is the location of higher mental faculties, such as reasoning ability. It thus was assumed that this part of the brain became larger as humans evolved, slowly changing the facial angle closer to the more evolved 90 degrees.[13]

History of the theory

The first angular measurement system for the comparative study of human crania was devised by the renowned Dutch anatomy professor Petrus Camper in his 1792

9. De Gobineau, A., *The Inequality of Human Races*, The Noontide Press, Los Angeles, pp. 108–109, 1966.
10. Lawrence, *Lectures on Physiology, Zoology, and the Natural History of Man*, p. 148.
11. Lawrence, W., *Lectures on Comparative Anatomy, Physiology, Zoology, and the Natural History of Man*, 9th edition, Henry G. Bohn, London, p. 115, 1848.
12. Haller, *Outcasts from Evolution*, p. 9.
13. Haller, *Outcasts from Evolution*, p. 9–13.

Dissertation on the Natural Varieties Which Characterize the Human Physiognomy.[14] His system exerted such a profound influence on the development of the physical anthropology field that he often is called "*the grandfather of scientific racism.*"[15]

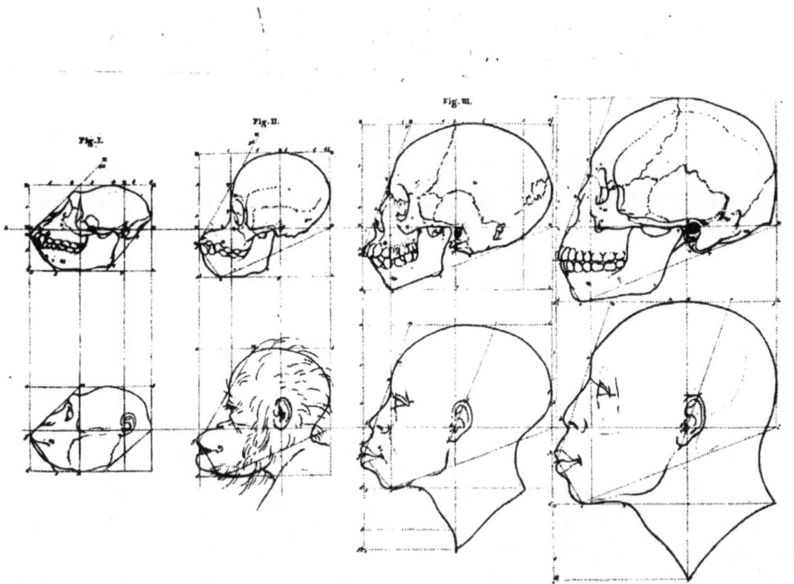

Figure 1
Camper's diagrams compare both ape and human skulls and also flesh-covered heads of both.
From Camper, P., Dissertation on the Natural Varieties Which Characterize the Human Physiognomy, 1792.

One study Camper completed involved comparing the heads of ancient Greek sculptures with those drawn by Dutch and Flemish artists.[16] He observed that, judging by these sculptures which now are known to be inaccurate, the face profile of the heads of famous Greek men was much steeper than those of Dutch and Flemish heads.

He then extended the comparison to animals and discovered that the jaw structure was important in determining the head and face angle (see Figure 3 on page 94).

---

14. Meijer, M.C., Facial Angle, in Frank Spencer, *History of Physical Anthropology: an Encyclopedia*, Garland, New York, p. 373, 1997.
15. Gould, Petrus Camper's angle, p. 12.
16. Greene, J.C., *The Death of Adam: Evolution and Its Impact on Western Thought*, The Iowa State University Press, Ames, Iowa, p. 190, 1959.

Camper concluded that, by comparing the heads of Negroes, Calmucks, Europeans, and apes, a line could be "*drawn from the forehead to the upper lip*" that reveals differences

> in the physiognomy of these peoples and makes apparent a marked analogy between the head of the Negro and that of the ape. After having traced the outline of several of these heads on a horizontal line, I added the facial lines of the faces, with their different angles; and immediately upon inclining the facial line forward, I obtained a head like that of the ancients; but when I inclined that line backwards, I produced a Negro physiognomy, and definitively the profile of an ape, of a Chinese, of an idiot in proportion as I inclined this same line more or less to the rear.[17]

Harvard Professor Stephen Jay Gould wrote that Camper's famous

> treatise is remembered today for one primary achievement—the definition of the so-called facial angle, the first widely accepted measurement for comparing the skulls of different races and nationalities. Camper's facial angle is the traditional beginning of craniometry, or the science of measuring human skulls, a major sub-discipline of physical anthropology.[18]

Although the facial angle hypothesis became a major plank for racists that is still used today, Meijer concluded that, because Camper was a creationist, the accusation that he introduced the system to sanction the view that Africans were racially inferior is incorrect.[19] Camper believed that all races were descended from Adam and Eve, and, thus, all races are brothers and equal.[20]

The racist interpretation of his idea came much later, especially after Darwin published his *Origin of Species* in 1859. Nonetheless, Camper's research was the basis of the later work that eventually became scientific racism.

Another researcher, Dr Charles White, took an interest in the facial angle when he noticed that a friend's skull collection could be lined up by facial angles and, starting with the smallest facial angle, produced a progression from monkey, to orangutan, to the 'lowest' human race, the African, to American Indian, to the Asiatics and, lastly, to the 'highest' races, the Europeans.[21]

White concluded "*that Nature would not employ gradation in one instance only, but would adopt it as a general principle.*"[22] Why 'nature' would do this was not stated.

17. Quoted in Greene, *The Death of Adam*, pp. 190–191.
18. Gould, Petrus Camper's angle, p. 12.
19. Meijer, Facial Angle, pp. 373–376.
20. Gould, Petrus Camper's angle, p. 18.
21. Jordan, W.D., *The White Man's Burden,* Oxford University Press, New York, p. 199, 1968.
22. Jordan, *The White Man's Burden*, p. 199.

White then *"composed a lengthy catalogue of the particular ways in which the Negro more closely resembled the ape than the European."*[23] He concluded that a major difference between 'Europeans and Negroes' was that the latter had a smaller brain capacity than Europeans. He eventually produced an enormous study called *An Account of the Regular Gradation in Man, and in Different Animals and Vegetables; and From the Former to the Latter* (1799). In this book he wrote that every person who has studied natural history

> must have been led occasionally to contemplate the beautiful gradation that subsists amongst created beings, from the highest to the lowest. From man down to the smallest reptile ... Nature exhibits ... an immense chain of beings, endued with various degrees of intelligence and active powers, suited to their stations in the general system."[24]

Professor Winthrop Jordan concluded that White's work was critical in spreading scientific racism:

> Dr. Charles White's book was of considerable importance not only because it was read (not widely but in important quarters) in America but because it established a striking precedent for grounding opinions about the Negro in the ostensibly ineluctable facts of comparative anatomy. His case for Negro inferiority rested upon an unprecedented if not always reliable array of physiological detail.[25]

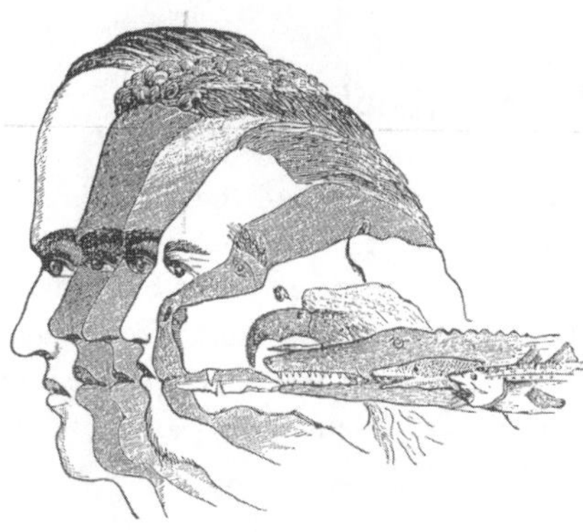

Figure 2
An example of the facial angle theory used to defend racism. Starting from the left, the first four show human races, from the highest to the lowest, followed by a dog, a bird, a reptile and last, two fish.
Source: R. Dexter, *Popular Science Monthly*, **4**:588, 1874.

23. Jordan, *The White Man's Burden*, p. 199.
24. White, C., quoted in Jordan, W.D., *White over Black*, The University of North Carolina Press, Chapel Hill, North Carolina, p. 499, 1968.
25. Jordan, W.D., *White over Black*, The University of North Carolina Press, Chapel Hill, North Carolina, p. 501, 1968.

Other researchers, such as German anatomist Samuel Soemmerring, continued this line of research until a "*racial hierarchy now seemingly based on genuinely scientific insights was established, and 'Camper's facial angle' became the means most often used in physical anthropology to demonstrate the superiority of the White race.*"[26]

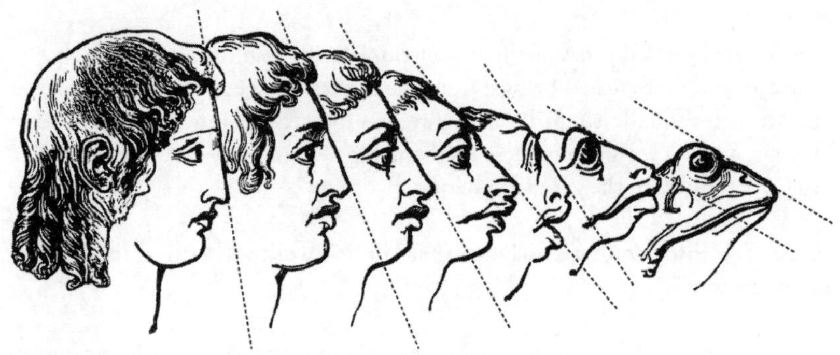

Figure 3
A common example of the facial angle reprinted in many pre-1900 science books. Redrawn by Richard Geer from a drawing by Jean Ignace Isidore Gerard in *Metamorphoses de jour,* Garnier Frères, Paris, 1869.

The facial angle incorporated into phrenology

As noted, the facial angle idea soon was incorporated into the now discredited pseudoscience of phrenology. For example, an article in *The Phrenological Journal* by an author named 'Cranium' includes the illustration commonly found in nineteenth-century literature ranking life from simple to complex, from snakes to humans (see Figure 4). It also ranks humans from inferior to superior.[27] The author showed photos of actual skulls of a "*civilized*" Caucasian and an African whom he called a "*savage*", one of "*the lower classes of men.*"[28]

26. Meijer, Facial Angle, p. 376.
27. Cranium, The Brain and Skull, *The Phrenological Journal*, p. 206, 1909.
28. Cranium, The Brain and Skull, p. 206–207.

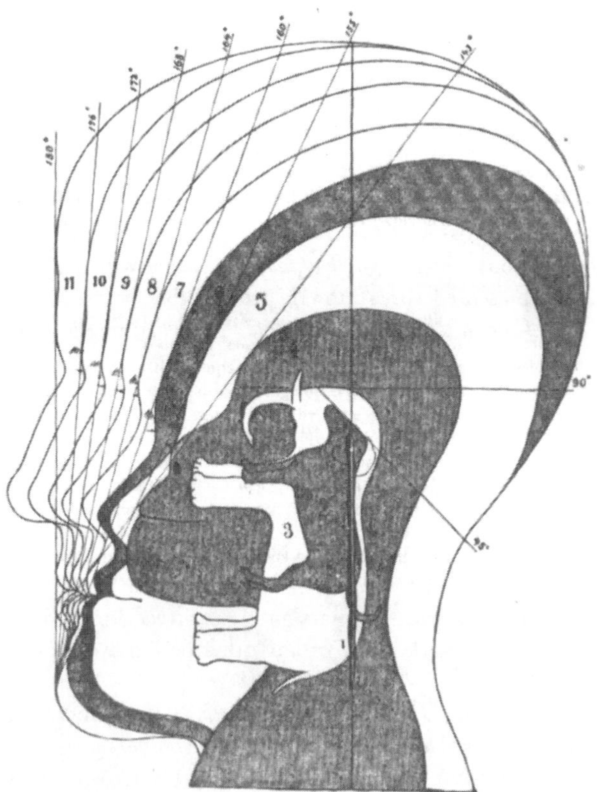

Figure 4

An example of the facial angle concept used to not only support racism but phrenology, the idea that skull shape can be used to determine personality traits.

Source: *The Phrenological Journal and Science of Health.* **122**(7):206. July 1909.

How facial angle was measured

The common method of determining facial angle was to draw a line from the occipital condyle along the floor of the nostrils, which was then intersected by a second line that touched the most prominent parts of the forehead and upper jaw (see Figure 1 on page 91). In Figure 4 on page 95 lines are drawn to show the angle. The intersected angle is called the facial angle.[29] The angle supposedly ranged from under 70 degrees for Africans to about 100 degrees for the 'highest' race, the

29. Dexter, The facial angle, p. 587.

Caucasians.[30] This measurement was used by evolutionists for decades to prove an inferiority-superiority hierarchy and is still widely used in racist literature today.[31,32]

Professor Dexter wrote that, although in the West the facial angle theory has occupied the attention of philosophers since antiquity, facial angle proponents now had physical evidence purportedly showing the intellectual differences in human races.[33] He then explained how facial angle is related, not only to intelligence and brain complexity, but also to the evolutionary progression of human traits. His major conclusion was that evolution from the lowest to the highest vertebrate progressed through almost "*imperceptible gradations*" as Darwin's theory required.[34]

Dexter then presented three human profiles that "*represent the savage, the half-civilized, and the cultivated races of man.*" The racial implications of his drawings were crystal clear.

In the first view, the picture next to the view of the 'idiot' which is the fourth profile from the profile on the far left of the illustration (see Figure 2 on page 93), is a drawing from a correct engraving of the celebrated North American Indian chief Black Hawk, and corresponds in brain capacity, facial angle, and mental powers, very nearly to the other 'savage' races, viz., the Malayan and Ethiopian. The next that is represented in the cut is the half-civilized Mongolian race, illustrating very nicely the ratio of the two factors physical and mental. The last is the representation of the highly-cultivated Caucasian man, and is a correct profile view of one of the most illustrious statesmen that this or any other nation ever possessed—that of Daniel Webster.[35]

Dexter concluded that "*In every vertebrate animal, then, are two factors, the physical and mental; the facial angle is the typical expression or exponent of the relative strength or condition of each.*"[36] Regarding the 'idiot', Dexter wrote that

> The profile of the idiot … illustrate[s] the influence upon the size and shape of the *cranium,* or skull, that an arrest of brain development has wrought, and which corresponds to the mental manifestations of its subject.[37]

Those with mental deficiencies, including Down syndrome, once called Mongoloid idiocy, were labelled idiots, morons and imbeciles—all once medical terms—and often described as atavisms, or evolutionary throwbacks to an earlier evolutionary

30. Haller, *Outcasts from Evolution*, p. 9.
31. Note figure 5 in Jeffries, *The Natural History of the Human Races*, p. 347.
32. See chapter 8 of Bergman, J. *The Darwin Effect. Its influence on Nazism, Eugenics, Racism, Communism, Capitalism & Sexism*, Master Books, Green Forest, Arkansas, 2014.
33. Dexter, The facial angle, pp. 588, 590–91.
34. Dexter, The facial angle, p. 590.
35. Dexter, The facial angle, p. 591.
36. Dexter, The facial angle, p. 591.
37. Dexter, The facial angle, p. 591.

ancestor of humans, such as Aborigines, meaning early, less evolved, man.[38] Even the level of "*stupidity*" of a normal human was associated with the facial angle—the greater the angle, the more stupid the subject.[39]

For adult humans, the facial angle varied from 65 to 85 degrees, and the former value is close to monkeys (see figure 3). Furthermore, the angle can be extended beyond humans "*as the Greeks have done in their representations of the Deity,*" but beyond 100 degrees

> the head would appear deformed. That angle, according to Camper, constitutes the most beautiful countenance; and hence he supposes the Greeks adopted it. "*For,*" says he, "it is certain no such head was ever met with, and I cannot conceive any such should have occurred among the Greeks, since neither the Egyptians, … nor the Persians, nor the Greeks themselves, ever exhibit such a formation on their medals, when they are representing the portrait of any real character.[40]

Another researcher, Professor John Kennedy, compared the baboon and, to use the term once common, but not properly used today, Negro, finding that the baboon facial angle is about 58 degrees, the Negro 70 degrees, and the European 80 degrees.[41] Thus the Negro, it implies here, is less intelligent than Caucasians, less evolved; but more intelligent, more evolved, than baboons.

By 1898 the facial angle was also used to measure human 'degeneracy'. Talbot noted that a chimpanzee has a facial angle of 40 to 50 degrees because the jaw occupies two thirds of the skull and the brain only one third. Negroes allegedly had facial angles close to 70 degrees compared to 75 to 80 degrees for Caucasians because the brain was encroaching and the jaw receding.[42] Although Talbot agrees that, in general, the facial angle is solid evidence for physical and behavioural degeneracy, he concludes it is not an ideal method to study this trait, but other factors, such as the shape of the ear pinna, may be more important![43]

The theory's demise

As early as 1848, it was recognized by at least one researcher that facial angle measurement was nothing more than "*one of the most simple (though often insufficient)*

38. Stephen Jay Gould, Dr. Down's syndrome, *Natural History* 89:142–148, 1980.
39. Lawrence, *Lectures on Comparative Anatomy …* , p. 147.
40. Lawrence, *Lectures on Comparative Anatomy …* , pp. 148–149.
41. Kennedy, J., *The Natural History of Man; or Popular Chapters on Ethnography*, John Cassell, London, pp. 17–18, 1860.
42. Talbot, E.S., *Degeneracy: Its Causes, Signs, and Results*, Walter Scott Ltd., Paternoster Square Charles Scribner's Sons, London, p. 182, 1898.
43. Talbot, *Degeneracy*, pp. 193, 212–218.

methods of expressing … the relative proportion of the cranium and face."[44] Lawrence noted that normal maturation changes the facial angle—for children the facial angle was as high as 90 degrees—a factor often ignored in research in this field. Other factors that eventually caused the demise of the theory included the advancement of scientific knowledge, the Civil Rights Movement, and a realization that the drawings used to illustrate the idea were horribly distorted, as is obvious in figures 1 and 4.

One of the first opponents of the facial angle theory, as well as the Negro inferiority claim, was President Samuel Stanhope Smith of Princeton University. His motivation was his belief that a "*sound study of natural philosophy could only confirm the revealed Word*" of God.[45]

He concluded from his studies that all "*mankind constituted a single species and that human varieties had come to differ in appearance through the operation of natural causes.*"[46] He then attempted to challenge Charles White and others, concluding that his critics

> failed to take into account the changes which the American environment was producing especially in domestic slaves and free Negroes. Was the formation of the jaw, the teeth, or the nose of the Negro of inferior quality? … "*in the United States, the physiognomy, and the whole figure and personal appearance of the African race is undergoing a favorable change.*" … but among the domestics of the South and even more among the free Negroes of Princeton are limbs "*as handsomely formed as those of the inferior and laboring classes, either of Europeans, or Anglo-Americans.*"[47]

Although his writings were "*written in defence of the Negro, … in effect Smith was denying inherent inferiority while conceding present inferiority.*"[48] Smith, Jordan concluded, was actually affirming human "*equality in the brotherhood of man as embedded in the story of Genesis.*"[49]

When skeptics objected to the racial implications of the face angle theory on the basis of the Bible's account of creation, White and others argued that the Bible is not a "*handbook of natural history.*"[50] Nonetheless, research increasingly has documented the fact that analysis of careful measurements showed that the theory was false because there were far too many exceptions to make any valid generalizations. Facial angle has nothing to do with intelligence except in the clear cases of disease.

---

44. Lawrence, *Lectures on Comparative Anatomy …* , p. 115.
45. Jordan, *The White Man's Burden*, p. 201.
46. Jordan, *White over Black*, p. 487.
47. Jordan, *The White Man's Burden*, p. 201.
48. Jordan, *The White Man's Burden*, p. 201.
49. Jordan, *White over Black*, p. 488.
50. Jordan, *White over Black*, p. 502.

The theory's historical influence in the propagation of evolution

The facial angle "*was maintained as a central measure of racial worth*" for many decades after it was falsified.[51] Unfortunately, the importance of such disproven ideas for establishing Darwinism and racism has, to some extent, been conveniently 'forgotten'.[52] Fortunately, scholars such as the late Harvard University Professor Stephen Jay Gould and others occasionally remind us of the historical importance of using the facial angle and other now debunked ideas for supporting both evolution and racism.

Summary

The facial angle system was widely considered fully valid for both documenting and demonstrating the evolution of life from fish to humans. Facial angle was even used to rank how close animals were evolutionarily to humans.[53]

Furthermore, as noted, the facial angle was "*one of the main initiators of racial craniology, which emerged during the nineteenth century*" to justify racism even though Camper himself, as a creationist, did not support this view. Thus, unfortunately, Camper was incorrectly "*accused of having introduced a measurement that sanctioned the opinion that the African was racially inferior and that this racial group occupied a position in the scala naturae midway between the European and the apes.*"[54]

As research accumulated, the evidence increasingly documented the fact that far too many exceptions existed for the theory to be valid. It was realized that often only cases that supported the theory were selected, and those that did not were ignored. Another reason for its demise was that facial angle was connected with phrenology, the now discredited 'science' of determining personality by evaluating skull bumps and indentations.[55]

The underlying assumption in both facial angle and phrenology is that intelligence increases directly with brain volume. This idea has long been refuted by scientific research, and factors other than volume are more highly correlated with intelligence, including the number of cortical neurons and their connection speed.[56]

---

51. Stepan, N., *The Idea of Race in Science: Great Britain 1800–1960*, Archon, Hamden, Connecticut, p. 34, 1982.
52. Wolpoff, M. and Caspari, R., *Race and Human Evolution: A Fatal Attraction*, Simon and Schuster, New York, 1997.
53. Lawrence, *Lectures on Physiology, Zoology, and the Natural History of Man*, pp. 115–116.
54. Meijer, Facial Angle, p. 373.
55. Cranium, The Brain and Skull.
56. Roth, G. and Dicke, U., Evolution of the brain and intelligence, *Trends in Cognitive Sciences* **9**(5):250–257, 2005.

CHAPTER 7

The failed attempt to use fingerprints to prove evolution and race inferiority

Introduction

A formal portrait of Francis Galton taken in the 1850s. He was Charles Darwin's half-cousin, sharing the common grandparent Erasmus Darwin.

Attempts to document Darwinism and eugenics by human fingerprints involved several famous scientists including Darwin's cousin, Francis Galton. Galton is sometimes remembered as *"an esteemed scientist who was interested in using Darwin's theories to improve the human race."*[1] Less well known is the fact that Galton's original purpose in developing the fingerprint system was primarily to further his eugenic goals by identifying members of what he judged as inferior races.[2] Galton even attempted to use fingerprints as a barometer to measure the evolutionary level of the various human races. The history of fingerprinting also reveals much about Galton and how he schemed to take credit for its discovery.

The history of fingerprint use

The first practical use of fingerprints was to establish the identity of a person, similar to how a driver's licence is used today.[3] In many countries, prison sentences for a first offence were very light compared to second or third offences. For this reason, offenders caught red-handed committing a crime often attempted to give a false name so that they would be sentenced as a first offender. Fingerprints were first used to determine the accused's true identity, often

1. Beavan, C., *Fingerprints: The Origins of Crime Detection and the Murder Case that Launched Forensic Science*, Hyperion, New York, p. 73, 2001.
2. Cole, S.A., *Suspect Identities: A History of Fingerprinting and Criminal Identification*, Harvard University Press, Cambridge, Massachusetts, 2001.
3. Cole, S.A., Fingerprint identification and the criminal justice system: historical lessons for the DNA debate, chapter 4, in Lazer, D. (Ed.), *DNA and the Criminal Justice System: The Technology of Justice*, MIT Press, Cambridge, Massachusetss, p. 65, 2004.

finding that the accused were not first offenders as they claimed, but *were* multiple repeat offenders.[4]

Another important use of fingerprints was to identify criminals by the print marks they left at the crime scene. Fingers contain over 3,000 sweat glands per square inch, a denser distribution than on any other part of the body.[5] When a finger presses against almost any surface, it leaves an impression similar to self-inking rubber stamp impressions on paper. At the scene of a crime, almost everything touched by bare hands leaves identifying fingerprint marks due to the fingerprints' unique ridges and valleys. The use of fingerprints for this purpose was one of the most important breakthroughs in forensic science. Less well known is the fact that fingerprints were closely tied to efforts to help determine certain character traits, such as intelligence, a propensity toward criminality, and attempts to correlate fingerprint pattern types with race, ethnicity, and even insanity.[6]

How fingerprinting works

Fingerprints are now recognized as a biologically unique trait for every person that has ever lived.[7] The pattern exists because the finger ridges are heavily influenced by individual factors, including genetics, but are also influenced by the womb environment and growth pressures and stresses. Even identical twins, although they cannot be distinguished by standard DNA tests, have different fingerprints because fingerprints are influenced by many factors.[8]

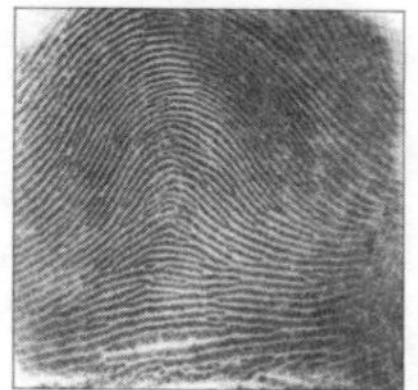

A fingerprint showing the arch.

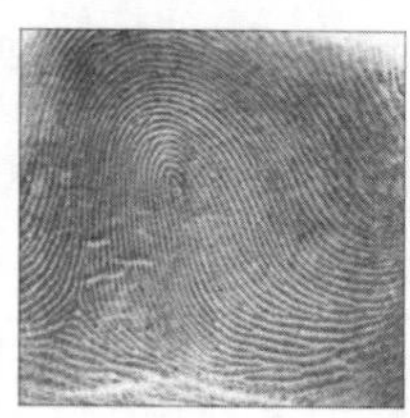

A fingerprint showing the loop.

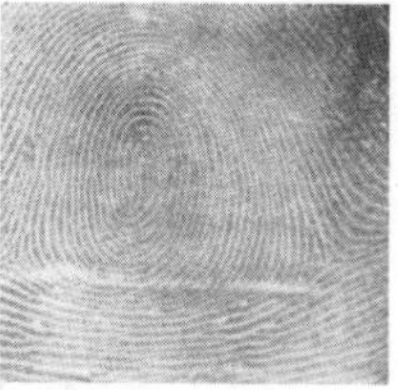

A fingerprint showing the whorl.

The genetic component is important and, consequently, the patterns on all of one's ten fingers usually are very similar, but they also contain unique ridge endings and bifurcations, called minutiae.[9] The fact that fingerprints on each finger are slightly different allows a collection of ten sets of data, which is why it is enormously

4. Beavan, *Fingerprints*, p. 12.
5. Rizzo, D., *Fundamentals of Anatomy and Physiology,* Cengage Learning, p. 123, 2003.
6. Cole, Fingerprint identification and the criminal justice system, pp. 65–66.
7. Beavan, *Fingerprints*, p. 202.
8. Beavan, *Fingerprints*, p. 202.
9. Beavan, *Fingerprints*, p. 203.

improbable for two different people to have identical fingerprints. No biological need exists for the unique differences found, and little evidence supports the idea that the ridges help to grip things, lending support to the idea that their purpose is identification.

The systematic use of fingerprints that was eventually developed to facilitate rapid identification involved analysis of several basic fingerprint patterns.[10] The most basic patterns were the arch (A), the loop (L), and the whorl (W), all typed by using A, L, and W standard values. A system was then developed using all ten fingers to classify the prints in such a way that they could be sorted according to an objective evaluation system. The researcher 'types' a suspect's ten fingers, then attempts to match the set to an existing file, allowing identification of the accused's name, birth date, city of birth, and verification of previous offences.

A typical whole fingerprint showing the major traits.

A major concern was whether or not a set of ten fingerprints from one person was different enough from other people's to achieve accurate identifications. The British were very concerned about falsely convicting innocent people, especially since the penalty in Britain often was hanging. For most of history, the only evidence allowed at court trials was eyewitness testimony because the use of physical evidence was considered too vulnerable to manipulation.[11]

Criminologists now realize that the eyewitness testimony used in modern society is notoriously inaccurate.[12] In a small town, or in the country where people have lived for most of their lives, one often recognizes almost everyone in the village. As a result, eyewitness identification was once more accurate than in typical communities today where one is likely to encounter a large number of strangers in one's daily life.

Faulds, Darwin, and Galton

Part of the fingerprint history is the struggle by the man who had priority, physician Henry Faulds, to counter the attempt by Darwin's cousin, Francis Galton, to claim credit for this systematized technology. Faulds had clear priority—he published the first discussion of the potential use of fingerprints as a method for identifying criminals in the October 1880 issue of *Nature*. Faulds had been trying to convince Scotland Yard to adopt his system of identification for a decade until "*an elite society scientist, Francis Galton, stumbled across Faulds' idea and claimed it as his own.*"[13] Scotland Yard ignored Faulds' work, and when the Yard finally did

10. Cole, Fingerprint identification and the criminal justice system, p. 66.
11. Beavan, *Fingerprints*, p. 18.
12. Starr, D., False eyewitness, *Discover* **33**(9):38–42, 64, November 2012.
13. Beavan, *Fingerprints*, on book jacket.

adopt the fingerprint identification system, they "*denied that Faulds had any part in the system's conception.*"[14]

Although one of the first people to utilize fingerprints for identification was William James Herschel, his technique was clearly inferior to Faulds' system. Herschel used the total handprint only to prove that people were who they said they were, and not for criminal identification. Herschel also began collecting the fingerprints of friends, colleagues, and family, which Galton eventually used for his research—becoming convinced that fingerprints were both unique to each individual, and that the fingerprint pattern did not change over time.[15] Herschel also discovered that patterns on the noses of cattle, horses and dogs could also be used to identify them in case of theft.[16]

Henry Faulds, who fought his entire life for the credit due him for developing the concept of fingerprints. Picture taken in the 1890s.

Faulds wrote to Charles Darwin in February 1880 about his fingerprint research.[17] Darwin, in turn, forwarded Faulds' letter to Francis Galton. In his reply to Darwin, Galton promised that he would help Faulds but, unfortunately, "*Galton did not keep his word, Faulds never heard from him*" about Darwin's letter.[18]

Faulds' *Nature* article specifically suggested using fingerprints for identifying criminals because these prints were unique and unchangeable. As evidence Faulds cited two criminal cases that he solved by the use of fingerprints.[19] Faulds' correspondence indicates one of the uses that late-nineteenth-century European scientists envisioned for fingerprints was to determine and rate human racial characteristics to produce a hierarchy from primitive to advanced races. Western science was then in the

throes of the Darwinian revolution wrought by the publication of *Origin of Species* in 1859. The most burning issue surrounding Darwinian theory was, not surprisingly, the evolutionary history of the human species, which Darwin had begun to address in *The Descent of Man* (1871). Western scientists were obsessed with tracing the relationship between humans and other primates, using evolutionary theory to delineate the various racial and

14. Beavan, *Fingerprints*, p. 12.
15. Forrest, D.W., *Francis Galton: The Life and Work of a Victorian Genius*, Taplinger, New York, p. 216, 1974.
16. Beavan, *Fingerprints*, p. 44.
17. Forrest, *Francis Galton*, p. 210.
18. Beavan, *Fingerprints*, p. 74.
19. Faulds, H., On the skin-furrows of the hand, *Nature* **22**(574):605, 1880.

> ethnic groups that made up the human species, and exploring the role of heredity in shaping human intelligence, personality, and other attributes.[20]

Furthermore, Darwinism

> ushered in the era of "*biological determinism,*" the belief that the character, abilities, and even destiny of each individual were strongly influenced, if not absolutely mandated, by biological inheritance. European scientists interested in fingerprint patterns, like Faulds, assumed that evolutionary theory would be crucial for explaining their origin and significance.[21]

Evolutionists then believed that fingerprint patterns might "*contribute to the scientific understanding of evolutionary history*" by functioning "*like a fossil record, providing clues about the evolutionary history of the species, the races, and individuals.*"[22]

Faulds' experimentation on finger ridges proved that, whether rubbed, burned away with acid, or sliced, they always healed in their original pattern, answering a major concern of the courts.[23] It has also been verified that fingerprints can be used to identify a person from infancy to old age. Once Faulds established their permanence and uniqueness, as a Darwinist he saw in "*fingerprint patterns … a visible trace of evolution, a code in which each individual's genealogy, racial and ethnical background, and even character traits might be encrypted.*"[24]

In addition, "*for Faulds the most intriguing thing about fingerprints was not that they were so individual but that they were so alike, that they fell into such regular patterns. …* [which] *had to have some evolutionary meaning.*"[25] Faulds believed that fingerprint patterns contained "*information about the history of the species, race, individual character, and even nature itself. Plumbing their mystery, he thought, might 'lead us close to the very centre of nature's great forge'.*"[26]

Galton's personality

Galton believed that people of "*upper-class birth were by nature superior to the lesser-born.*"[27] This belief reflected itself in how he reacted to Henry Faulds: "*much of what Francis Galton got in life, he never had to work for, while much of what Faulds worked for, thanks in part to Galton, he never got.*"[28]

---

20. Cole, *Suspect Identities*, p. 97.
21. Cole, *Suspect Identities*, p. 97.
22. Cole, *Suspect Identities*, pp. 97–98.
23. Forrest, *Francis Galton*, p. 212.
24. Cole, *Suspect Identities*, p. 98.
25. Cole, *Suspect Identities*, p. 98.
26. Cole, *Suspect Identities*, p. 99.
27. Beavan, *Fingerprints*, p. 94.
28. Beavan, *Fingerprints*, p. 99.

Galton "*benefited from the hard work of a member of a lower class* [Faulds]" and "*felt entitled to do so without credit or acknowledgement.*"[29] Thus Galton refused to acknowledge the true discoverer of the technique that he later published in his classic book on fingerprints.[30] Those who "*dared to oppose*" Galton soon "*learned that he was, by all accounts, that dangerous breed of dog who bites before even bothering to growl.*"[31] Galton referenced Faulds only once in his writings, and that one time he misspelt Faulds' name.[32]

Galton was a very wealthy man, able to do a great deal to help humanity. His £26,000 inheritance was worth several million dollars by today's standards.[33] Nonetheless, he "*treated with ingratitude and callousness both those who helped him win his prestige and those who through hard work had won acclaim on their own—such as … Faulds.*"[34] One acquaintance opined that Galton "*was essentially a doctrinaire* [exemplified in the way he rigidly adhered to his Darwinian worldview—Ed.] *not endowed with much sympathy,*" and was unable to make an allowance for the failings of others. He also lacked tact, openly letting others know what he thought of those he judged as inferior human beings.[35] Galton characteristically either liked or disliked people, and Faulds was among those he disliked.[36]

Galton robs Faulds of credit

Beavan noted that "*Faulds had published a far more significant and valuable contribution on fingerprints,*" but Galton began promoting Herschel as the originator of fingerprint identification, ignoring Faulds' contributions.[37,38] In a *Nature* paper that Galton published, although he cited Faulds, he cited Herschel's paper first, giving "*the appearance that Herschel came first. Whether this subtle falsehood was a mistake or deliberate attempt to rewrite history, only Galton knew.*"[39] Beavan concluded that the result was clear: it "*effectively robbed Faulds of his priority of publication and his rightful place as the first announcer of a new discovery.*"[40]

The fact is, Faulds' system was vastly superior to Galton's. Fingerprinting was also a superior identification system compared to Bertillon's complex and unwieldy

29. Beavan, *Fingerprints*, p. 94.
30. Gillham, N.W., *A Life of Sir Francis Galton*, Oxford University Press, New York, pp. 246–247, 2001.
31. Beavan, *Fingerprints*, p. 94.
32. Galton, F., *Finger Prints*, Macmillan, London, p. 26, 1892.
33. Beavan, *Fingerprints*, p. 97.
34. Beavan, *Fingerprints*, p. 97.
35. Beavan, *Fingerprints*, p. 98.
36. Forrest, *Francis Galton*, p. 211.
37. Beavan, *Fingerprints*, pp. 104–105.
38. Gillham, *A Life of Sir Francis Galton*, p. 240.
39. Beavan, *Fingerprints*, p. 106.
40. Beavan, *Fingerprints*, p. 106.

body measurement system. Unfortunately, "*Galton had already undermined Faulds' reputation*" and, as a result, Faulds was ignored.[41]

Even though Faulds knew that his ideas had been stolen,[42] he continued to be cordial toward Galton, once writing that Galton deserved the "*greatest credit*" for his masterly exposition of the subject in his comprehensive book titled *Finger Prints*.[43,44] The fact that Galton knew of Faulds' early work—such as Faulds' letter to Darwin on fingerprints that Darwin had passed on to Galton—must have bothered Faulds greatly.[45] Faulds eventually tried to set the record straight and published a letter in the October 1894 *Nature* pointing out that he had priority because his article was "*absolutely the first notice of the subject contained in English literature.*"[46]

Improvements required

A major problem that had to be overcome to make a fingerprint system practical was to develop procedures that did not require extensive scientific training to allow it to be used by the average investigator. A workable system also required that fingerprints be categorized in such a way that the person's file could be located by their fingerprint marks alone. Because Galton's system was clearly inferior to Faulds' system, Faulds' system is used today. Galton himself proved that even a collection of hundreds of thousands of prints could be accurately classified with precision by Edward Henry's fingerprint cataloguing system, which utilized Faulds' ideas.[47]

Once the technology became widely accepted, Faulds continued to fight for the recognition that he deserved, but "*Galton had ensured that credit would not come to Henry Faulds until long after*" both Galton and Faulds had died.[48] Even after Faulds died on March 19, 1930, it would be 57 years before his contributions were formally recognized. In 1987, two American fingerprint experts located Faulds' grave in Britain, restored it, and raised money for the cost of maintaining it as a tribute to his work.[49]

---

41. Beavan, *Fingerprints*, p. 131.
42. Forrest, *Francis Galton*, pp. 210–211.
43. Faulds, H., On the identification of habitual criminals by finger prints, *Nature* **50**(1301):548, 1894.
44. Beavan, *Fingerprints*, p. 132.
45. Beavan, *Fingerprints*, p. 134.
46. Beavan, *Fingerprints*, p. 134.
47. Beavan, *Fingerprints*, p. 150.
48. Beavan, *Fingerprints*, p. 190.
49. Beavan, *Fingerprints*, p. 198.

Bertillon's body measurement system

One reason Faulds' research was largely ignored was that in the late 1800s, Alphonse Bertillon developed an extensive system of identification based on physical traits.[50] His system involved translating body measurements, including height, weight, and specific anatomical measurements such as the forehead, foot size, out-stretched arm measurement, and even the length of the middle finger into a coding system that allowed some logical filing system so that a specific file could be located when a suspected offender was measured.

The system, although unwieldy, successfully identified people and became so well known that when Galton visited Bertillon's laboratory, he recognized that it had potential for applying

> Darwin's theories to create a master race of men. He hoped to identify Britain's most able-bodied and nimble-minded and to mate them the way a horse breeder creates winners of the grand national. To do this, he needed to identify which members of the population had the greatest genetic potential. Galton had decided bodily measurements might be one way to accomplish this and, for this purpose, four years before he visited Bertillon in Paris, Galton had opened an anthropometric lab of his own.[51]

Unfortunately, Bertillon's system was later used by others for nefarious purposes, including the Nazis in Germany, who used the system in an attempt to determine who belonged to those races they judged as inferior. Galton also tried to use the method to identify inferior individuals or groups.[52] Today, the anthropometric system with its meticulous skull measurements and attention to body size evokes the pseudosciences of phrenology, craniometry, and somatotyping and their contributions to racist science. What is less known, however, is that both identification systems—fingerprinting as well as anthropometry—were closely tied to biologically determinist efforts to find bodily markers of character traits like intelligence and criminality.[53]

Criminal anthropology

The scientific discipline called "*criminal anthropology*" attempted to determine indications of a criminal mind by measuring "*skull sizes and shapes, facial features, and body types.*"[54] Bertillon's system was "*an ark of salvation for the nascent field of*

50. Beavan, *Fingerprints*, pp. 80–83.
51. Beavan, *Fingerprints*, p. 93.
52. Cowan, R.S., *Sir Francis Galton and the Study of Heredity in the Nineteenth Century*, Garland, New York, 1985.
53. Cole, Fingerprint identification and the criminal justice system, p. 65.
54. Cole, Fingerprint identification and the criminal justice system, p. 66.

criminal anthropology", and there soon developed a "*thriving research program*" that still exists today "*albeit in greatly diminished and increasingly marginalized form.*" It sought to "*correlate fingerprint pattern types with race, ethnicity, and character traits, such as insanity and criminality.*"[55] Galton, though, became discouraged with Bertillon's system, partly because body traits could change—people gain or lose weight, their hair turns grey, aging causes height loss, and illness affects body shape, but fingerprints were stable throughout life.[56]

Used to prove evolution

Fingerprints were also used in an attempt to prove evolution somewhat like genetic testing is used today, by making a "*connection between fingerprint pattern types and human types*" from "*primate studies, racial studies, and character studies of fingerprints.*" Cole notes that it "*seemed patently obvious*" to the "*late-nineteenth-century scientific mind*" that "*fingerprint patterns were probably inherited and therefore should correlate with race, ethnicity, disease propensity, abilities, and various behavioral characteristics.*"[57]

In 1867, French anatomist Professor A. Alix published a study of palm print patterns of a large sample of primate species, and concluded that

> though there was great variety even within a given species, the frequency of pattern types was characteristic for each species. … humans shared patterns with the monkeys of the Americas, carnivorous apes, and rodents, but not with the African monkeys. In light of Darwin's theory, these findings suggested that papillary ridge patterns might reflect evolutionary history—that evolutionary lineages might be traced using fingerprint patterns and that some patterns might be "*more evolved*" than others.[58]

Eugenics

When Galton became interested in fingerprints, his focus was primarily on eugenics and not identification: his "*passion was the improvement of the human race by artificial selection. He took to fingerprints, thinking their intricate ridge patterns might somehow reveal their owners' physical and mental capacities—their worth as breeding stock.*"[59] Galton was "*less interested in the function of fingerprint patterns than in how those patterns might be exploited … to provide a physical marker of heredity, ethnicity, and race.*"[60] The

55. Cole, Fingerprint identification and the criminal justice system, p. 66.
56. Cowan, R.S., Francis Galton's statistical ideas: the influence of eugenics, *Isis* **63**(4):509–528, 1972.
57. Cole, Fingerprint identification and the criminal justice system, p. 66.
58. Cole, *Suspect Identities*, p. 105.
59. Beavan, *Fingerprints*, p. 13.
60. Cole, *Suspect Identities*, p. 75.

> convergence of fingerprinting and eugenics … is often treated as a mere coincidence, but in fact Galton's ideas about eugenics were closely bound up in the development of criminal identification. Indeed, Galton's chief contribution to the development of the fingerprint system—his tripartite classification scheme for sorting all fingerprint patterns into three groups: arches, loops, and whorls—was devised chiefly for the purpose of using fingerprint patterns as bodily markers of heredity and character.[61]

Galton is well known for coining the term eugenics and for the idea that Adolf Hitler's government would appropriate when they passed the 1933 Eugenic Sterilization Law.[62] The law required compulsory sterilization of all German citizens with presumably inherited handicaps. Galton was heavily influenced by Darwin, and "*if Galton ever needed proof of his ideas of the genetic superiority of some people over others, it had come … with the 1859 appearance of his cousin Darwin's theory of evolution.*"[63]

Galton became convinced that the "*children of the intellectually and physically well-endowed were naturally superior*" and launched a quest to prove this.[64] This goal became a major motivation for his fingerprint research. He admitted that "*one of the inducements to making these inquiries into personal identification has been to discover independent features for hereditary investigation.*"[65] Galton had rejected theistic evolution, believing that

> evolution was not divinely directed, and man might just as easily evolve backward toward the apes as forward into the image of his once-fancied Creator. Man's true religious duty, therefore, … should be to the deliberate and systematic forward evolution of the human species."[66]

He reasoned, just as we breed dogs, one could likewise breed a race of highly gifted men. Galton also concluded from Darwin's theory "*that God did not exist*" and, in a letter to Darwin, he wrote "*that [The] Origin had driven away 'the constraint of my old superstition as if it had been a nightmare'.*"[67]

Galton's "*overriding concern*" in his research was with the application of eugenics because he concluded that the "*environment has little influence on the character of men.*"[68] One just had to determine who the genetically gifted men were, a goal

61. Cole, Fingerprint identification and the criminal justice system, p. 66.
62. Beavan, *Fingerprints*, pp. 98–99.
63. Beavan, *Fingerprints*, p. 99.
64. Beavan, *Fingerprints*, p. 99.
65. Galton, F., Personal identification and description, *Nature* 1888 June 28, pp. 201–202.
66. Beavan, *Fingerprints*, p. 100.
67. Beavan, *Fingerprints*, p. 100.
68. Cowan, Francis Galton's statistical ideas, p. 509.

fingerprints could help to facilitate. The theory of evolution radically changed the worldview of many Westerners, even affecting

> the notion of the "*born criminal*"—that criminals were born of bad heredity rather than made by poor social conditions. Criminals and other deviants were biologically different from "*normal,*" law-abiding citizens. On the basis of the Darwinian theory of evolution, which was then gaining in popularity, the Italian School posited that criminals were products of bad stock—individuals who were less evolved than the rest of the population, in much the same way that "*savages*" and other indigenous peoples were less evolved than Europeans.[69]

Darwinian theory taught that the chief causes of born criminals was "*'atavism,' the reversion to a primitive evolutionary state, and 'degeneration,' the tendency of some subcultures to 'evolve backwards,' weakening, rather than improving, their evolutionary fitness.*"[70]

Fingerprint eugenics program fails

Although in the 1890s Galton believed that fingerprints were "*the most important of anthropological data,*" twenty years later he was "*profoundly disappointed that his fingerprint research had not provided a reliable way of tracing hereditary relationships, assessing character, determining racial or ethnic background, or predicting criminality.*"[71] Galton, in his landmark book *Finger Prints* (1892), published a study of the frequency with which various fingerprint patterns appeared in various races. He found

> almost no significant variations, other than slightly fewer arches among the Jews. This was what the anthropologist Paul Rabinow has called "*Galton's regret*" in his provocative essay of that title. Despite Galton's "*regret,*" however, a scientific research program arose beginning in the 1890s that *did* attach biological significance to Galton's three pattern types.[72]

Galton had first expected to find clear racial differences, but in the late 1800s he realized that this "*hope* [was] *no longer justifiable.*" After studying the fingerprints of "*races and classes*" Galton concluded that "*there is no peculiar pattern which characterizes persons of any of the above races*" [that is, "English, pure Welsh, Hebrew, and

69. Cole, *Suspect Identities*, p. 23.
70. Cole, *Suspect Identities*, p. 23.
71. Cole, *Suspect Identities*, p. 103.
72. Cole, Fingerprint identification and the criminal justice system, p. 66.

Negro"—Ed. Emphasis added].[73] This conclusion was very disappointing to Galton because he had

> published several books arguing that virtually every human attribute could be traced to heredity. Galton's strong belief in the power of heredity would later blossom into the eugenics movement, which sought to control mating practices in order to improve the human race through directed evolution.[74]

The rise and fall of fingerprints as evidence of evolution, and to track the evolution of the races, began in the 1890s when

> Galton called fingerprints "*the most important of anthropological data.*" Twenty years later, however, Galton would be profoundly disappointed that his fingerprint research had not provided a reliable way of tracing hereditary relationships, assessing character, determining racial or ethnic background, or predicting criminality. Although biometricians like Galton, who believed that the key to heredity lay in the measurement of the body, did find differences in the distribution of fingerprint patterns among different races and did believe they could arrange fingerprint patterns into an evolutionary hierarchy, these findings were hardly convincing enough—even to them—to warrant judicial, or even actuarial, decision making. The effort to read criminality, heredity, and race in the fingertips ultimately failed.[75]

Although slight fingerprint differences do exist between races, the assumption "*that pattern types appeared with different frequencies among different racial and ethnic populations … and that fingerprint patterns contained information that would … be able to predict individuals' propensity for certain diseases and even their behavioral characteristics, including criminal propensity*" was falsified.[76]

In other words, "*although fingerprints did provide a powerful device for the identification of criminals (and everyone else, for that matter), they revealed nothing about individual character. …* [E]*xamining prints from English, Welsh, Jews, Negroes, and Basques, … scientists, and idiots revealed no systematic differences*" between these groups.[77] We now know that the relationship found was of little or no use to predict criminality or any other abnormal behavior propensity.[78] Nonetheless, Cole notes that this line of

---

73. Galton, *Finger Prints*, p. 192.
74. Cole, *Suspect Identities*, p. 99.
75. Cole, *Suspect Identities*, p. 103.
76. Cole, Fingerprint identification and the criminal justice system, p. 67.
77. Rabinow, P., Galton's Regret: Of Types and Individuals, in: Billings, P.R. (ed.), *DNA on Trial: Genetic Information and Criminal Justice*, Cold Spring Harbor Laboratory Press, Woodbury, New York, p. 7, 1992.
78. Cole, Fingerprint identification and the criminal justice system, p. 7.

research continued well into the 1920s. In Galton's laboratory, researchers studied the inheritance of fingerprint patterns. Other researchers measured the frequency with which pattern types appeared in different ethnic groups. The most ambitious study of this kind … found that Asians had a higher proportion of whorls, and fewer arches, than Europeans. In 1922, the *New York Times* reported, a German professor, Heinrich Poll predicted that life insurance companies would soon be able to "*tell from finger prints what will be the insured's career.*" This research never died out completely. The most recent publication claiming to be able to diagnose criminality from fingerprint pattern types dates from 1991.[79]

Fingerprints show evidence of design

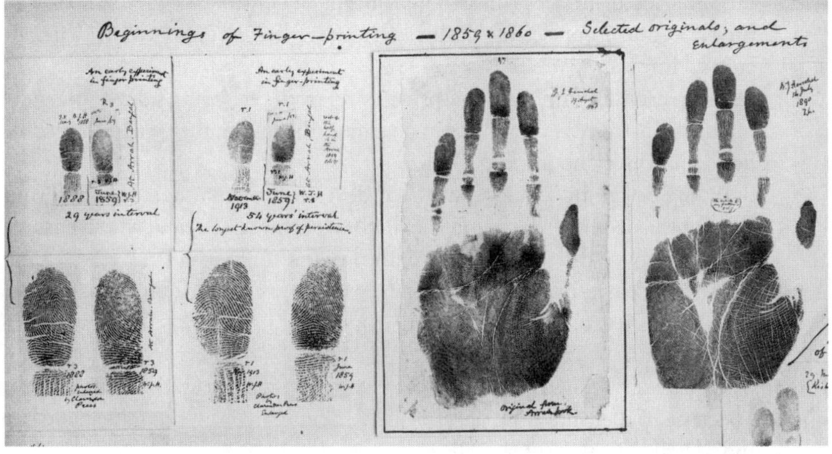

Some examples of early fingerprints taken about 1859 to 1860 by William James Herschel showing the detail he was able to achieve very early in the development of the technique's history.

Evolutionary biologists have not been able to explain the origin of fingerprints in humans and no known biological need exists for the unique differences found. One claim was that its ridges aided in gripping items. Research has shown that the fingerprint system is completely irrelevant to physical gripping or any other biological function. Since the ridges provide no tactile benefits, fingerprints could not have evolved by neo-Darwinist mechanisms of mutation and natural selection because no survival benefit in the wild could possibly be conferred by any of the functional

79. Cole, Fingerprint identification and the criminal justice system, p. 67.

requirements in this complex multi-part system. Nor could the equivalent systems existing in gorillas, chimpanzees, and koalas have evolved by any Darwinian process.

Lacking a theoretical survival value means that Darwinism cannot explain their existence, or their individual unchanging uniqueness, by natural selection, because the system provides no survival value, thus the large commitment of resources to develop and transmit this system from generation to generation cannot be explained by evolution. Furthermore, the process of new skin formation, including the programmed cell death of billions of skin cells to constantly renew the epidermis, does not alter the programmed fingerprint pattern, indicating that it is a designed system created for the identification of individuals. To function as an identification system fingerprints must:

- vary the design in noticeable and definable patterns so that it will accurately identify billions of individuals
- produce raised surfaces consisting primarily of continuous curved lines
- produce non-intersecting pathways that create clean patterns without crossed lines
- begin to establish unique fingerprints early in the offspring's development
- retain the pattern as tiny digits in an infant through puberty and into adulthood and throughout life
- draw the design by an algorithm that develops and maintains the information for the pattern throughout the lifetime of the person, and which ensures that the pattern differs even for identical twins
- ensure the pattern will survive and even re-emerge through most finger surface injuries.

Perhaps the Creator designed unique, life-long fingerprints (and footprints) on humans because of their importance, especially for effective and accurate identification of individuals throughout their lives.

Summary

Biometricians such as Galton "*believed that the key to heredity lay in the measurement of the body.*"[80] Although scientists did find some differences in the distribution of fingerprint patterns among different races that they believed could be used to "*arrange fingerprint patterns into an evolutionary hierarchy*", the research findings failed to support this goal.[81] In the end, all attempts "*to read criminality, heredity, and race in the fingertips ultimately failed.*"[82] The attempts by Darwinists to use fingerprints to determine something about race is a long story of yet another failed attempt to classify and judge humans on a superior-inferior scale based on evolution.

80. Cole, *Suspect Identities*, p. 103.
81. Cole, *Suspect Identities*, p. 103.
82. Cole, *Suspect Identities*, p. 103.

CHAPTER 8

The Ancon sheep blunder: A now falsified proof of macroevolution

Introduction

The Ancon sheep 'breed' was once widely believed to have provided critical support for the validity of macroevolution. It was also thought to support the once common belief that major evolutionary changes or jumps called 'sports' drove evolution. Putative examples of sports have been used as evidence of rapid macroevolution since Darwin first discussed the Ancon sheep mutation in 1859. Ancon sheep had very short legs that shepherds considered an advantage because the sheep were less likely to escape over fences. Oxford University Professor Wilma George writes "*the short-legged Ancon sheep that appeared … in 1791 and became the ancestor of a new breed of sheep*"[1] is a good example of evolution, a claim long ago disproved.

A picture of Ancon Sheep, which *Life* magazine described as a short-legged lamb mutant that could not jump even low fences.

Source: *Life* **22**(11):83, 17 March, 1947.

Textbooks and articles implied that the breed was an example of how a major new trait or even a new species could evolve in a single generation. The Ancon sheep example has been used not only to prove Darwinism, but also to argue for rapid evolution as opposed to Darwinian gradualism. It is now recognized that Ancon sheep were not a new breed, but the result of a genetic disease called achondroplasia. The so-called new breed had so many major health problems that the condition caused its extinction decades ago, yet it was mentioned in textbooks as evidence for macroevolutionary jumps as recently as 2005.

1. George, W., *Darwin*, Fontana Paperbacks, Glasgow, p. 55, 1982.

Mutations

Mutations *"are the foundation of evolutionary change. Without mutations there would be no evolution."*[2] Mutations that produce phenotypic changes are usually 'loss mutations' that result in the loss of efficiency or effectiveness of the structure the gene produces. Loss mutations resulting in a non-functional protein or structure, or the total elimination of such protein or structure, can in rare cases be beneficial for the organism or, more often, beneficial to humans—as in the case of mutations causing the loss of seeds, producing the now popular seedless fruits.

FIG. 126. Mutation in sheep. Sheep with normal legs at the right and short-legged Ancon sheep (mutant) at the left. *Photograph furnished by Dr. W. Landauer, University of Conn.*

The white-eyed fly was a mutation. About 1800 a New England farmer found a male lamb with short bowed legs in his flock of long-legged sheep, from which he developed a race of short-legged sheep, which, as Walter suggests, proved a real labor-saving device since the sheepraiser now built lower fences than formerly (Fig. 126). Some other new varieties of animals resulting from mutations are hornless Hereford cattle, which arose from a mutant in a herd of Herefords at Atchison, Kansas, in 1891; tailless dogs and cats; and chickens with bare necks.

A picture of Ancon sheep from a leading biology textbook. This example was used for decades as proof of evolution by the accumulation of mutations.

Source: Bernal Weimer. *Man and the Animal World.* 1951 New York: Wiley. p. 247.

One of the earliest, and for years one of the most commonly cited, examples of a beneficial mutation was the Ancon sheep, an animal claimed to be a new sheep breed typified by very short legs. Many labelled it a new species and Thomas Huxley called it a new race, writing that *"this short-legged sheep of America was not produced gradually, but originated in the birth of an original parent of the whole stock,"* and maintained *"by a rigid system of artificial selection."*[3]

2. Audesirk, T., Audesirk, G. and Byers, B., *Life on Earth*, Prentice Hall, Upper Saddle River, New Jersey, p. 289, 2002.
3. Quoted in Phelps, L. and Cohen, E., The Wilberforce-Huxley debate, *Western Speech* **37**(1):64, 1973.

The 'new species' produced by macromutations was first noticed by Massachusetts farmer Seth Wright[4] in 1791.[5] Wright bred a number of this short-legged sheep 'species', all of which were unable to jump over short stonewalls or fences.[6,7] He called them 'Otter sheep' because Otters have short, stubby legs. The Ancon 'breed' reduced the requirement for taller, more costly fences used to contain the herd.[8] The short legs also interfered with the sheep's ability to run. Consequently, the animals were less active and, as a result, gained weight more easily than most other sheep.[9] Edward Blyth wrote that macromutations (he used the term monsters) can produce animals that

> often become the origin of a new race. Such, for example, is the breed of sheep, now common in North America, and known by the name of *ancons*, or *otter* sheep … . This variety was extensively propagated, in consequence of being less able to jump over fences than the ordinary breeds of sheep.[10]

The new breed was announced at the Royal Society on January 14, 1813, by David Humphreys[11] while reviewing several breeding experiments carried out by various sheep breeders. Darwin seized on this finding and exploited it to support his theory. Genetic blending would dilute the new traits, eventually resulting in their loss. The "*Ancon sheep are important to the history of biology because Charles Darwin used them to support his argument that animals inherit parental traits without blending.*"[12]

Charles Darwin's use of Ancon sheep

The first person known to use the Ancon sheep as evidence for evolution was Charles Darwin. He discussed it at least four times in his published writings. In his first

4. Davenport, C., Home of the Ancon sheep, *Science* **86**(2236):422, 1937. Please note Davenport spelled the farmer's name as Wite.
5. Schwartz, K. and Vogel, J., Unraveling the yarn of the Ancon sheep, *Bioscience* **44**(11):764–768, 1994.
6. Curtis, H., and Barnes, N.S., *Biology*, 5th edition, Worth Publishers, Inc., New York, p. 982, 1989.
7. Dodge, R.A., *Elements of Biology*, Allyn and Bacon, Boston, Massachusetts, p. 598, 1959.
8. Schwartz and Vogel, Unraveling the yarn of the Ancon sheep.
9. Dwight, T., *Travels in New England and New York*, Vol. 3, Harvard University Press, Cambridge, Massachusetts, pp. 89–90, 1969.
10. Blyth, E., An attempt to classify the 'varieties' of animals, with observations on the marked seasonal and other changes which naturally take place in various British species, and which do not constitute varieties, *Magazine of Natural History* **8**(1):47, 1835.
11. Humphreys, D., On a new variety in breeds of sheep, *Philosophical Transactions of the Royal Society*, London, **103**:88–95, 1813; pp. 88–89.
12. Schwartz and Vogel, Unraveling the yarn of the Ancon sheep, p. 764.

book on evolution, he wrote about "*sports ... called hereditary monsters*" or a new race, using as his example cases where "*all the limbs are stunted (as in the Ancon sheep).*"[13] Darwin speculated in the *Origin of Species* (1859), that animal variations could have "*arisen suddenly, or by one step*" in a single generation. Darwin also wrote that such 'one step' rapid evolution is also "*known to have been the case with the Ancon sheep.*"[14]

Darwin concluded in a later work that whole new breeds had "*suddenly originated*" by evolution, and he gave the example of 'a ram-lamb' born in Massachusetts. The animal had "*short crooked legs and a long back, like a turnspit-dog.*"[15] Darwin claimed that from this lamb "*the otter or ancon semi-monstrous breed was raised.*"[16] He stated that these sheep can transmit

> their character so truly that Colonel Humphreys never heard of "*but one questionable case*" of an ancon ram and ewe not producing ancon offspring. When they are crossed with other breeds the offspring, with rare exceptions, instead of being intermediate in character, perfectly resemble either parent; even one of the twins has resembled one parent and the second the other. Lastly, "*the ancons have been observed to keep together, separating themselves from the rest of the flock when put into enclosures with other sheep.*"[17]

If the Ancon mutation is a Mendelian recessive, as research has indicated, Darwin's claim—quoting Colonel Humphreys, that "*When they are crossed with other breeds the offspring, with rare exceptions, instead of being intermediate in character, perfectly resemble either parent*" and are not blended—is incorrect. Either Darwin was wrong or the research reviewed by Schwartz and Vogel[18] is incorrect. Likely Darwin was wrong.

After a "*long discussion of artificial selection*" and "*sports ... e.g., Ancon sheep,*" according to Hull, Darwin reasoned that "*if breeders could do so much with so little, one can only imagine how powerful natural selection must be.*"[19] This example discussed by Darwin has been cited ever since, partly because it fitted the expectations of many evolutionists—namely "*the appearance of a new inheritable characteristic*" in only one generation.[20]

13. Darwin, Francis (Ed.), *The foundations of The Origin of Species. Two essays written in 1842 and 1844,* Cambridge University Press, Cambridge, p. 59, 1909.
14. Darwin, C., *On the Origin of Species,* John Murray, London, p. 30, 1859.
15. Darwin, C., *The Variation of Animals and Plants Under Domestication*, D. Appleton, New York, p. 104, 1896.
16. Darwin, *The Variation of Animals and Plants Under Domestication*, p. 104.
17. Darwin, *The Variation of Animals and Plants Under Domestication*, p. 104.
18. Schwartz and Vogel, Unraveling the yarn of the Ancon sheep.
19. Hull, D.L., Strategies in meme theory—A commentary on Rose's paper: Controversies in meme theory, *Journal of Memetics—Evolutionary Models of Information Transmission* **3**(2):70–72, 1999.
20. Moody, P.A., *Introduction to Evolution,* Harper and Brothers, New York, p. 337, 1953.

Huxley believed the answer to the lack of transitional forms lay "*in large-scale mutations*", and he concluded that the Ancon sheep provided key evidence for this view.[21] Huxley further argued that the reason for seizing on the Ancon sheep example is because it supported the idea that

> "*transmutation may take place without transition*"—by leaps, leaving no string of middle stages. Look at the sudden appearance of Ancon sheep, a long-bodied strain with "*short bandy legs*", once bred in Massachusetts for the canny reason that they could not jump fences.[22]

Thomas Huxley claimed the Ancon sheep was one of the best-known examples of the 'spontaneous' production of new variation.[23]

Ancon sheep becomes an icon of evolution

The Ancon sheep example of "*rapid evolution*" became an icon of Darwinism, repeated for decades in hundreds of textbooks, books and articles. The Ancon sheep also soon became a "*classic example of evolution*" by mutations and an important evidence for the origin of species.[24]

The argument usually ran as follows: The Ancon sheep proves that complete major structural changes can occur in one single generation. Furthermore, the sheep legs were either very short (all of the Ancon breed) or of normal size (all other breeds), proving that a mutation can produce major biological changes in only one generation. This example is, therefore, a dramatic confirmation of macroevolution.

Darwinists argued that this example proved a new species that was "*unknown in the world*" before this time could evolve in a *single generation* or, at the least, a major beneficial change caused by a mutation could occur in one generation.[25] Jones notes that Darwin's *Origin of Species*

> describes the improvement of sheep using a "*short-stemmed*" mutation. The Ancon gene shortened the legs of the sheep who bore it. This was convenient as it stopped them from jumping over stone walls, and the breed became popular. … Other useful genes for disease resistance in tropical cattle,

---

21. Desmond, A., *Huxley: From Devil's Disciple to Evolution's High Priest*, Addison-Wesley, Reading, Massachusetts, pp. 256, 262, 1997.
22. Desmond, *Huxley*, p. 256.
23. Huxley, T., *Lay Sermons, Addresses, and Reviews*, D. Appleton, New York, p. 264, 1915.
24. Bayles, E.E. and Burnett, R.W., *Biology for Better Living*, Silver Burnett Company, New York, p. 606, 1946.
25. Landauer, W. and Chang, T.K., The Ancon or otter sheep, *The Journal of Heredity* **40**(4):105–112, 1949; p. 106.

> increased growth in pigs, and so on have been bred into farm animals and spread by selection in the Darwinian way.[26]

The claim was that all four legs and their accessory structures, such as nervous tissue, simultaneously became shorter, while the sheep otherwise appeared to be normal. If this major change could occur in one generation, why could not other drastic morphological changes that were beneficial occur just as rapidly? Consequently, 'sports' soon became a very important support for Darwinism.

Dutch botanist Hugo de Vries completed extensive research on mutational 'sports' in evening primroses and fruit flies. He concluded that these 'sports' were

> the key to a new evolutionary scheme. He argued that small-scale differences between individuals—the fuel of Darwinian evolution—had nothing to do with the origin of species. To de Vries, new species were the product of giant evolutionary leaps. He did not discount Darwinism entirely. Natural selection would still pick the cream of the crop. But it would pick from a motley assortment of meaty mutants instead of slight, individual variations.[27]

Professor Herbert Conn described the Ancon sheep as one of the best examples of a "*new chord in nature*" or new breed that appeared suddenly and, he claimed, due to its superior traits "*soon supplanted the original variety.*"[28] This discovery was also of "*extreme importance, since it shows genetic crossing will not always eliminate variations,*"[29] a problem in Darwinism because it was thought that new varieties would be lost through interbreeding. The Ancon sheep, Conn believed, negated this major objection to Darwinism.

The Ancon example of a beneficial 'sport' mutation was for this reason discussed in many major biology textbooks for decades. A few representative examples include Smith,[30] Bayles and Burnett,[31] Weimer,[32] Dodge,[33] Moody,[34] Simpson and

---

26. Jones, S., *The Language of Genes*, Anchor Doubleday, New York, pp. 212–213, 1993.
27. Brookes, M., *Fly; The Unsung Hero of 20th-Century Science*, HarperCollins, New York, p. 29, 2001.
28. Conn, H.W., *Evolution of today; a summary of the theory of evolution as held by scientists at the present time, and an account of the progress made by the discussions and investigations of a quarter of a century*, G. P. Putnam's Son, New York, p. 257, 1886.
29. Conn, *Evolution of today*, p. 226.
30. Smith, E.T., *Exploring Biology*, Harcourt, Brace and Company, New York, p. 553, 1940.
31. Bayles and Burnett, *Biology for Better Living*, p. 606.
32. Weimer, B.R., *Man and The Animal World*, John Wiley & Sons Inc., New York, p. 247, 1951.
33. Dodge, *Elements of Biology*, p. 598.
34. Moody, *Introduction to Evolution*.

Beck,[35] Kroeber, *et al.*,[36] Gardner and Snustad,[37] Curtis and Barnes,[38] Nelson,[39] and Boolootian and Stiles.[40] The example of the Ancon sheep is still being used even in some current college textbooks.[41,42] The first proof of macromutations in one of the most widely used high school biology textbooks in North America was the Ancon sheep example:

> We have historic records that even such larger mutations have occurred in single generations. In the year 1791 a New England farmer found a lamb in his flock which had short and crooked legs. With the eye of a thrifty Yankee, he saw what an advantage it would be to have a breed of sheep which could not jump fences, so he carefully took care of the freak lamb, bred from it, and got other animals with short and crooked legs. It was thus that the breed of Ancon sheep came into existence.[43]

In 1950, Landauer claimed that the "*Ancon mutant apparently was accepted by all contemporary observers as a new 'breed' of sheep.*"[44] The 10th edition of the major college text by Boolootian and Stiles[45] also taught that the Ancon mutation resulted in a new and valuable breed of sheep. As late as 1989 Nelson, under the subtopic "*The Origin of New Genes: Mutation,*" stated that Seth Wright "*set out to develop a flock of short-legged sheep*" based on this new trait that "*suddenly appeared.*" In their text book Gardner *et al.* include a colour picture of an Ancon sheep as an example of a beneficial mutation which the authors erroneously concluded caused a new species

---

35. Simpson, G.G and Beck, W.S., *Life: An Introduction to Biology*, 2nd edition (1965), 3rd Edition (1969), Harcourt, Brace & World, Inc., New York.
36. Kroeber, E., Wolff, W.H., and Weaver, R.L., *Biology*, Revised 2nd edition, D.C. Heath and Company, Lexington, Massachusetts, 1969.
37. Gardner, E. and Snustad, D.P, *Principles of Genetics*, John Wiley, New York, 1984.
38. Curtis and Barnes, *Biology*, p. 982.
39. Nelson, G.E., *Biological Principles with Human Applications*, 3rd edition, John Wiley and Sons, New York, p. 301, 1989.
40. Boolootian, R. and Stiles, K., *College Zoology*, Macmillan, New York, pp. 684–685, 1981.
41. Hickman, C. *et al.*, *Integrated Principles of Zoology*, McGraw-Hill, New York, p. 123, 2006.
42. Hickman, C., *Animal Diversity*, McGraw-Hill, New York, p. 22, 2003.
43. Kinsey, A.C., *An Introduction to Biology*, J.B. Lippincott, Philadelphia, pp. 189–190, 1926. See also Kinsey, A.C., *New Introduction to Biology*, J.B. Lippincott, Philadelphia, p. 414, 1938.
44. Landauer, W., The Massachusetts Ancon sheep, *The Journal of Heredity* **41**(6):144, 1950.
45. Boolootian and Stiles, *College Zoology*, pp. 684–685.

to arise, fulfilling evolutionary expectations.[46] Ancon sheep also were featured as proof of Darwinism in the popular literature.[47]

Another example of the use of Ancon sheep to support the claim that macro-evolution can occur in one generation was a debate between Dr Duane Gish and Dr Ken Miller, Professor of Biology at Brown University. Miller used the Ancon sheep example

> to support his contention that something akin to Goldschmidt's "*hopeful monster*" mechanism can and does occur. He used two examples: four-winged flies and Ancon sheep. He maintained that each of these examples lends support to Goldschmidt's suggestion that sudden large evolutionary changes, caused by macro-mutations, can give rise to abrupt, large evolutionary advances.[48]

The late Harvard Professor Stephen Jay Gould concluded that the need for evidence of rapid evolution, what Goldschmidt called 'hopeful monsters', is critical to neo-Darwinism for many reasons, especially because of lack of evidence for significant intermediate forms.[49]

Unable to find fossil intermediates connecting today's vertebrates, mollusks, insects, and other animals, critics long ago and still today ask "*where was the proof that they had come from a common stock*" in the course of thousands of generations?[50]

Many Darwinists pointed to sports or macromutations such as the Ancon sheep as the answer. This idea has been resurrected to support Gould's idea which he calls punctuated equilibrium or "*punk eck*", often called evolution "*by jerks*" as opposed to gradual evolution "*by creeps.*"[51]

The vital importance of the Ancon sheep and other "*evolutionary jumps*" for neo-Darwinism was that they helped to explain the existence of the many major classes of animals in existence today that lack evidence for gradual transitions.

Others agreed that sports, including the Ancon sheep, exist but argued that sports could not be the major source of evolution. Darwin's co-author of his first paper on evolution, Alfred Russel Wallace, argued that the Ancon sheep and other sports cannot explain the origin of new species. The reasons Wallace provides include:

---

46. Gardner, E, Simmons, M. and Snustad, D.P., *Principles of Genetics*, 8th edition, John Wiley, New York, 1991.
47. For example, Gehr, H., Genetics: young science studies continuity of life, *Life* **22**(11):83, 1947.
48. Gish, D., *Creation Scientists Answer Their Critics*, Institute for Creation Research, El Cajon, Calafornia, p. 93, 1993.
49. Gould, S., Evolution's erratic pace, *Natural History*, vol. 86, p. 14, 1977.
50. Desmond, *Huxley*, p. 256.
51. Frymire, P., *Impeaching Mere Creationism*, San Jose Writers Club Press, San Jose, Calafornia, p. 17, 2000.

- sports are extremely rare;
- they often do not leave offspring, and;
- repeated crossing with normal animals often causes the trait to disappear.

Claims which, in his words, were eventually proven to be correct:

> The short-legged Ancon sheep, and the six-toed cats, are other examples of such remarkable abnormalities or sports which have the curious property of being strongly hereditary, and yet, apparently, of never leading to the formation of new species. Almost all students of evolution now admit that "*sports*" or large and sudden divergencies from the specific type are *not* the materials from which new species have been formed, the reason being that they are extremely rare occurrences; and when any such "*sport*" appeared in a species, the individual presenting it would either be avoided by its fellows and leave no offspring, or by repeated crossings with the normal type the sport would disappear.[52]

Research soon documented that the claim made by neo-Darwinists that these sheep were widely bred because they are short-legged and thus cannot jump fences—an advantage for those who raise sheep—was problematic because the sheep had major health problems and, as the next section shows, breeding from them was very limited.[53]

Health problems discovered early in the Ancon sheep

When Seth Wright first found a male lamb with remarkably short, bowed legs, some of the 15 ewes in his flock were apparently heterozygous (had two different genes for the trait of concern here) not homozygous (one gene for the trait, thus breeding true) for the condition.[54] When he bred the Ancon ram, of the 15 lambs produced during the first season, two were Ancon sheep. By interbreeding Ancon sheep, he claimed that he produced a "*pure-breeding*" Ancon "*race.*"

Unfortunately, as has now been confirmed, the Ancon mutation produced so many major anatomical problems that this sheep 'breed' soon became extinct.[55] Hámori claims that the Southdown sheep—phenotypically similar to Ancon sheep—had thyroid gland lesions, among other harmful ailments, and that the

52. Wallace, A.R., *Studies: Scientific & Social*. New York: The Macmillan Company, p. 393, 1900. From *The Problem of Utility: Are Specific Characters Always or Generally Useful?*, a paper originally read before the Linnean Society on June 18th, 1896.
53. Gehr, Genetics, p. 83.
54. Dwight, *Travels in New England and New York*, pp. 88–89.
55. Schwartz and Vogel, Unraveling the yarn of the Ancon sheep.

majority of the dwarf lambs died before reaching two months of age.[56] They also described other Ancon dwarf sheep, many of which also had serious health problems.

The mutation has proved lethal even in a protected environment and, for this reason, no Ancon sheep herd exists today anywhere in the world.[57] The use of Ancon sheep to argue for evolutionary jumps is also deceptive because we now know that the mutation actually causes a pathological condition that results in a form of dwarfism called achondroplasia or a related pathology.[58]

Achondroplasia is a genetic dwarfism characterized by slow limb growth relative to the rest of the skeleton. Some prefer the term chondrodystrophy because the condition in animals is often due to an inadequate level of cartilage growth, not cartilage absence.[59] The term achondroplasia is widely used to describe this condition, so it was used in this chapter.

In harmony with our experience with mutations, other abnormalities, aside from short legs, have been discovered in Ancon sheep post-mortems. Some of these include abnormal spines and skulls, flabby subscapular muscles, looser leg joint articulations, and crooked, bent inward forelegs that caused the sheep legs to have an elbow-like appearance while walking.[60,61]

This trait was so prominent that the term *Ancon* (Greek for *elbow*) was used to describe them. This description fits the abnormality; Ancon sheep resemble the clubfoot condition because the adults were clumsy cripples that could neither run nor jump like other sheep.[62]

Landauer and Chang, who studied the sheep firsthand, describe the particular characteristics of these sheep, including

> the extreme shortness of their legs, which are also turned out in such a manner as to render them rickety. They cannot run or jump, and even walk with some difficulty. They appear as if their legs had been broken, and set by an awkward surgeon. To me there is something so disgusting in the sight of a flock of these poor lame animals, that even a strong conviction of their superior utility could hardly induce me to keep them.[63]

---

56. Hámori, D., *Constitutional Disorders and Hereditary Diseases in Domestic Animals*, Elsevier Scientific, New York, p. 347, 1983.
57. Schwartz and Vogel, Unraveling the yarn of the Ancon sheep.
58. Maroteaux, P. and Lamy, M., Achondroplasia in man and animals, *Clinical Orthopaedics and Related Research* **33**:91–103, 1964.
59. Maroteaux and Lamy, Achondroplasia in man and animals, p. 91.
60. Schwartz and Vogel, Unraveling the yarn of the Ancon sheep, p. 764.
61. Maroteaux and Lamy, Achondroplasia in man and animals, p. 101.
62. Dwight, *Travels in New England and New York*, p. 89.
63. Landauer and Chang, The Ancon or otter sheep, p. 110.

Early observers even concluded that Ancon sheep were so "*seriously handicapped*" that they were actually deformed, "*unsightly*" cripples.[64] One major problem is that the distal ends of their long bones disintegrate and may even largely disappear at birth.[65] The finding that the Ancon sheep mutation, and other mutations that cause dwarfism, are pathological, even in captivity, resulted in many evolutionists abandoning the hopeful monster theory early in Darwinian history:

> At one time, it was proposed that evolution takes place in sudden, large jumps such as this—a concept sometimes referred to as the "*hopeful monster*" theory. One reason this concept has been abandoned is that nearly all mutations producing dramatic changes in the phenotype are harmful.[66]

It was not advantageous in the wild to be unable to jump walls or run fast. Such an animal would not survive long in the wild, even if it was healthy. Moreover, this particular mutation also adversely affected the animal's reproductive rate, and this is one reason why the Ancon type became extinct.[67]

Recurrence also is characteristic of many mutations. The Ancon sheep mutation has reappeared at least four times in history (in Massachusetts, Texas, New Hampshire, and Norway). The most well-known case, aside from the one in Massachusetts, was in the flock owned by a Norwegian farmer in 1925. Although it is possible that most of the Ancon varieties were caused by similar genetic mutations, the Massachusetts and Norway examples may have been caused by separate mutations.[68] All four lines of sheep became extinct.[69]

Achondroplasia in humans causes a defect in the growth regions of the long bones, producing short limbs in comparison to the trunk and also redundant skin folds in the arms and legs.[70] It also causes a large skull, vertebral abnormalities, various bone and hand deformities, and other problems such as bow-leggedness.[71] In humans, the deformity is caused by an autosomal gene, and can be of various severity levels.

---

64. Landauer and Chang, The Ancon or otter sheep, pp. 108–109.
65. Shelton, M., A recurrence of the Ancon dwarf in merino sheep, *Journal of Heredity* **59**(5):267–268, 1968.
66. Curtis and Barnes, *Biology*, p. 982.
67. Klotz, J., *Genes, Genesis and Evolution*, Concordia, Saint Louis, Missouri, p. 258, 1970.
68. Schwartz and Vogel, Unraveling the yarn of the Ancon sheep, p. 767.
69. For other examples, see Shelton, A recurrence of the Ancon dwarf in merino sheep; and Wray, C., Mathieson, A.O., and Copland, A.N., An achondroplastic syndrome in South County Cheviot sheep, *Veterinary Record* **88**(20):521–522, 1971.
70. Bonaventure, J. *et al.*, Common mutations in the fibroblast growth factor receptor 3 (FGFR 3) gene account for achondroplasia, hypochondroplasia, and thanatophoric dwarfism, *American Journal of Medical Genetics* **63**(1):148–154, 1996.
71. Maroteaux and Lamy, Achondroplasia in man and animals.

In humans, the life expectancy of the heterozygotes for achondroplasia is about a decade less than normal, and homozygotes usually are stillborn or die in infancy due to respiratory failure and other problems.[72] It is often a *de novo*, or spontaneous, mutation, arising in about ten per million gametes (reproductive cells).[73] The cause of achondroplasia in most cases is a mutation in the transmembrane domain of the fibroblast growth receptor-3 gene.[74] Those people who survive often require extensive reconstructive surgery to reduce the many negative effects of the condition.

Achondroplasia in other animals

Achondroplasia has been found in many animals, including cows, rabbits, rhinoceroses, goats (in goats it can be caused by pituitary or thyroid disorders), mice, dogs, horses, pigs, birds, cats, turtles, and even humans.[75,76,77,78,79,80,81,82,83,84,85] The same gene is involved in causing the disease in different animals, but different genes evidently can cause the disorder in humans.[86,87]

72. Jorde, L., Carey, J., and White, R., *Medical Genetics*, Mosby, New York, p. 65, 1995.
73. Lewis, R., *Human Genetics*, McGraw Hill, New York, pp. 218–219, 2008.
74. Martinez, S., Valdes, J., and Alonso, R.A, Achondroplastic dog breeds have no mutations in the transmembrane domain of the FGFR-3 gene, *Canadian Journal of Veterinary Research* **64**(4):243–245, 2000; p. 243.
75. Mohanty, B.B. and Mohanty, B.N., Congenital malformations in bovines. 2. Incidence of achondroplasia, *Indian Veterinary Journal* **47**(9):765–766, 1970.
76. Becker, R.B., Neal, F.C. and Wilcox, C.J., Prenatal achondroplasia in a Jersey, *Journal of Dairy Science* **52**(7):1122–1123, 1969.
77. Bowden, D.M., Achondroplasia in Holstein-Friesian cattle, *Journal of Heredity* **61**(4):163–164, 1970.
78. Konyukhov, B.V. and Paschin, Y.V., Abnormal growth of the body, internal organs and skeleton in the [sic] achondroplastic mice, *Acta Zoologica Academiae Scientiarum Hungaricae* **21**(4):347–354, 1970.
79. Kaikini, A.S. and Malkhede, P.S., Achondroplasia in a goat (Capra hircus L.), *Indian Veterinary Journal* **46**(10):904–906, 1969.
80. Bruere, A.N., Dwarfism in beef cattle: diagnosis and control, *New Zealand Veterinary Journal* **17**(10):205–209, 1969.
81. Oostra, R.J., Baljet, B., Dijkstra, P.F. and Hennekam, R.C. Congenital anomalies in the teratological collection of Museum Vrolik in Amsterdam, The Netherlands. II: Skeletal dysplasias, *American Journal of Medical Genetics* **77**(2):116–134, 1998.
82. Sande, R.D. and Bingel, S.A., Animal models of dwarfism, *Veterinary Clinics of North America, Small Animal Practice* **13**(1):71–89, 1983.
83. Frye, F.L. and Carney, J.D., Achondroplastic dwarfism in a turtle, *Veterinary Medicine, Small Animal Clinician* **69**(3):299–301, 1974.
84. Basrur, P., and Bhola, Y., Genetic diseases of sheep and goats, *Veterinary Clinics of North America* **6**(3):779–802, 1990.
85. Martinez *et al.*, Achondroplastic dog breeds … .
86. Martinez *et al.*, Achondroplastic dog breeds … .
87. Maroteaux and Lamy, Achondroplasia in man and animals.

In dogs, like sheep, achondroplasia causes "*tortuous limbs endowed with rolls of loose skin.*"[88] In bovine achondroplasia, the victim suffers from a "*disturbance of cartilage growth in the extremities, including complete or temporary absence of perichondral and endochondral ossification* [normal bone development—Ed.]."[89] They typically have so many deformities that, if they are born alive, many do not survive very long.[90] In calves, achondroplasia causes a variety of major abnormalities, producing so-called 'bulldog calves'.

The Ancon mutation is a loss mutation

A major problem for Darwinists is that the Ancon mutation (most are evidently a Mendelian recessive) is a loss mutation, as is true with most other putative useful mutations, such as seedless fruit. This type of mutation does not result in a functional information gain, as Darwinism requires, but an information loss, often resulting in a complete structure or protein loss.

A huge difficulty in arguing for macroevolution by mutations is the fact that most expressed mutations are either near-neutral, semi-lethal, or lethal to the individual. Near-neutral mutations cannot be eliminated by natural selection, and so they continuously accumulate, causing eventual mutational meltdown.[91] Semi-lethal recessive mutations only rarely become homozygous lethal, when one copy is inherited from both parents. This eliminates that individual, but not the gene, which can still be passed on by relatives (carriers) who have only one copy. Lethal mutations are those in which even a single copy kills the organism outright. Mutations may cause the fertility rate to be reduced as well as causing the loss of certain structures.

Other common examples used to prove sports, such as seedless fruit, hornless Hereford cattle, tailless dogs and cats, and bare-neck chickens, are also all loss mutations.[92] Yet, some evolutionists try to claim that sports are a major source of new variety for neo-Darwinism, such as by implying that the loss mutation caused the Ancon sheep to gain a "*new character.*"[93]

Conclusions

The Ancon sheep was a widely cited evidence of macroevolution for over a century, and still is discussed in a few textbooks today. The textbooks implied that a radically new breed of sheep that was ideally suited for sheep farmers was produced in only

88. Ludders, J.W. and Brunson, D.B., A technique for ear-vein catherization, *Veterinary Medicine & Small Animal Clinician* **79**:769, 1984.
89. Hámori, *Constitutional Disorders and Hereditary Diseases in Domestic Animals*, p. 341.
90. Hámori, *Constitutional Disorders and Hereditary Diseases in Domestic Animals*, p. 344.
91. Sanford, J.C., *Genetic Entropy and the Mystery of the Genome*, FMS Publications, New York, 2008.
92. Weimer, *Man and The Animal World*, p. 247.
93. For example, see Kroeber *et al.*, *Biology*, p. 441.

one generation. In fact, the condition was a result of one or more mutations that caused a debilitating, and often lethal, disease called achondroplasia. Ancon sheep deformity is now classified as a harmful mutation, a Mendelian inheritance causing dwarfism.[94] That the 'new strain' was actually the result of serious deformities is a fact not mentioned in any of the textbooks or popular articles reviewed that touted the sport as evidence for evolution. All gave a misleading, distorted review of the true condition of these malformed sheep and what they mean to Darwinism.

The Ancon sheep example is still occasionally used to support neo-Darwinism. Professor Ken Miller's use of the Ancon sheep recently to prove that beneficial sport mutations exist is an example. Gish argued that this ploy was deceptive because Miller failed to note that the condition is caused by a mutation that results

> in the failure of the cartilage between the joints to develop. There is thus little or no cartilage between the joints of their legs, causing them to be short. This abnormal condition would, of course, result in their rapid extinction in a natural environment and could never be considered an evolutionary advance. Miller did not explain this to the audience, of course, and much to my chagrin, neither was I able to do so, since I was not aware of these facts at that time.[95]

As the results of the research on the Ancon 'breed' become more widely known, this icon of evolution is one more that will no longer be used to argue for macroevolutionary sports.

94. Mendelian Inheritance in Animals reference number 000004-9940 : Achondroplasia in Ovis aries.
95. Gish, *Creation Scientists Answer Their Critics*, p. 93.

CHAPTER 9

Darwin's peacock tail proof of sexual selection myth

Introduction

Many claimed examples of sexual selection exist, such as flycatchers with tails five times longer than their bodies and the mating calls, beautiful colour, and plumage of many birds.[1] The "*great feathered display of the male peacock is … the most famous example of nature's exuberance*" and of sexual selection. Darwin realized that natural selection could not explain these creatures so "*he came up with the idea of sexual selection.*"[2] Darwin argued that this theory explains many animal traits which actually can hinder survival, such as the unwieldy cumbersome peacock tail.

A peacock dragging its long, cumbersome tail which slows it down when attempting to escape from enemies.

In fact, the major theory today that attempts to explain all sexual dimorphism is Darwin's theory of sexual selection. Sexual selection involves an animal preferring to mate with animals that have certain physical traits. For example, birds with more attractive tails may be preferred as mates, causing this trait to become more prominent in the bird population over a period of time. The process, similar to human selection, or breeding, was used by Darwin to explain a wide variety of traits that seemed to have nothing to do with survival and even made an animal more visible

1. Rothenberg, D., *Survival of the Beautiful*, Bloomsbury Press, New York, pp. 4–5, 2011.
2. Rothenberg, *Survival of the Beautiful*, p. 5.

in most environments. They were, for this reason, actually *less* likely to survive due to their increased visibility to predators. Darwin used as a central illustration of his sexual selection theory the example of the Peacock's ostentatious tail. New research that has largely falsified this example is reviewed in this chapter.

Terminology

Peacocks (family *Phasianidae* and order *Galliformes)* are male birds, members of the pheasant family, that possess resplendent 'tails' called trains. These trains are raised and spread in displays of stunning colors, including iridescent green and gold ornamented with richly coloured bright blue-green eye-like markings. The females, called peahens, lack a train and are far less colourful.[3] Peacocks, although native to Africa and Asia, have been introduced elsewhere and are now found on every continent except Antarctica.

Peacock tail important in Darwin's theory

The ordinary peacock provided both inspiration and important evidence for Darwin's theory of sexual selection. Darwin at first had difficulty explaining why certain traits existed in animals that seemed to hurt their chances of survival in the wild because, while these traits may have effectively attracted mates, they also often attract many predators. Furthermore, these traits often were very gaudy and impractical. The peacock's tail is heavy, impedes its flying ability, slows the animal down when trying to escape predators, and requires much energy to grow and drag around.

Futuyma wrote about the large tail problem: "*Do the creation scientists really suppose their Creator saw fit to create a bird that couldn't reproduce without six feet of bulky feathers that make it easy prey for leopards?*"[4] Darwin also recognized these problems for his theory. For example, on April 3, 1860, he wrote the following to botanist Asa Gray: "*I remember well the time when the thought of the eye made me cold all over, but … now … The sight of a feather in a peacock's tail, whenever I gaze at it, makes me sick.*"[5]

3. Nehamas, A. and Long, P., The year of Darwin: the peacock problem, *American Scholar* **78**(2):118–121, 2009.
4. Futuyma, D., *Science on Trial: The Case for Evolution*, Pantheon, New York, p. 122, 1983.
5. Darwin, C., *The Correspondence of Charles Darwin*, Vol. 8. Edited by Burkhardt, F., Cambridge University Press, New York, p. 140, 1993.

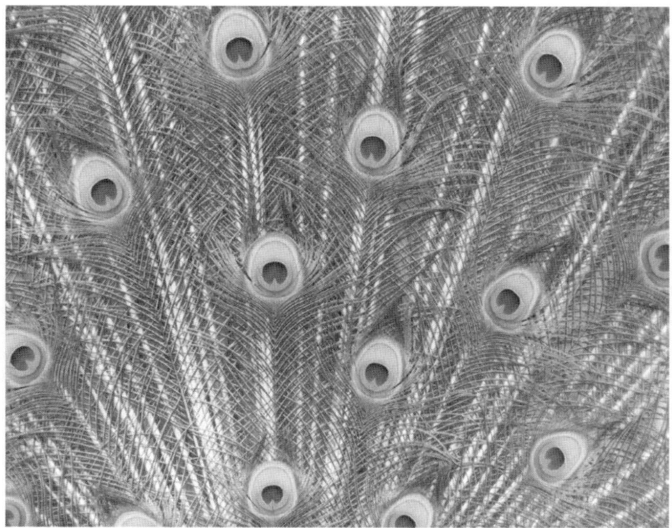

The famous iridescent colourful ocelli (eyespots) design. Note the eyespot has dark and light blue placed in a bed of pink surrounded by a green border.

The famous peacock display shown in all of its colourful glory.

Darwin's comment is not surprising. The stunning colours of the peacock's feathers and its enormous size have proven very difficult for evolutionists to deal with, both then and now. Peacocks are 'exhibit one' in the problem of evolution's attempts to explain the existence of certain features in animals as a result of natural selection. Natural selection explains traits in animals because they give them a distinct survival advantage over those animals that do not have that trait. Futuyma explains:

> The peacock's train of feathers is a perfectly natural result of a process in which genes that affect his plumage either succeed or not, depending on the whim of the female's sexual preference—a process that doesn't in any way enhance the peacock's adaptation to anything except the act of reproduction. … What we see exemplified by the *t* gene in the peacock's tail is this: whenever a gene, for whatever reason, can bequeath more copies of itself to subsequent generations than any other gene, it takes over—without forethought and without regard for whether it will be good for the individuals who inherit it or good for the species as a whole. Perpetuation of the species is not a cause but a result of reproduction.[6]

Many traits not only do not seem to give animals a survival advantage, but rather a clear survival disadvantage, and the peacock is only one of many examples. University of Chicago Professor Jerry Coyne explained that few animals are

> more resplendent than a male peacock in full display, with his iridescent blue-green tail, studded with eyespots, fanned out in full glory behind a shiny blue body. But the bird seems to violate every aspect of Darwinism, for the traits that make him beautiful are at the same time *maladaptive* for survival. That long tail produces aerodynamic problems in flight, as anyone knows who has ever seen a peacock struggle to become airborne. This surely makes it hard for the birds to get up to their nighttime roosts in the trees and to escape predators, especially during the monsoons when a wet tail is literally a drag. The sparkling colors too attract predators, especially compared to the females, who are short-tailed and camouflaged a drab greenish brown. And a lot of metabolic energy is diverted to the male's striking tail, which must be completely regrown each year.[7]

Coyne then stresses that

> not only does the peacock's plumage seem pointless, but it's an impediment. How could it possibly be an adaptation? And if individuals with such plumage left more genes, as one would expect if the raiment evolved by natural selection, how come the females aren't equally resplendent?[8]

Coyne documents the fact that this tail logically would *reduce* the animal's survival rate, and this is what made Darwin "*sick*" about the problem of the origin of the peacock's tail. Dawkins claims that both the female and the chicks are dull-coloured,

---

6. Futuyma, *Science on Trial*, p. 122.
7. Coyne, J.A., *Why Evolution is True*, Viking, New York, p. 144, 2009.
8. Coyne, *Why Evolution is True*, pp. 144–145.

"obviously well camouflaged, and that's the way the male would be if individual survival were his priority."[9]

The sexual selection solution

Darwin solved the problem by concluding that the tail gave the peacock a survival advantage in competing for mates, a theory he called sexual selection. He wrote that the peacock's tail is *"good evidence that the most refined beauty may serve as a charm for the female, and for no other purpose."*[10]

In his *Origin of Species,* Darwin wrote that sexual selection *"depends, not on a struggle for existence, but on a struggle between the males for the possession of the females; the result is not death to the unsuccessful competitor, but few or no offspring."*[11]

A peahen, the female bird that lacks a train. Notice it is a very dull bird by comparison. Darwin for this reason had to explain the difference between the colourful male and the female whose tail lacked the dynamic colour of the male.

A major example that Darwin used to illustrate his sexual selection theory was the peacock. All of his peahen birds, he claimed, found the peacock's tail attractive—and the larger and more colourful the tails, the more attractive they found them. For this reason, Darwin argued, peahens selected peacocks with more attractive tails with which to mate. As a result, the tail slowly became larger and more colourful with each generation.

9. Dawkins, R., *The Greatest Show on Earth: The Evidence for Evolution*, Free Press, New York, p. 45, 2009.
10. Darwin, C., *The Descent of Man*, Vol. II, John Murray, London, p. 92, 1871.
11. Darwin, C., *On the Origin of Species*, John Murray, London, p. 88, 1859.

Darwin concluded, "*I can see no good reason to doubt that female birds, by selecting, during thousands of generations, the most melodious or beautiful males, according to their standard of beauty, might produce a marked effect.*"[12]

In a summary of "*the most influential piece of popular science writing ever published,*" Darwin's *Origin of Species,* Professor Jones wrote that the

> Males of many species are forced to compete for the attention of females, and it pays a female to choose the best mate to father her offspring, the vessel of her own precious genes. This struggle for sex can lead to the evolution of bizarre structures such as the peacock's tail. Far from helping their bearers to stay alive, these sexually attractive traits are often a handicap. That may be why they work, for they indicate that those who bear them have what it takes to survive despite their costly sexual signal.[13]

Dawkins opined that, just as humans breed trees for larger fruit and horses for speed, so too "*peahens breed for more appealing peacocks.*"[14] In his 1871 book, Darwin discussed in detail his solution to the peacock problem, namely sexual selection, and discussed the peacock example in more detail to document his argument. Johnson wrote that the example of sexual selection

> illustrates the skill of Darwinists at incorporating recalcitrant examples into their theory. Sexual selection is a relatively minor component in Darwinist theory today, but to Darwin it was almost as important as natural selection itself. (Darwin's second classic, *The Descent of Man,* is mainly a treatise on sexual selection.) The most famous example of sexual selection is the peacock's gaudy fan, which is obviously an encumbrance when a peacock wants to escape a predator. The fan is stimulating to peahens, however, and so its possession increases the peacock's prospects for producing progeny even though it decreases his life expectancy.[15]

This is the standard explanation for the peacock tails. As Dawkins wrote:

> On the face of it, the tail of a peacock is a *jeu d'esprit par excellence.* It surely does no favours to the survival of its possessor. But it does benefit the genes that distinguish him from his less spectacular rivals. The tail is an advertisement, which buys its place in the economy of nature by attracting females.[16]

---

12. Darwin, C., *On the Origin of Species,* John Murray, London, p. 89, 1859.
13. Jones, S., *On the Origin of Species Revisited,* inset in *New Scientist*, p. 4, November 14, 2009.
14. Dawkins, *The Greatest Show on Earth*, p. 61.
15. Johnson, P., *Darwin on Trial*, Regnery Gateway, Washington, DC, p. 30, 1991.
16. Dawkins, R., *The God Delusion*, Houghton Mifflin Company, Boston, p. 163, 2006.

Coyne claimed that "*Enigmas like the peacock's tail abound.*"[17] Yet evidently no-one had properly scientifically evaluated the peacock tail theory until 2008. Before this time the few studies that had been completed on this question produced somewhat conflicting results. For example, Petrie *et al.* reported a clear correlation between the number of ocelli (eyespots) in the male train and mating success, and Petrie reports that the offspring of peacocks with more elaborate trains grow and survive better under nearly-natural conditions; however when elaborating further Petrie and Halliday cite research pointing to symmetry or overall colour in the train as potentially significant in female mate-choice.[18,19,20] Manning suggests age is a factor, finding a strong correlation between the number of ocelli in the train and the age of the bird, though Petrie and Halliday dispute some of his findings.[21] Yasman and Yahya demonstrate mating success has a high correlation with the length of fishtail feathers, and also some correlation with mating calls with more than five notes.[22] The study also raised the possibility of a link between the two traits such that it could be mating calls which are the deciding factor and not train quality. Other studies give differing explanations for female choice, though usually it is just *assumed* that male appearance is a significant factor.

Recent research overturns the peacock theory

Darwin's theory sounds plausible but a recent and thorough study by Takahashi *et al.* involving detailed observations of mating behaviour found that a more colorful array of peacock's tail feathers does *not* give it a mating advantage. The elaborate tail may actually put it at a survival disadvantage because, as Coyne noted, the ostentatious tail both attracts predators and is a major hindrance in fleeing from enemies. Takahashi, *et al.,* note that the "*peacock's train has been proposed not only as a target of current female choice, but also as an indicator of good genes,*" adding that at least four problems exist with this hypothesis:

> First, male train morphology seems not to be the universal cue of choice because there is evidence both for and against the effect of male train morphology on male mating success. Successful peacocks are individuals either

17. Coyne, *Why Evolution is True*, p. 145.
18. Petrie, M. and Halliday, T., Experimental and natural changes in the peacock's (*Pace cristatus*) train can affect mating success, *Behavioral Ecology and Sociobiology* **35**(3):213–217, 1994.
19. Petrie, M., Improved growth and survival of offspring of peacocks with more elaborate trains, *Nature* **371**(6498):598–599, 1994.
20. Petrie, M., Halliday, T., and Sanders, C., Peahens prefer peacocks with elaborate trains, *Animal Behaviour* **41**(2):323–331, 1991.
21. Manning, J.T., The peacock's train and the age-dependency model of female choice, *Journal of The World Pheasant Association*, pp. 12, 44–56, 1987.
22. Yasmin, S. and Yahya, H., Correlates of mating success in Indian peafowl. *Auk*, 113, 490–492, 1996.

> with or without longer trains and with or without a greater number of eyespots. The trait itself does not seem to be the single cue for choice; several peafowl researchers have pointed out the functional importance of behavioral cues. Second, the ways in which females assess male trains (unless females have the ability to count eyespots per se) have been questioned repeatedly.[23,24]

Their third reason is the study determined through photographs taken each season that both the eyespot number and symmetry fluctuated. Last, the shivering display involving shaking directly toward a visiting female also varied both in number and intensity.

The details of the Tokyo study

For seven years, University of Tokyo researchers studied a population of both peacocks and peahens in Izu Cactus Park, carefully photographing each male during the tail-fanning display ritual. They then analyzed their data to determine if females were more likely to have chosen mates with the highest quality tails over those with inferior tails. The researchers used factors such as the number of eyespots and tail size as a measure of the tail's quality.

During their observation period, they found that of the 268 successful matings observed, females were just as likely to mate with drab-tailed peacocks as with flashy train-gifted males. The researchers concluded that the male peacocks' tail quality was *not* related to female attraction—a result dramatically at odds with Darwin's theory. The researchers concluded that their study of mate choice using male- and female-centred observations

> found no evidence that peahens expressed any preference for peacocks with more elaborate trains (i.e. trains having more ocelli, a more symmetrical arrangement or a greater length), similar to other studies of galliforms showing that females disregard male plumage. Combined with previous results, our findings indicate that the peacock's train is not the universal target of female choice, [and] shows small variance among males across populations.[25]

The importance of this research is clear. Coyne wrote that we need to determine if males that "*are more highly ornamented, or perform the best displays, actually get more mates*" because "*If they don't, the whole theory of sexual selection collapses.*"[26] The fact

23. Takahashi, M., Arita, H., Hiraiwa-Hasegawa, M., and Hasegawa, T., Peahens do not prefer peacocks with more elaborate trains, *Animal Behaviour* **75**(4):1209–1210, 2008.
24. Takahashi *et al.*, Peahens … , pp. 1209–1219.
25. Takahashi *et al.*, Peahens … , p. 1209.
26. Coyne, *Why Evolution is True*, p. 149.

is, central questions about the validity of sexual selection exist, at least in the case of Darwin's peacock example.

A question never answered is: "*Why would females be attracted to the peacock's tail? Would not the traits they found attractive also be shaped by sexual selection?*" In other words, the females who found the typical existing bird attractive *before* it evolved its train would be more likely to mate and pass on the genes that caused it to be attracted to typical pre-train males. The "*prediction that choosy females produce sexy sons is critical to all models of indirect selection on choice*", but has never been carefully studied to the level of detail reported by these Tokyo researchers.[27]

This field of research has been problematic since Darwin first proposed his sexual selection theory. Previous studies were biased by Darwin's claims, and the researchers tended to find what they were looking for—called the research bias problem—or else the research was found to be inadequate in other ways.

Darwin once noted that he prided himself as an expert "*in the master art of wriggling*" out of problems with his theory.[28] Would Darwin have come up with an explanation to salvage his theory of sexual selection if he knew about these results, or would he try to wriggle out of the implications of this study?

The theory of sexual selection now being questioned

These findings have caused some researchers to question the validity of the whole sexual selection theory research field. The field and laboratory research has undermined the sexual selectivity theory based on the perceived attractiveness of an animal to potential mates. Some scientists, such as Stanford University Professor Joan Roughgarden, have concluded that an impressive catalogue of biological studies, such as the Takahashi *et al.* research, shows that the facts often *fail* to support the sexual selection theory.[29,30] Brooks, in a review of the literature, wrote that

> the standard view of sexual selection, choosing a mate, is meant to be a straightforward affair. It is based on the display of "*good genes,*" usually manifest in the adornments and athleticism of the male of the species. For the most part the females choose (their eggs are limited; sperm is cheap and plentiful), and males slug it out for the chance to be chosen. However, recent studies showed that all that talk about females choosing males with the biggest antlers, or loudest roar, or, as in the case of peacocks, the most

27. Kokko, H., Jennions, M.D. and Brooks, R., Unifying and testing models of sexual selection, *Annual Review of Ecology, Evolution, and Systematics* **37**:43–66, 2006; p. 58.
28. Darwin, F., *Life and Letters of Charles Darwin*, Vol. III, p. 55–56, 1887.
29. Roughgarden, J. *Evolution's Rainbow: Diversity, Gender and Sexuality in Nature and People*, University of California Press, Los Angeles, 2004.
30. Roughgarden, J., *The Genial Gene*, University of California Press, Berkeley, California, 2009.

> elegant tail feathers in order to get the "*best genes*" is just far too simplistic to describe what happens in the real world.[31]

The many problems with the sexual selection theory were noted by John Maynard Smith, who used the

> red deer as an example of where things go wrong for sexual selection theory. The powerful males get busy rutting in an exhausting, drawn-out, and impressive display of antler bashing. Often, though, the females aren't impressed and slope off to have sex with the less macho males of the herd.[32]

Brooks added that there does not even exist

> strong evidence that females really are impressed by the antler bashing or link it with the good genes that they supposedly seek for their offspring. And are there really so few good genes out there that the females are willing to focus all their attention on just one or two males? ... if the theory holds together, all the males are the progeny of strong, fit males from the previous generation. It's hard to imagine that there is such a marked difference that females would be so discerning. The issue, known as the *Lek Paradox*, is well known to biologists. Although there are some explanations for why female choosing should persist, it still stands as a point of contention in standard sexual selection theory.[33]

Summary

Darwin's sexual selection idea has been applied to explain many traits that cannot be explained by natural selection, such as the most extravagant plumage ornaments in some male birds, but more careful research has lent serious doubt to the theory, especially in the one case that Darwin emphasized.[34] We now know that the plumage clearly interferes with its survival ability.

The male peacock in full display, "*with his iridescent blue-green tail, studded with eyespots, fanned out in full glory behind a shiny blue body*" is one of the most beautiful birds known to mankind.[35] This may be the only reason for its design and not sexual selection.

Futuyma asked whether creationists "*really suppose their Creator saw fit to create a bird that couldn't reproduce without six feet of bulky feathers that make it easy prey*

31. Brooks, M., *13 Thing That Don't Make Sense: The Most Baffling Scientific Mysteries of Our Time*, Doubleday, New York, p. 237, 2008.
32. Brooks, *13 Thing That Don't Make Sense*, p. 237.
33. Brooks, *13 Thing That Don't Make Sense*, p. 238.
34. Takahashi *et al.*, Peahens ... , p. 1209.
35. Coyne, *Why Evolution is True*, p. 144.

for leopards?"[36] Solidly refuting him, Johnson noted that a peacock and peahen are the kind of creatures that an innovative Creator would design, but that an "*uncaring mechanical process*" like natural selection would never permit to evolve.[37] If neither natural nor sexual selection can explain the peacock, one has to agree with him that a peacock is just the kind of animal an artistic creator would favour.

Furthermore, Roughgarden's research found that "*there are so many exceptions to this idea* [of sexual selection] *that we should look elsewhere for an explanation of courtship displays. Secondary sexual characteristics, such as the peacock's tail, might not be indicators of good genes, but of general good health.*"[38] Brooks concluded that it is true that some animals expend an effort to

> scrutinize the males, but it is by no means the norm. As the biologist Steven Rose pointed out, although it seems like a compelling idea, the empirical evidence for sexual selection based on impressive male traits is weak—and that is even true among peacocks, the "*classic*" example. What's more, there is evidence suggesting that the key to reproductive success lies somewhere other than a display of brute strength.[39]

36. Futuyma, *Science on Trial*, p. 122.
37. Johnson, *Darwin on Trial*, p. 31.
38. Brooks, *13 Thing That Don't Make Sense*, p. 239–240.
39. Brooks, *13 Thing That Don't Make Sense*, p. 238.

CHAPTER 10

A century-old fraud debunked: Haeckel's biogenetic law

Introduction

Darwinists once commonly believed that the basic life-forms which existed in our putative past multi-millions of years of evolution are repeated in humans during the first few months between conception and birth. In other words, as the human embryo develops, it passes through most of the major past evolutionary stages from which it was believed to have evolved. This theory—also commonly known as 'ontogeny recapitulates phylogeny', the biogenetic law, or the recapitulation law—was cited as a major proof of evolutionism for over a century. Mid-20th century discoveries in embryology and re-evaluation of the evidence showed that the theory is without foundation, and it has now been discarded by embryologists. Biogenetic law claims commonly used in pre-1980s textbooks, including the gill slits, tail, and yolk sac claims, have also been found to be invalid.

Background

Ernst Haeckel as an old man.

Professor Ernst Haeckel gave to the world the generalization that *ontogeny (individual development) recapitulates (repeats) phylogeny (evolutionary descent)*, which means that "*the development of the individual repeats the evolution of the race.*"[1] This notion later became known simply as recapitulation or the biogenetic law.[2] A review of older biology textbooks reveals that the biogenetic law once was considered "*one of the most important sources of biological evidence for evolution*" and for this reason, until recently, almost always was discussed in textbooks that covered biological evolution.[3] In the words of Princeton's Professor Conklin,

1. Moore, J.A. (Ed.), *Biological science: an Inquiry into Life*, Harcourt Brace and World, New York, p. 608, 1963.
2. Hickman, C., Roberts, L. and Larson, A., *Integrated Principles of Zoology*, William C. Brown, Dubuque, Iowa, p. 116, 2006.
3. Smallwood, W.M., *A Textbook of Biology*, 6th edition, Lea and Febiger, Philadelphia, p. 391, 1930.

> ontogeny, or the origin of individuals, and phylogeny, or the origin of races, are two aspects of one and the same thing, namely, organic development. There is a remarkable parallelism between the two, and in particular the factors or causes of development are essentially the same in both.[4]

In other words, the embryonic stage of an animal reveals the evolutionary stages that the animal supposedly has passed through

> in the course of its evolution. Embryonic development is a brief and condensed repetition of a series of ancestral stages through which the race has passed. Or, as often stated, ontogeny (the development of the individual) recapitulates phylogeny (the development of the race).[5]

Some authorities have tried to claim that even plant embryo development documents recapitulation. An example is: "*Germinating moss and fern spores produce a short filament of green cells*" that

> resembles a filamentous green algae. Soon the moss protonema develops into the male and female leafy shoots, while the filament of fern cells develops into the mature prothallus. For a brief period, though, mosses and ferns both pass through a stage reminiscent of the algae from which we think they evolved.[6]

The long-discredited, now-abandoned theory taught that human life begins as a single cell as did the first life-forms, then develops into a fish stage with fish gills, next a reptile stage, then a mammal stage with a tail like a dog, an ape stage and, before birth, the embryo develops into the highest life-form that evolution has so far achieved, the human stage.[7] The recapitulation law also taught that each successive stage in the development of an individual represents an adult form that appeared in its evolutionary history, and that there is evidence of this past in the embryo and fetus.

For example, small depressions in the human embryo neck were said to be evidence that humans once had a fish-like ancestor because the depressions were at the same location where gills later develop in fish. Related to the biogenetic law argument is the belief that some structures in the developing embryo and fetus are useless. Darwin did much to popularize the theory and included a detailed discussion of it in his *Origin of Species*.[8]

---

4. Conklin, E.G., Embryology and evolution in *Creation by Evolution*, Frances M. (Ed.), MacMillan, New York, p. 64, 1928.
5. Haupt, A., *Fundamentals of Biology*, McGraw Hill, New York, p. 345, 1940.
6. Kimball, J.W., *Biology*, Addison-Wesley, Reading, Massachusetts, p. 546, 1965.
7. Rimmer, H., *Embryology and the Recapitulation Theory*, Research Science Bureau, Los Angeles, p. 8, 1929.
8. Darwin, C., *On the Origin of Species*, John Murray, London, pp. 439–450, 1859.

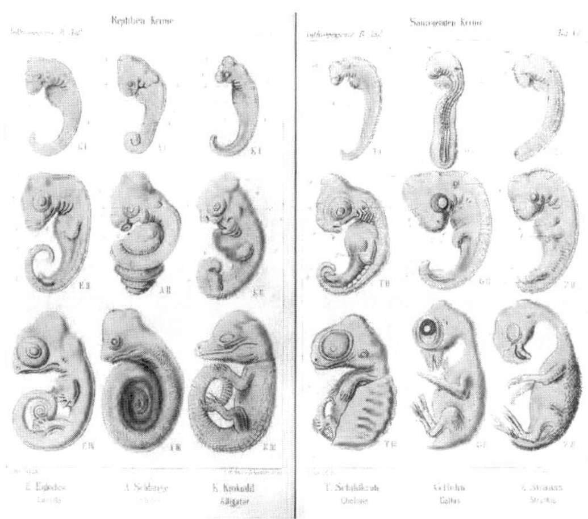

Plates VI and VII from the 4th edition of Haeckel's influential textbook *Anthropogenie*. Haeckel first published his embryo diagrams in his 1868 book *Natürliche Schöpfungsgeschichte*. These pictures have been reprinted hundreds of times, often redrawn slightly, in high school and college biology and evolution textbooks.

Although the theory was comprehensively discredited by the end of 1915, it remained popular and was not abandoned, and is still occasionally claimed as valid evidence for evolution.[9]

Some modern biology texts still try to argue that the resemblances embryos display to their putative ancestors as they develop is critical evidence for evolution. The biogenetic law was even widely taught in popular lay books, such as Dr Spock's *Baby and Child Care,* which sold over 40 million copies in 39 languages. Under the subheading "*They're repeating the whole history of the human race,*" Spock wrote that watching a baby grow is "*full of meaning*" because the development of each child retraces the entire

> history of the human race, physically and spiritually, step by step. Babies start off in the womb as a single tiny cell, just the way the first living thing appeared in the ocean. Weeks later, as they lie in the amniotic fluid in the womb, *they have gills like fish* and tails like amphibians. Toward the end of the first year of life, when they learn to clamber to their feet, they're celebrating that period millions of years ago when our ancestors got up off all fours and learned to use their fingers with skill and delicacy [emphasis added].[10]

9. Frair, W., Embryology and evolution, *Creation Research Society Quarterly* **36**(2):62–67, 1999.
10. Spock, B., *Dr. Spock's Baby and Child Care*, 7th edition, Dutton, NewYork, p. 18, 1998.

This passage implies that the embryo breathes by using gills to extract oxygen from the amniotic fluid! As will be documented, this once common conclusion has been proven false.[11,12] Nonetheless, the influence of the biogenetic law in convincing the public of the validity of macroevolution has been enormous, and even though it has been refuted, it is still mentioned in some biology textbooks.[13]

> So great was the desire on the part of some to strengthen this [biogenetic] idea, that a classic series of drawings showing embryonic similarities was produced in which the resemblances of the embryos of fish and man were remarkable. They were so remarkable, in fact, that further investigation showed that overzealous artistry had indicated a few resemblances that did not quite exist![14]

The basis for the theory

Extensive comparisons of most animals has confirmed that a great deal of similarity exists in both the structure and function of body morphology including skeletons, muscles, nerves, body organs, and cell ultrastructure. For example, Haupt argues for evolution by claiming that fish gill slits exist during human embryo development when the human

> heart is two chambered and the circulatory system distinctly fish-like. The heart then passes through a three-chambered stage, characteristic of amphibians and reptiles, and finally becomes four chambered, as in birds and in other mammals. Similarly the human brain, in its embryonic development, passes through a series of stages corresponding to adult conditions in the lower vertebrate groups.[15]

Although many animal kinds look superficially very similar in the zygote, cleavage, blastula, gastrula, and other stages of development, profound differences exist. Many vertebrates, from amphibians to humans, share fundamental resemblances in fetal development, but biological research has increasingly revealed differences between the life-forms the animal supposedly evolved from, eventually disproving

11. McNamara, K., Embryos and evolution, *New Scientist* **164**(2208):1–4, 1999.
12. Hopwood, N., *Haeckel's Embryos: Images, Evolution, and Fraud*, The University of Chicago Press, Chicago, 2015.
13. Examples include: Prothero, D., *Bringing Fossils to Life: An Introduction to Paleobiology*, McGraw-Hill, 3rd edition, p. 29, 2013; Prothero, D., *Evolution: What the Fossils Say and Why it Matters,* Columbia University Press, New York, p. 110, 2007; and Whalley, K., *et al.*, Science Focus 4, Pearson Educational Australia, Melbourne, p. 244, 2005.
14. Moore, *Biological science: an Inquiry into Life*, p. 608.
15. Moore, *Biological science: an Inquiry into Life*, p. 347.

the biogenetic law. One major difference is the organism's DNA, that can differ by many hundreds of thousands or millions of base pairs. This contrast eventually results in the more obvious morphological differences that produce the divergence which occurs in the animal's later developmental stages.[16]

Even vertebrate eggs of many animals display profound differences. Most obvious is their great variation in size, ranging from the microscopic eggs of mammals to the enormous eggs of some birds. Eggs also differ in the conditions required for them to develop: some eggs begin as naked cells independent of their parents; others, although enclosed in both protective membranes and shells, are incubated by their parents. Still other eggs, such as those of most mammals, develop within the mother's body. Associated with these varying developmental conditions are many differences in egg colour, rate of development, and nutritional requirements.[17]

History of biological recapitulation

The theory that the "*ontogeny*" of the embryo "*recapitulates*" or duplicates the evolution of the organism probably was first expounded in modern times by Kielmeyer in 1793 partly from the observation that a frog tadpole resembles a fish.[18]

The theory was further developed by embryologist Karl Von Baer (1792–1876) and also by Fritz Müller in 1864. In chapter 14 of *The Origin of Species,* Darwin further developed the idea that the embryo's evolutionary history was recorded in its developmental stages.[19] It was later elaborated and popularized by German Professor of Comparative Anatomy, Ernst Haeckel (1834–1919), spelled Häckel in German.[20]

Haeckel, an accomplished artist, produced a series of excellent, but sometimes very inaccurate, illustrations that have been widely reproduced in textbooks throughout the world. Darwin and Huxley were both very impressed by Haeckel's illustrations and referred to them in their own writings. Haeckel's drawings were first published in his own books starting from 1868, then later in the 1897 book *Darwin, and After Darwin* by George Romanes.[21] From this source they were widely reproduced in English language biology texts for the next century, no doubt because his pictures appeared to provide clear evidence for macroevolution.

16. Richardson, M. *et al.*, There is no highly conserved embryonic stage in the vertebrates: implications for current theories of evolution and development, *Anatomy and Embryology*, **196**(2):91–106, 1997.
17. Burton, R., *Eggs: Nature's Perfect Package,* Facts on File, New York, 1987.
18. Rusch, W., Ontogeny recapitulates phylogeny, *Creation Research Society Quarterly* **6**(1):27–34, 1969.
19. Darwin, *On the Origin of Species,* pp. 483–486.
20. Rusch, Ontogeny recapitulates phylogeny.
21. Romanes, G., *Darwin, and after Darwin*, The Open Court Publishing Co., Chicago, 1901.

In a review of the history of the biogenetic law and why it was important, Conklin claimed the "*law*" taught that every animal climbs up its own ancestral tree when developing from egg to adult, a "*god-send*" for evolutionists. As a result, the study of embryology was pursued with "*feverish zeal*" because the method

> promised to reveal more important secrets of the past than would the unearthing of all the buried monuments of antiquity—in fact nothing less than a complete genealogical tree of all the diversified forms of life which inhabit the earth. It promised to reveal not only the animal ancestry of man and the line of his descent but also the … origin of his mental, social, and ethical faculties.[22]

As research revealed more and more flaws in his idea, many scientists realized Haeckel's biogenetic law went "*far beyond anything resembling science*" and later became "*an embarrassment to Darwin himself*."[23]

The biogenetic law has proved critically important in converting people to Darwinism, and has been cited as a major proof of evolution in science textbooks from high school to graduate school for over a century.[24] One reason recapitulation was so popular with text book authors was because it was a simple, easily grasped concept that could be illustrated effectively by diagrams that superficially appeared to prove Darwinism.

As Rusch[25] noted, "*in most cases, recapitulation was considered to be sufficient cause for the various stages in embryological development,*" a belief that was valid in some cases, but may have discouraged research into other causes. De Beer wrote that the biogenetic law also influenced the direction of embryology research and, importantly, it also distorted conclusions about past research findings. "*Seldom has an assertion like that of Haeckel's 'theory of recapitulation', facile, tidy, and plausible, widely accepted without critical examination, done so much harm to science. The puerile notion that the past evolution of a race was sufficient to explain the mechanism of the process of embryonic development of descendants, blinded biologists for a time …*". He added that Haeckel's theory "*took a long time to expose … So seductive did this picture appear.*"[26] One case where it actually produced valid results was when Darwin won favour with scientists because he took Hooker's advice and studied one group of

22. Conklin, Embryology and evolution, p. 70.
23. Milner, R., *The Encyclopedia of Evolution: Humanity's Search for Its Origins*, Facts on File, New York, p. 205, 1990.
24. Taylor, I., *In the Minds of Men*, TFE, Toronto, p. 276, 1984.
25. Rusch, Ontogeny recapitulates phylogeny, p. 27.
26. De Beer, G., Darwin and embryology in *A century of Darwin*, Barnett, S. (Ed.), Heinemann, London, pp. 159–161, 1958.

organisms in detail. He became a world expert on barnacles and used embryology to correctly place barnacles, earlier thought to be mollusks, in the arthropods.[27]

Doubts about the universality of the theory began to emerge very early in its history. At first

> embryology was studied chiefly to learn the course of past evolution, but owing to the highly speculative character of such studies and to the differences of opinion as to what were original (palingenetic) and what were acquired (coenogenetic) characters, there gradually arose a widespread skepticism concerning the value of embryology for this purpose.[28]

In 1889, Gegenbaur wrote the "*growing opinion among zoologists*" was that if coenogenetic traits are intermingled with palingenetic traits

> then we cannot regard ontogeny as a pure source of evidence regarding phyletic relationships. Ontogeny accordingly becomes a field in which an active imagination may have full scope for its dangerous play, but in which positive results are by no means everywhere to be attained. To attain such results the palingenetic and the coenogenetic phenomena must be sifted apart, an operation that requires more than one critical *granum salis* [grain of salt—Ed.].[29]

Since then serious problems with the 'law' have accumulated, and scientists have increasingly discounted the theory, some even declaring that no evidence exists that ontogeny ever recapitulates phylogeny, and that Haeckel's 'biogenetic law' has no foundation in fact.[30] Many of the major difficulties in the theory had become well known by 1928, when it was realized that many developmental events are

> adaptations to the conditions of embryonic or larval life and could never have been present in adult animals, [therefore] Haeckel separated such characters, which he called "*coenogenetic,*" from the truly ancestral ones, which he called "*palingenetic.*" Unfortunately there was no certain method of always distinguishing these *two* types of embryonic characters, but in spite of this difficulty embryology was supposed to afford a short and easy method of determining the ancestral history of every group.[31]

No certain criterion existed by which the various ancestral features existing in development could be distinguished from the recently acquired ones. Therefore

---

27. Stott, R., *Darwin and the Barnacle: The Story of One Tiny Creature and History's Most Spectacular Scientific Breakthrough,* Norton, New York, 2003.
28. Conklin, Embryology and evolution, pp. 70–71.
29. Quoted in Conklin, Embryology and evolution, pp. 70–71.
30. Rusch, Ontogeny recapitulates phylogeny, p. 28.
31. Conklin, Embryology and evolution, p. 70.

> what one embryologist regarded as ancestral another might consider a recent addition. Furthermore, when there were no living or fossil animals resembling certain embryological forms the fancy was given free rein to invent hypothetical ancestors corresponding to such forms. As a result of such speculations multitudes of phylogenetic trees sprang up in the thin soil of embryological fact and developed a capacity of branching and producing hypothetical ancestors which was in inverse proportion to their hold on solid ground.[32]

Unfortunately, in his enthusiasm to prove the law and, thereby, vindicate evolution, the biogenetic law's major popularizer resorted to outright fraud.

Fraud proven

Many of Haeckel's drawings used to support his biogenetic law were demonstrated to be grossly fraudulent as soon as they were published. In 1977, Michael Richardson, an embryologist at St George's Hospital Medical School in London, has concluded that generations of biology students were

> misled by a famous set of drawings of embryos published 123 years ago by the German biologist Ernst Haeckel. They show vertebrate embryos of different animals passing *through* identical stages of development. But the impression they give, that the embryos are exactly alike, is wrong. … [Richardson] hopes once and for all to discredit Haeckel's work, first found to be flawed more than a century ago.[33]

The fraud was exposed in 1868 by Uni. of Basel comparative anatomy professor L. Rütimyer, immediately after Haeckel's first publication of the images, and then again in 1875 by leading embryologist Wilhelm His Sr (1831–1904), after Haeckel republished them in 1874. Dr His, a comparative embryologist and Professor of Anatomy at the Uni. of Leipzig, concluded that both Haeckel's drawings and his conclusions were gross distortions of the facts. In a review of His's work, Taylor argued that His proved that Haeckel had engaged in blatant fraud and, therefore, Haeckel

> had eliminated himself from the ranks of scientific research workers of any stature … His, whose work still stands as the foundation of our knowledge of embryological development, was not the first to point out the deficiencies of Haeckel's work, nor indeed was he the last, yet Haeckel's fraudulent drawings have continued to the present day to be reproduced throughout the biological literature.[34]

32. Conklin, Embryology and evolution, p. 70.
33. Pennisi, E., Haeckel's embryos: fraud rediscovered, *Science* **277**(5331):1435, 1997.
34. Taylor, *In the Minds of Men*, pp. 276–277.

Cambridge University biologist Michael Pitman even wrote that, after Haeckel formulated his 'fundamental biogenetic law' in 1868, he claimed that the

> entire animal kingdom was descended from an organism resembling the gastrula—an early stage in the embryonic development of most animals. To support his case he began to fake evidence. Charged with fraud by five professors and convicted by a university court at Jena, he agreed that a small percentage of his embryonic drawings were forgeries; he was merely filling in and reconstructing the missing links when the evidence was thin, and he claimed unblushingly that "*hundreds of the best observers and biologists lie under the same charge*".[35]

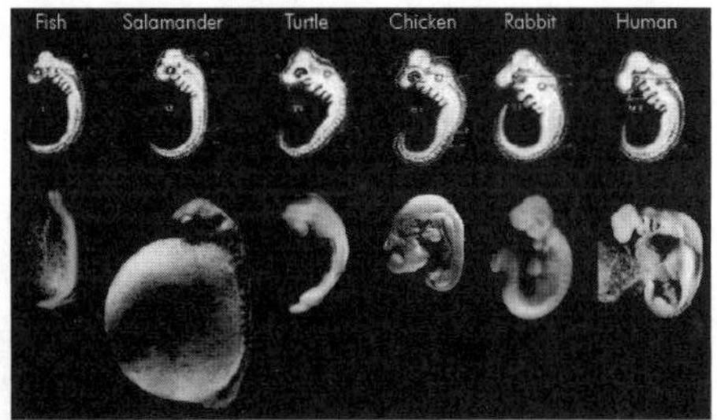

First row, Haeckel's embryo sketches, from *Anthropogenie* (1874).
Second row, several of Professor Richardson's published photos of embryos, showing Haeckel to have greatly distorted his pictures.

From: Richardson, M.K., *et al.*, There is no highly conserved embryonic stage in the vertebrates: implications for current theories of evolution and development, *Anatomy and Embryology* **196**(2):91–106, 1997.

Assmuth and Hull wrote a whole book on Haeckel's "*many frauds and forgeries,*" concluding that Haeckel deliberately falsified his evidence in an effort to convince others of Darwinism's validity. Nonetheless, the early promising beginning of the new theory soon fell on hard times for scientific reasons, even though many biologists contemporary with Haeckel believed that embryology would be an important evidence for phylogeny.[36] The fact is "*few aspects of evolutionary science have been so heavily attacked in recent years*".[37]

Assmuth and Hull's report added that "*Haeckel has in many cases freely invented embryos, or reproduced the illustrations given by others in a substantially changed form,*" quoting anatomist F. Keibel of Freiburg University.[38] Haeckel's distorted drawings were even labelled "*a sin against scientific truthfulness.*"[39]

35. Pitman, M., *Adam and Evolution*, Rider, London, p. 120, 1984.
36. Assmuth, J. and Hull, E., *Haeckel's Frauds and Forgeries,* P. J. Kenedy & Sons, New York, 1915.
37. Dodson, E.O., *Evolution Process and Product*, Reinhold, New York, p. 51, 1960.
38. Assmuth and Hull, *Haeckel's Frauds and Forgeries*, p. 26.
39. Assmuth and Hull, *Haeckel's Frauds and Forgeries*, p. 24.

The major reason for the attack was that, as "*biological knowledge increased … the biogenetic law has been subjected to considerable criticism.*"[40] It soon became clear that the law is lethally flawed, even though some Darwinists still cling to remnants of it today. Its flaws were openly discussed in mainline textbooks as early as 1963:

> The similarities of embryological development among multicellular animals were intensively studied during the latter half of the nineteenth century. These studies led to the conclusion that the embryonic development of the individual repeated the evolutionary history of the race. Thus, it was thought to be possible to trace the evolutionary history of a species by a study of its embryonic development. This idea was so attractive as to gain the status of a biological principle. … Today the idea of embryonic resemblances is viewed with caution. We can see and demonstrate similarities between embryos of related groups. … However … the old idea that a human passes through fish, amphibian, and reptile stages during early development is not correct.[41]

Thanks to the work of Richardson *et al.*, the many fatal flaws in Haeckel's work have now been widely publicized. Pennisi quotes Richardson as concluding from his extensive study of Haeckel's work that it may be "*one of the most famous fakes in biology.*"[42] Haeckel once even admitted that he "*used artistic license in preparing his drawings*" but Haeckel's confession was either forgotten or ignored by those who wanted to use his biogenetic law to support evolution.[43]

Examples of his distortion

Many embryo types share certain features at the early developmental stages, including what appears to be a tail-like structure on their posterior and certain identifiable body segments. These features were distorted in Haeckel's embryo drawings. One example was that the so-called 'tailbud' stage is nearly identical in all of the different species he drew. Richardson's team found that tailbud stage embryos, which were thought to correspond to a conserved stage of evolution, actually showed many major variations in form due to allometry, heterochrony, and differences in body plan and somatic segment number.

These variations foreshowed critical differences in the adult body form.[44] Richardson concluded that studying the many *differences* in embryos may prove

40. Carlson, B.M., *Patten's Foundations of Embryology*, McGraw-Hill, New York, p. 38–39, 1996.
41. Moore, *Biological science: an Inquiry into Life*, p. 608.
42. Quoted in Pennisi, Haeckel's embryos: fraud rediscovered, p. 1435.
43. Quoted in Pennisi, Haeckel's embryos: fraud rediscovered, p. 1435.
44. Richardson *et al.*, There is no highly conserved embryonic stage in the vertebrates, p. 91.

to be far more fruitful than focusing on their similarities. In an interview in *The London Times* Dr Michael Richardson stated:

> This is one of the worst cases of scientific fraud. It's shocking to find that somebody one thought was a great scientist was deliberately misleading. ... What he [Haeckel] did was to take a human embryo and copy it, pretending that the salamander and the pig and all the others looked the same at the same stage of development. They don't ... These are fakes.[45]

Embryos of different animal types possess many major differences which also negate the biogenetic theory. Evidence in favor of the biogenetic law was exploited by Haeckel, and the numerous examples against the law were ignored. For example, by the time human embryos have developed to the extent of having the number of body segments shown in Haeckel's drawings, they possess prominent protrusions called *limb buds* that later develop into limbs. These structures are all absent in Haeckel's drawings.

Haeckel not only left out limb buds in his drawings, he also even added structures to the select few examples he used to prove his law to make the embryos of different animals appear more similar than they actually were. The additions were chosen because they seemed to prove his recapitulation theory. For example, he added a curl to the bird embryo 'tail' so it would more closely resemble a human 'tail'.

Furthermore, in the examples Haeckel used, he fudged the scale by as much as tenfold in order to exaggerate similarities among species. A comparison of Haeckel's drawings with accurate drawings or photographs shows how enormously distorted, actually outright fraudulent, his drawings were.[46]

In most cases Haeckel also neglected to name the species he drew to illustrate his theory, falsely implying that the one example he chose was representative of the entire group, such as all fish. Even embryos presumed in evolutionary theory to be closely related, such as those of different species of fish, can vary greatly in appearance at both the embryo stage and in their developmental pathway.[47]

Professor Richardson's work scientifically disproving Haeckel's claims was "*a great service to developmental biology*" which helped us understand that far more variation exists in vertebrate embryo development than was once assumed.[48] As a result of Richardson's work and that of others, Haeckel's phylogenetic tree and embryo drawings, based in part on the biogenetic law strongly influenced by "*Darwin's theory of common descent ... including the unilateral progression of evolution toward humans, ... have since been refuted.*"[49] Dodson demonstrated that the biogenetic law

---

45. Hawkes, Nigel, An embryonic liar, interview with Michael Richardson, *The Times (London)*, p.14, August 11, 1997.
46. Pennisi, Haeckel's embryos: fraud rediscovered, p. 1435.
47. Carlson, *Patten's Foundations of Embryology*, p. 39.
48. Gilbert, S., quoted in Pennisi, Haeckel's embryos: fraud rediscovered, p. 1435.
49. Hickman *et al.*, *Integrated Principles of Zoology*, p. 15.

failed when applied to echinoderms, the organisms that were important in establishing the biogenetic law in the first place. He wrote that the recent comprehensive studies of echinoderm embryology revealed

> extensive differences among various groups of echinoderms, and these differences are referable to embryonic adaptations. [Professor of invertebrate zoology at the Harvard Museum of Comparative Zoology, Howard Fell—Ed.] even casts doubt on the echinoderm-chordate relationship, for the hemichordate larva does not fit into the scheme of larval relationships which he has worked out.[50]

As recently as 1997, the very year Richardson conclusively reconfirmed Haeckel's deception, the embryo drawings were still being presented as valid in at least one major textbook,[51] despite having been immediately exposed as fraudulent each time Haeckel published them, starting in 1868.[52] Worse, Luskin documents a number of textbooks published between 1998 and 2003 which either reproduced the drawings exactly, or made new images of their own based on Haeckel's work.[53] I can also remember drawings similar to Haeckel's pictured on an advertisement for another college embryology text,[54] but interestingly, Haeckel's ideas were never mentioned in the text itself. Perhaps the authors felt they couldn't bear to give up on such a valuable 'proof' of evolution, even if the recent work of Richardson *et al.* necessitated removing all references to it from the text.

The current most optimistic representation of the 'ontogeny recapitulates phylogeny' law, penned in an effort to save as much of it as possible, was summarized by Trefil as follows:

> Nineteenth-century biologists noted that, as an embryo of an advanced organism grows, it passes through stages that look very much like the adult phase of less advanced organisms. … In the nineteenth century, this so-called biogenetic law was taken to prove that evolution had proceeded on more or less a straight line from the simplest organisms to its epitome in human beings. We no longer have this view of evolution, but the biogenetic law remains a useful generalization about the way an embryo develops.[55]

---

50. Dodson, *Evolution Process and Product*, p. 52.
51. Gerhart, J. and Kirschner, M., *Cells, Embryos and Evolution*, Blackwell Science, Malden, Massachusetts, figs. 7–16, 1997.
52. Assmuth and Hull, *Haeckel's Frauds and Forgeries*, pp. 4–5.
53. Luskin, C., *What do Modern Textbooks Really Say about Haeckel's Embryos?*, Discovery Institute, Seattle, 2007.
54. Gilbert, S.F. and Raunio, A.M. (Eds.), *Embryology: constructing the organism*, Sinauer Associates, Sunderland, Massachusetts, 1997.
55. Trefil, J., *1001 Things Everyone Should know about Science*, Doubleday, New York, p. 23, 1992.

Although most current textbooks no longer use Haeckel's fraudulent drawings, some

> evolutionists still ignore the overwhelming evidence against recapitulation theory and use the often vague similarities found in developing species to argue for Haeckel's theory—or a watered-down version of it. A major reason why Haeckel got away with passing off his theory for so long was because his drawings "*became famous and have been repeatedly reproduced by publishers over the course of the last 120 years or so*" to prove evolution.[56]

The human embryo tail

The putative human embryo 'tail' which is gradually reduced until it usually disappears before birth, is also misinterpreted as an example of recapitulation. Interpreted as evidence of our tailed ancestors, this 'tail' is actually the human spine and the developing vertebrae that end in the coccyx. The 'tail' develops very early in the embryo because the brain and spinal chord mature very early in development in order to coordinate the rest of the body's development, and, at this developmental stage, the developing spinal column system is longer than the embryo torso.

This is why humans, and most mammals possess what superficially *appears* to be a tail during their early development. Tailed animals do not have a spinal cord in their tail as does a part of the 'tails' of embryos. Unfortunately, many older textbooks published highly misleading and often totally erroneous claims about the human embryo spine. A good example is Haupt's 1940 text that claimed embryology teaches that

> many structures which are permanent in the lower members of a group appear only in embryonic stages in the case of the higher members, and then either later disappear completely, persist as vestiges, or become modified to form other structures. For example, during an early period of prenatal development, the human embryo has a tail as well developed as that of any of the other vertebrates.[57]

A survey of modern biology textbooks indicated that few texts today even mention the now disproved tail claims.

The conserved stage theory

The biogenetic law now is widely recognized as both erroneous and misleading because so many exceptions have been found. It is also flawed for the reason that Haeckel based his biogenetic law on the

56. Youngson, R., *Scientific Blunders, a Brief history of How Wrong Scientists can Sometimes be*, Carroll and Graf, New York, p. 176, 1998.
57. Haupt, *Fundamentals of Biology*, p. 347.

> flawed premise that evolutionary change occurs by successively adding stages onto the end of an unaltered ancestral ontogeny, compressing the ancestral ontogeny into earlier developmental stages. This notion was based on Lamarck's concept of the inheritance of acquired characteristics.[58]

A major problem with the 'conserved stage' hypothesis of recapitulation is that different organs develop at different times in different species, making it impossible to point to a single conserved stage when all species have the same body plan.[59] Furthermore, organ development often was contrary to what recapitulation predicted. For example, if the human embryo repeated its assumed evolutionary ancestry as it developed, the human heart should begin with a single chamber and then develop successively into two, then three, and finally four chambers. Instead, the human heart begins as a two-chambered organ which fuses to a single chamber, which then develops directly into four chambers. In other words, the sequence is 2-1-4, not 1-2-3-4 as required by the theory. The human brain develops before the nerve cords, and the heart before the blood vessels, both out of the assumed evolutionary sequence. It is because of many similar contradictions and omissions that the theory of embryological recapitulation has been abandoned by embryologists.[60]

Another excellent example is that the development of similar forms of animals from very dissimilar pathways is common at later stages of development. The fact is, many animals pass through a larval developmental stage, such as

> most frogs [which] begin life as swimming tadpoles, and only later metamorphose into four legged animals. There are many species of frogs, however, which bypass the larval stage and develop directly. Remarkably, the adults of some of these direct developers are almost indistinguishable from the adults of sister species which develop indirectly. In other words, very similar frogs can be produced by direct and indirect development, even though the pathways are obviously radically different. The same phenomenon is common among sea urchins and ascidians.[61]

Many other examples exist of organs and structures that do not develop in the order predicted by the biogenic law. Examples Rusch lists include the tongue in mammalian embryos developing before the teeth, and the fact that certain environmental

---

58. Hickman *et al.*, *Integrated Principles of Zoology*, p. 116.
59. Richardson, M., Heterochrony and the phylotypic period, *Developmental Biology* **172**:412–421, 1997.
60. Gish, D., *The Fossils Still Say No*, Institute for Creation Research, El Cajon, California, p. 358, 1995.
61. Wells, J. and Nelson, P., Homology: a concept in crisis, *Origins and Design* **18**(2):16, 1997.

conditions can change the sequence order in which embryo differentiation occurs.[62] Nor do anatomical evaluations of the developing embryo support recapitulation:

> while many authors have written of a conserved embryonic stage, no one has cited any comparative data in support. … the phylotypic stage is [evidently] regarded as a biological concept for which no proof is needed. This has led to many problems, not the least of which is the lack of consensus on exactly which stage is conserved.[63]

Other problems with the biogenetic law

The biogenetic law has misled researchers who for years have looked for evidence that does not exist and who have ignored, or tried to explain away, the large body of evidence that contradicted the biogenetic law. For example, proponents of the biogenetic law originally tried to explain virtually *all* aspects of development. An example is the claim that the human embryo has

> gill slits and aortic arches, which undergo exactly the same transformations that take place in other mammals. Man's heart is at first like that of a fish, consisting of one auricle and one ventricle. His backbone begins as a notochord, is next a segmented cartilaginous rod, then each segment or vertebra consists of five separate bones, and finally each fuses into a single bone. He has in the course of his development three different pairs of kidneys, first a pronephros (or forekidney), like that of the lower fishes, then a mesonephros (or mid-kidney), like that of the frogs, and finally a metanephros (or hind-kidney) like that of reptiles, birds, and mammals, which alone survives in the adult.[64]

Conklin claims that the embryo's "*brain, eye, ear, in fact, all his organs, pass through*" certain development stages

> that are characteristic of lower vertebrates. Even in those adult features that are distinctively human, such as the peculiar form of the hand and the foot, the number of bones in the ankle and wrist, the number of pairs of ribs, the absence of a tail and the relative hairlessness of the skin—in all these respects the human fetus resembles anthropoid apes more than adult man. Why are not these and a hundred other structures made directly? Why this roundabout process of making a man? There is no answer but evolution.[65]

62. Rusch, Ontogeny recapitulates phylogeny, p. 28.
63. Richardson *et al.*, There is no highly conserved embryonic stage in the vertebrates, p. 92.
64. Conklin, Embryology and evolution, pp. 74–75.
65. Conklin, Embryology and evolution, pp. 74–75.

Recapitulation almost certainly would *not provide the animal with any selection advantages* but instead would likely result in many major selection *disadvantages* during the embryonic stage.

Biogenetic law and racism

The biogenetic law problem is no minor matter, of interest only to biologists. The biogenetic law "*became extremely influential outside of science*" and "*caused a great deal of mischief.*"[66] One example Milner cites is the idea that the brains of certain races were stuck at a lower, childlike stage of evolutionary development. Gould claimed that the theory was one of the two or three leading scientific arguments for racism.[67] In Gould's words, for "*a half century the proponents of recapitulation had collected*" evidence that "*argued adults of 'lower' races were like white children.*"[68] Gould notes that proponents of recapitulation asserted the fact that "*women are more childlike in their anatomy than men*" and this claim was used as proof of their inferiority.[69]

Many other examples of the use of the biogenetic law to endorse racism exist, such as the argument that black males are more primitive than whites because in contrast to white children, the distance between their navel and penis remains small relative to body height as adults. The rising belly button was seen as a mark of evolutionary progress and could be used to rank the evolutionary "*level*" of many primates including the apes.[70] Gould also noted:

> Recapitulation had its greatest political impact as an argument to justify imperialism. Kipling, in his poem on the "*white man's burden,*" referred to vanquished natives as "*half devil and half child.*" If the conquest of distant lands upset some Christian beliefs, science could always relieve a bothered conscience by pointing out that primitive people, like white children, were incapable of self-government in a modern world.[71]

Biologist Randy Moore concluded that "*recapitulation was a leading argument for racists in the late 19th century.*"[72] Furthermore, some of Sigmund Freud's more radical (and now discredited) ideas came directly from Haeckel's biogenetic law.[73]

---

66. Milner, *The Encyclopedia of Evolution*, pp. 177–178.
67. Gould, S.J., Racism and recapitulation, ch. 27 (pp 214–221) in *Ever since Darwin*, Norton, New York, p. 216, 1977.
68. Gould, Racism and recapitulation, pp. 219.
69. Gould, Racism and recapitulation, pp. 221.
70. Gould, Racism and recapitulation, p. 218.
71. Gould, Racism and recapitulation, p. 218–219.
72. Moore, R., Science, objectivity and racism, *American Biology Teacher* **61**(4):240, 1999.
73. Milner, *The Encyclopedia of Evolution*, p. 177.

This view of development has also been used as an argument to justify abortion in the early stages of pregnancy based on the reasoning that it is not wrong to kill life at this developmental stage because the embryo is not yet human, but is only a fish or less.[74]

Milner even concludes that Haeckel's views "*became a major cultural force in shaping the militant nationalism in Germany*" that led to the Holocaust resulting in the loss of over six million lives.[75]

The end of the law

As a result of the growing knowledge of biology and development in the 1950s, the 'law' was definitively discredited around half century ago, even though it took decades before this new knowledge was reflected in the textbooks. The evidence supports Sir Arthur Keith's statement of a century ago regarding embryology and evolution, in which he said biologists

> expected that the embryo would recapitulate the features of its ancestors from the lowest to the highest forms in the animal kingdom. Now that the appearances of the embryo at all stages are known, the general feeling is one of disappointment; the human embryo *at no stage* is anthropoid in its appearance.[76]

The many flaws that eventually mortally wounded the biogenetic law included the fact that it lost favour due to the rise of experimental embryology, and finally became

> *untenable in theory* (when the establishment of Mendelian genetics converted previous exceptions into new expectations). The biogenetic law was not disproved by a direct scrutiny of its supposed operation; it fell because research in related fields refuted its necessary mechanism.[77]

Attempts have been made throughout the years to repair and revise the law, but all have failed. One early attempt offered by nineteenth-century embryologist K. E. von Baer argued that early developmental features were *more* widely shared among

> different animal groups than later ones ... The adults of animals with relatively short and simple ontogenies often resemble preadult stages of other animals whose ontogeny is more elaborate, but the embryos of descendants do not necessarily resemble the adults of their ancestors. Even early

74. Major, T., Haeckel: The legacy of a lie, *Reason and Revelation* **14**(9):175–177, 1994.
75. Milner, *The Encyclopedia of Evolution*, p. 205.
76. Keith, A., *A History of the Human Body*, Williams and Norgate, London, pp. 93–94, 1912.
77. Gould, S.J., *Ontogeny and Phylogeny*, Harvard University Press, 1977, p. 168.

> development undergoes evolutionary divergence among groups, however, and it is not quite as stable as von Baer believed.[78]

As noted, many biologists recognized that the biogenic law was falsified as long as one half-century ago and:

> during the latter half of the nineteenth century this theory was received with great enthusiasm, and it was predicted that a study of living things in the light of this "*law*" would revolutionize biology. But, unfortunately, the predictions are not being verified. As a working hypothesis the theory has been a great help, but there are so many exceptions, apparently even contradictions, that its application is frequently misleading.[79]

No reason now exists to believe that the recapitulation theory is true except that it appears to support evolution. Harvard's Stephen Jay Gould even wrote a 501-page book[80] (cited earlier) on Haeckel's biogenetic law, documenting its history from its appearance in the pre-Socrates days to its demise in the early twentieth century.

Why the biogenetic law still is taught

The reason the biogenetic law still is taught in some textbooks is not because the realization that it is erroneous is recent, but because many scientists, at least nominally, still accept the biogenetic law, or remnants of it.

> The biogenetic law has become so deeply rooted in biological thought that it cannot be weeded out in spite of its having been demonstrated to be wrong by numerous subsequent scholars. Even today both subtle and overt uses of the biogenetic law are frequently encountered in the general biological literature as well as in more specialized evolutionary and systemic studies.[81]

While Bock wrote this in 1969, we find the same complaint appearing in more recent literature, as noted above.

Many scientists and scholars are either unaware of the criticism of the law, or choose to ignore the evidence against it. Dr Warwick Glover claims that the "*vast majority*" of his medical students believe the human embryo has gill slits, even though their medical text on embryology correctly explains that the human embryo

78. Hickman *et al.*, *Integrated Principles of Zoology*, p. 115
79. Hauber, V.A and O'Hanlon, M.E., *Biology: A Study of the Principles of Life for the College Student*, F.S. Crofts, New York, p. 156, 1946.
80. Gould, *Ontogeny and Phylogeny*.
81. Bock, W.J., Evolution by orderly law, *Science* **164**(3880):684, 1969.

does not possess gill slits, but rather, pharyngeal grooves.[82] And Youngson concluded that while "*Haeckel's theory of recapitulation was*" once

> almost universally believed, the debunking of Haeckel was not widely known … His book *The Riddle of the Universe,* an extraordinary mishmash of real science and imaginary nonsense, was a great popular success and ran into numerous editions. So, although his ontogeny ideas were brushed aside at a fairly early stage by the serious scientists, they continued to be accepted by the lay public.[83]

Another major reason for the continued acceptance of the biogenetic law by some evolutionists is because it now is part of the accepted worldview of scientists, a belief that they were exposed to from the earliest days of their training. Most scientists are influenced by social pressure, and many fear recriminations from their fellow scientists if they do not conform to what is currently viewed as orthodox. To prove their orthodoxy, many scientists have become unscientific and have embraced the worldview of twentieth century naturalism.[84]

Implications for creationism

The ontology law was a major weapon in the arsenal used to attack, not only creationism, but also Christianity, minorities, and even the existing social order in favor of communism. Recapitulation was Haeckel's favorite argument "*to attack nobility's claim to special status—are we not all fish as embryos?—and to ridicule the soul's immortality—where could the soul be in our embryonic, wormlike condition?*"[85]

Our ability to reason, to determine right and wrong, to live according to a conscience, to exercise dominion over plants and animals, to enjoy music and art, and to worship our Creator are all only a small part of the enormous chasm that separates humans from *every other living creature.* The biogenetic law is only one of many hypotheses that Darwinists have used in attempting to support their naturalistic theory and which are gradually being proven wrong as more and more new evidence accumulates.

Naturalistic evolution required faith in an embryological theory that has now been disproved,[86] and belief in evolutionism still requires a blind, often unthinking faith induced partly by pressure to conform to the science establishment that is saturated with naturalism. The history of the biogenetic law should force all people

82. Ham, K., A surgeon looks at creation, *Creation,* **14**(3):46–49, 1992; creation.com/glover.
83. Youngson, *Scientific Blunders*, p. 177.
84. Johnson, P., Science without God, *Wall Street Journal,* May 10, p. A10, 1993.
85. Gould, Racism and recapitulation, p. 217.
86. Frair, Embryology and evolution.

to look critically at the current lack of evidence for the whole evolutionary model of origins.

Conclusions

The biogenetic law was based on very superficial similarities in different developing embryos. As our knowledge of embryology, and especially genetics, increased, it became increasingly obvious that the 'law' was fundamentally in error. The three major early scientific objections to Haeckel's version of the biogenetic law can be summarized as follows:[87]

1. The path of embryological development in different species varies enormously for organs and body structures. Each ontogenetic 'stage' is actually an inseparable mixture of structures in *different* stages of putative ancestral repetition, some embryos during a specific stage of growth somewhat resemble very early stages in other animals, others at that same time of development resemble those of animals at much later developmental stages.
2. Larvae and embryos possess many features that help them adapt to their individual modes of life. New characters often are introduced at stages of embryological development that do not follow the biogenetic law.
3. Development can be retarded as well as accelerated compared to the predictions of the biogenetic law. Embryonic or larval stages of alleged ancestors can sometimes superficially resemble the adult stages of descendants—a phenomenon directly opposite to the recapitulation law prediction.

Some stages of embryological development of many animals do show some similarities, but the major reason for this fact is design constraints. Likewise, adult organs show much similarity because only so many ways exist to design a heart or lung, and we would expect the *earlier* in development, the *fewer* the design possibilities that exist. All sexually reproducing organisms start out as one-celled zygotes that superficially look remarkably similar and, as development and differentiation proceed, they increasingly look different.

All hearts begin as a single contracting artery tube which, depending on the animal type, develops into a one, two, three or four-chambered heart. A human heart does not start as a simple one-chambered heart because our ancestor had a one-chambered heart, but because embryological development in general mandates simple to complex progression. The same is true for all other organs. Because all life begins as one cell does not prove all life evolved from one cell, but that this is the only way that life can reproduce itself.[88]

---

87. Adapted from Gould, Racism and recapitulation, pp. 214–221.
88. Milton, R., *Shattering the Myth of Darwinism*, Park St Press, Rochester, Vermont, 1997.

CHAPTER 11

The Piltdown Man hoax: The most infamous blunder in science

Introduction

Piltdown Man was a critical icon in convincing the world of the validity of Darwin's theory of evolution. When it was eventually exposed as a forgery, the *London Star* headline screamed that it was "*the biggest scientific hoax of the century.*"[1] Even though compelling evidence existed soon after it was discovered that it was a forgery or, at the very least, was not evidence for human evolution, it was touted in textbooks, articles, and major museums for almost four decades as critical evidence of human evolution. The hoax is an excellent example of the difficulties in drawing conclusions about evolution from fossils.

Although Piltdown Man originally convinced many people of the validity of Darwinism, its final, definitive exposure as a forgery did little to reverse the basic acceptance of evolution by the public and even most Darwinists. The embarrassment it caused still angers evolutionists. One paleoanthropologist stated about the Piltdown hoax "*I'd like to see the anniversary commemorated by the crushing of all the material and the burning of the Piltdown archive.*"[2]

History of the hoax

One of the most important, and most successful (and now the most infamous), fossil forgeries was *Eoanthropus dawsoni* (a.k.a. Piltdown Man), which soon became an entire race of prehumans, the Piltdown race.[3,4] The new "*discoveries made headlines throughout the world.*"[5] In the end, no other forgery in the history of paleoanthropology has "*caused more trouble, nor has received such wide publicity as that*

1. Russell, M., *The Piltdown Man Hoax: Case Closed*, The History Press, Gloucestershire, UK, p. 10, 2012.
2. Quoted in Stringer, C., The 100-year mystery of Piltdown Man, *Nature* **492**(7428):177–179, 2012; p. 177.
3. Hammond, M., A framework of plausibility for an anthropological forgery: the Piltdown case, *Anthropology* **3**(1–2):47–58, 1979.
4. Osborn, H.F., *Men of the Old Stone Age*, Charles Scribner's Sons, New York, p. 130, 1916.
5. Stringer, The 100-year mystery of Piltdown Man, p. 178.

of Piltdown Man."[6] For almost 40 years, the fossil "*was taught as fact*" in textbooks throughout the world, and was a primary exhibit used in attempts to prove evolution at major museums the world over including the American Museum of Natural History in New York.[7,8] It now has been proven that, of the 18 Piltdown fossil fragments tested, more than half were stained to appear old and to match the gravel bed in which they were found. Furthermore, the weight of the evidence indicates that all of the finds had been planted, and none actually originally came from Piltdown.[9]

In the early 1900s, most scientists excluded Neandertals from the evolutionary line leading to humans, and the only other candidate was Java Man, a finding that was widely debated.[10] Piltdown Man fitted Darwin's predictions and, as a result, was the answer to the Darwinists' dreams.[11] The headline of *The New York Times* for September 22, 1912 announcing the discovery read, "*Darwin Theory Is Proved True*", indicating how important it was.

As a result, Piltdown Man "*absorbed the professional attention of many fine scientists* [and] … *led millions of people astray for forty years.*"[12] The many famous scientists involved in the hoax include Sir Arthur Smith Woodward (1864–1944), Director of the Natural History Museum of London, and Sir Arthur Keith (1866–1955), Professor of Anatomy at the London Hospital Medical School and later Conservator of the Royal College of Surgeons Museum. Piltdown was so important that Walsh concluded it

> *played a pivotal role in one of the most critical scientific pursuits of modern times,* the theory of human evolution … the fraudulent bones receiving "*nearly as much attention as all the legitimate specimens in the fossil record put together*" [emphasis added]. Young scientists and old alike wasted untold thousands of hours on the Piltdown phenomenon. The laborious study, and the writing and publishing of the several hundred research reports and papers worldwide, the sheer, enormous amount of space in books and articles given to sober discussion of its every smallest aspect, make a picture sad to contemplate.[13]

6. Hutchinson, G.E., The Piltdown Man, *American Scientist* **42**(2):305, 1954.
7. Blinderman, C., *The Piltdown Inquest*, Prometheus Books, Buffalo, New York, p. 238, 1986.
8. Eiseley, L., *The Immense Journey*, Random House, New York, p. 80, 1957.
9. British Museum of Natural History, *The Piltdown Man Hoax*, London, 1973.
10. Wells, J., *Icons of Evolution: Science or Myth*, Regnery, Washington, DC, p. 216, 2000.
11. Hammond, A framework of plausibility for an anthropological forgery, p. 48.
12. Gould, S., *Hen's Teeth and Horse's Toes*, W.W. Norton, New York, p. 225, 1983.
13. Walsh, J.E., *Unraveling Piltdown: the Science Fraud of the Century and its Solution*, Random House, New York, p. xvi, 1996.

Figure 1
An example of a reconstruction of Piltdown Man used for decades in textbooks and popular sources such as *The National Geographic* (**29**(2):119, February 1916, "How old is Man" by President Theodore Roosevelt). This reconstruction was by J. H. McGregor.
Source: Henry Fairfield Osborn, *Men of the Old Stone Age*, Scribner's, New York, p. 145, 1916.

No minor fossil, University of California Anthropologist Craig Stanford concluded that "*Piltdown occupied a place of pride on every scholar's genealogy of humans throughout the first half of the twentieth century.*"[14] Piltdown fossils were major evidence used to corroborate Darwinism and were used as a major proof of Darwinism in textbooks for decades.[15] The drawings showing that the Piltdown brain's size was physically in between modern humans and chimpanzees were especially effective in convincing the public and scientists alike of human evolution,[16] as were statues showing the Piltdown Man's ape-like body in detail (see fig. 1).[17] Piltdown Man helped to establish the careers of some of the most eminent paleoanthropologists of the twentieth century.

When Arthur Smith Woodward retired, he was as busy studying Piltdown fossils as he was during his 40 productive years at the London Natural History Museum. The highest civilian honour for a British citizen, conferral of knighthood, was awarded to Woodward in the spring of 1924. Walsh notes that Woodward's eminence was fairly earned by "*sheer brilliance*" and "*unflagging energy.*" At the young age of 37, he was appointed the director of a world-famous geology department and a fellow of the Royal Society before he was 40. He continued to achieve scientific awards and

14. Stanford, C., *Upright: The Evolutionary Key to Becoming Human*, Houghton Muffin, Boston, p. 6, 2003.
15. Baitsell, G., *The Evolution of Earth and Man*, Yale University Press, New Haven, Connecticut, 1929.
16. Osborn, *Men of the Old Stone Age*, p. 140.
17. Simpson, J., *Man and the Attainment of Immortality*, Doran, New York, p. 99, 1922.

> by the time of his retirement he had been president at different times of three prominent scientific bodies. A recipient of the Gold Medal of England's Royal Society, he had also been awarded the Lyell Medal, the Linnean Medal, the Wollaston Prize, the Prix Cuvier of the French Academy, and the Thompson Medal of the American Museum.

Furthermore, aside from his half-dozen books, his total number of

> scientific writings exceeded a remarkable four hundred papers. *Capping all was the association that had brought him fame and secured his place at the pinnacle of his profession, the central role he took in the drama of Piltdown Man* [emphasis added]. Hailed by most as evolution's first true "*missing link,*" that sensational find since its arresting debut in 1912 had usurped a large portion of his time at the museum, and through his twenty-year retirement it continued to rivet his attention ... To a reporter from a London paper who interviewed him on the day he quit the museum for good, *Woodward readily admitted that the Piltdown discovery had been "the most important thing that ever happened in my life"*[emphasis added].[18]

Piltdown Man was so important that its dethronement "*set the stage for a major revision of human phylogeny.*"[19]

The sloppy, inept forgery

A critical fact in the case was that the forgery had been so poorly executed that it was remarkable it fooled anybody, let alone many leading paleontologists, and could have easily been exposed. Furthermore, although the techniques existed then to expose the forgery, the focus was instead on the morphological problems involved in reconstructing the Piltdown fossil.[20] The reason for concluding that the jaw belonged with the skull

> was the fact that the tops of the teeth were worn down in a manner which seemed to be characteristic of humans and not of apes. But no one noticed that the teeth had been artificially ground down to look like human teeth. No one noticed the scratches left by the abrasive agent, which the careless perpetrator of the hoax did not polish away. No one noticed that the job of flattening the surfaces of the teeth was overdone and the surfaces were too flat to be realistic. No one noticed that the teeth were so flat on top that the edges were angular instead of rounded. No one even noticed that

18. Walsh, *Unraveling Piltdown*, pp. 3–4.
19. Spencer, F., *Piltdown: a Scientific Forgery*, Oxford University Press, New York, p. xvi, 1990.
20. Hammond, A framework of plausibility for an anthropological forgery, p. 48.

> the job had been done so carelessly that the tops of the different teeth were flattened at different angles. Also, because of the crudeness of the operation, "*the Piltdown cusps exhibit dentin quite flat and flush with surrounding enamel, a state of affairs explicable only by rapid artificial rubbing down of the surface.*"[21]

Figure 2
Piltdown discovery site showing Dawson (left) and Smith-Woodward searching for more bones.
Source: *Illustrated London News*, p. 143, 1913.

The teeth were filed down to obliterate obvious orangutan traits, but they still did not resemble human teeth. For example, human teeth normally are worn down faster on the buccal (cheek) side compared to the lingual (tongue) side. Zoologist Bolton Davidheiser added that X-ray analysis of the loose canine tooth found near the Piltdown skull showed the tooth had been filed down so far that its

> pulp cavity was exposed, a phenomenon which does not happen as a result of natural wear, and someone had filled the pulp cavity with sand! Besides all this, it was an immature tooth which would not have had time to wear down a great deal. All of this was not only overlooked as evidence that something unnatural had happened, but it was rejected when it was pointed out. A dentist named Lyne pointed out that the canine tooth could not have been worn down naturally, but his "*cogent arguments were brushed aside by Woodward.*" Professor Woodward let himself be influenced by a Dr. Underwood who "*spoke in violent disagreement with Mr. Lyne's contention of the immaturity of the canine and its paradoxical nature,*" and who declared that the wear of the canine was "*indubitably natural.*"[22]

21. Davidheiser, B., *Evolution and Christian Faith*, Presbyterian and Reformed, Nutley, New Jersey, p. 342, 1969.
22. Davidheiser, *Evolution and Christian Faith*, pp. 342–343.

History has proved Dr Courtney Lyne correct and Dr Underwood wrong—a point that should have been obvious to anyone with a basic knowledge of human teeth. To help the bones appear old and apelike they were stained with potassium bichromate and the canine tooth was painted with ordinary hardware store paint, probably Vandyke Brown.[23,24] Furthermore, the site where the skull was found appears to have been a most unlikely place for bones to have survived hundreds of years, much less thousands, partly because it was frequently under water or very damp (See Figure 2 on page 165 for an illustration of the location site).[25]

History of the Piltdown discovery

The story began with Charles Dawson, a geologist awarded the coveted fellowship of the London Geological Society at the young age of 21.[26,27] The story varies, but one account says Dawson claimed that when workers were digging gravel from a shallow pit near the village of Piltdown in Sussex County, England, he noticed several small pieces of brown flint. The flint indicated the site might contain humanoid fossils, so Dawson asked the workers to contact him if they found any bones.

Dawson later claimed that the men found some "*old bones*" in 1908, and four years later, on December 18, 1912, Dawson and Woodward introduced Piltdown Man, the "*most important archaeological discovery of all time,*" to the world in front of a packed and excited audience at the Geological Society of London.[28,29]

The find not only fulfilled Charles Darwin's (and many other Darwinists') predictions of an evolutionary link with both an advanced brain and an ape-like jaw with large teeth, but was also judged "*the ideal missing link*" by many experts.[30] The fossil evidence, found in shallow gravel, consisted of nine skull fragments, two teeth, and the right side of a mandible with two teeth still in place.[31] The Piltdown brain capacity was first estimated to be about half-way between that of humans and apes, but later evaluations indicated its brain size to be about 1,400 cubic centimetres—close to that of modern Piltdown town residents.

Later named *Eoanthropus dawsoni* by Woodward in honor of Dawson, there was general agreement among evolutionists that it came from Pleistocene gravel, roughly around the last ice age [despite the frequent claims to the contrary, "The only clear

23. Walsh, *Unraveling Piltdown*, p. 70.
24. Elliott, D., *The Curious Incident of the Missing Link*, Bootmakers of Toronto, Toronto, p. 6, 1988.
25. Spencer, *Piltdown*, pp. 160–163.
26. Youngson, R., *Scientific Blunders, a Brief History of How Wrong Scientists can Sometimes be*, Carroll and Graf, New York, p. 53, 1998.
27. Lubenow, M., *Bones of Contention*, Baker Book House, Grand Rapids, Michigan, p. 40, 1992.
28. Youngson, *Scientific Blunders*, p. 54.
29. Millar, R., *The Piltdown Men*, St Martin's Press, New York, 1972.
30. Millar, *The Piltdown Men*, p. 9.
31. Spencer, *Piltdown*.

evidence we have is for one Ice Age"[32]—Ed.]. In 1915, there were further finds, including a lower canine tooth, cranial fragments, and a "*molar exactly like those in the jaw.*" These fragments were allegedly found 3.2 km (two miles) away at a second site called Piltdown II, which dispelled much of the doubt about the validity of the original finds.[33,34,35]

Some Piltdown II fragments—a piece of the forehead and an isolated molar—later were found to be part of the Piltdown I skull.[36,37] Also allegedly found near the site of Piltdown I, besides the bones and teeth, were crudely flaked flint stones (called eoliths), and antlers of a variety of extinct animals including mastodons and some non-extinct animals.[38]

Many scientists—and most Darwinist non-scientists—were so elated by the discovery that they uncritically accepted the sloppy forgery. Now evolutionists felt that, for the first time, they finally had solid empirical evidence of human evolution. Piltdown was judged by many of the world's leading paleontologists as neither monkey nor human, but rather as an ape/man link that bridged the gap between humans and lower primates. The find was soon widely regarded as the earliest known human fossil—older than anything the French, Germans, or anyone else had found.[39]

The world celebrates the discovery

As a close associate of Dawson, Sir Arthur Smith Woodward, who by then was head of the British Museum geology department, was so enthusiastic about the find that he publicized it at every opportunity. Piltdown Man was so important that it became the basis for many beliefs about putative 'missing links' discovered since then. The importance of the find is clear in a contemporary account of the introduction of Piltdown to the world:

> A GREAT company assembled in the rooms of the Geological Society of London on the evening of December 18th, 1912, to receive the first authentic account of the discovery at Piltdown. … It was quite plain to all assembled that the skull thus reconstructed by Dr. Smith Woodward was a strange

32. Batten, D. *et al., The Creation Answers Book*, Creation Ministries International, p. 199, 2006.
33. Kurtén, B., *How to Deep-Freeze a Mammoth*, Columbia University, New York, pp. 66, 1986.
34. Gould, S., Piltdown revisited, *Natural History* **88**(3):87, 1979.
35. Lubenow, *Bones of Contention*, p. 41.
36. Walsh, *Unraveling Piltdown*, p. 70.
37. Millar, *The Piltdown Men*, p. 228.
38. Winslow, J.H. and Meyer, A., The perpetrator at Piltdown, *Science* **83**(4):33–43, American Association for the Advancement of Science, September 1983.
39. Winslow and Meyer, The perpetrator at Piltdown, p. 33.

> blend of man and ape. At last, it seemed, the missing form—the link which early followers of Darwin had searched for—had really been discovered. No one had ever suspected that a secret of this kind lay hid away in the Weald of Sussex.[40]

The primitive and ape-like fossil was the perfect missing link, discussed prominently in detail in scientific works as well as books written for the public by scientists.[41] The renown of Piltdown Man soon spread rapidly throughout the world. Only one day after the Piltdown find was announced to the world, a *New York Times* headline announced the find as "*Bones Probably Those of a Direct Ancestor of Modern Man.*"[42]

The very next day, the *Times* followed up with an interview with Woodward who stated, "*Hitherto the nearest approach to a species from which we might have been said to descend that had been discovered was the cave-man, but the authorities constantly asserted that we did not spring direct from the cave-man. Where, then, was the missing link in the chain of our evolution? … the answer lies in the Piltdown skull, for we came directly from a species almost entirely ape.*"[43] Many American and European newspapers carried similar claims.

In its next Sunday edition, the *New York Times* continued its laudatory coverage of the Piltdown discovery with a front-page summary of the find and its evidence for evolution. The banner headline proclaimed, "*Darwin Theory is Proved True*" and added the sub-heading that the skull was "*thought to be a woman's.*" Another sub-heading added, "*English Scientists Say the Skull Found in Sussex Establishes Human Descent from Apes.*"

This article added Keith's conclusion that the discovery was what paleoanthropologists had been seeking for 40 years. Keith concluded that scientists finally had proof of "*a stage in the evolution of man which we have only imagined since Darwin propounded the theory.*" He then added that

> *there is no doubt at all* that this is the most important discovery concerning ancient man ever made in England. It is *one of the three most important discoveries* of … [fossil man] *ever made in the world* [emphasis added]. The other two were the discovery of the individual known as Pithecanthropus, made in Java in 1892 by Prof. Eugene Dubois. The other, which equals it in instructiveness and importance, is the skull discovered at Heidelberg six years ago.[44]

With the support of many eminent scientists, nearly all others were soon convinced that Piltdown was a critical find "*even more wonderful in many ways than the*

40. Keith, A., *The Antiquity of Man*, Williams and Northgate, London, p. 306, 1915.
41. Elliot, G.F.S., *Prehistoric Man and His Story*, Seely Ltd, London, p. 127, 1925.
42. Quoted in *The New York Times*, p. 6, December 19, 1912.
43. Quoted in *The New York Times*, p. C-6, December 20, 1912.
44. Quoted in *The New York Times*, p. C-1, December 22, 1912.

ape-creatures of Java."[45] Jesuit priest Pierre Teilhard de Chardin assisted Dawson with the digs, which vastly improved Dawson's credibility. Professor de Chardin, who was then teaching at a seminary in Hasting, soon uncovered another part of the missing link—this time a canine tooth. After these further discoveries, major challenges to Piltdown Man appeared unlikely. As Peake and Fleure concluded, the find "*very clearly*" shows the evolution of the human skull and the complexity of evolution as well.[46]

Piltdown was critical in convincing the common people of the validity of human evolution, and was widely featured in school textbooks. Other fossil finds of the time included a jawbone found near Heidelberg, Germany, (Heidelberg man), and a skull cap, thighbone, and three teeth discovered in Java (Java Man). At the time, these were the only known fossil evidence of alleged modern human ancestors, and for years both "*remained the subject of intense scientific controversy.*"[47] Neandertals "*contributed little to the story of human evolution because they came from a later era, were fully human and died out.*"[48]

Peake and Fleure conclude that the general view then was that the Neandertal type was not ancestral to modern humans, and the *only* evidences of human ancestry were the "*slight clues from Piltdown and perhaps ... the Broken Hill skulls.*"[49] This left Piltdown as a critically important link between humans and the higher apes.[50]

One reason why the Piltdown fraud was so successful was because it conformed to what many evolutionists expected to find, namely a large-brained human ancestor. Sir Grafton Elliott Smith had successfully predicted that a fossil very similar to Piltdown Man would be found. This successful prediction was one reason why Smith was regarded as a suspect once the hoax was discovered.[51]

Replicas of the famous skull made from the original, which was considered priceless and thus was locked away safely in the British Museum to protect it from vandals and skeptical investigators alike, soon found their way into many state museums and college science classrooms.[52] For years Professor Henry Fairfield Osborn exhibited his best evidence for human evolution in the 'Hall of the Age of Man' at the American Museum of Natural History.

He placed a bust of the Piltdown Man conceived by Professor J.H. McGregor in the exhibit case number two. Described as a restoration of a missing link, the Piltdown half-ape/half-human bust was designed to convince the uninitiated, such

---

45. Henderson, K., *Prehistoric Man*, E.P. Dutton, New York, p. 28, 1927.
46. Peake, H. and Fleure, H.J., *Apes and Men*, Oxford University Press, New York, p. 115, 1927.
47. Larson, E., *Summer of the Gods*, Basic Books, New York, pp. 11–12, 1997.
48. Larson, *Summer of the Gods*, p. 12.
49. Peake and Fleure, *Apes and Men*, p. 124.
50. Larson, *Summer of the Gods*, p. 12.
51. Lubenow, *Bones of Contention*, p. 43.
52. Johnson, P., *Darwin on Trial*, Regnery Gateway, Washington, DC, p. 186–187, 1991.

as high school students and their teachers who visited the museum in ever-increasing numbers, that human evolution is fact supported by scientific evidence.[53]

The eminent Sir Arthur Keith even wrote a 520-page scholarly book on the human fossil record that discussed Piltdown Man in enormous detail, including extensive discussions of its biology, life habits, and even its death. He wrote that

> the peculiar and characteristic features of this ancient form of man were centered in the region of the chin. Such features had never been found or seen in any mandible or skull to which the term human could be applied … . There is no projection of the anterior surface at the lower border of the symphysis to represent a chin in the chimpanzee; the anterior or labial surface of the jaw slopes downwards and backwards to a chinless lower border. On the hinder surface of the symphyseal region—the surface directed towards the tongue—there is seen a deep pit, almost large enough to take the tip of the little finger. … Such is the conformation of the symphyseal or chin region of the lower jaw in apes … . When a corresponding section is made of the symphyseal region of a human lower jaw, a very different conformation is seen [spelling modernized—Ed.].[54]

This and other writings vividly reveal the proliferation of unfounded speculations involved in establishing evolutionary theory. An example is Henderson's claim that "*evidence from other parts of the neighborhood show the Piltdown species to be clearly defined, racially, and of the short-headed type … . Essentially, however, she is human.*"[55] Henderson added that

> although her brain is remarkably under-developed and with only very simple convolutions, as one would naturally expect, she has quite a distinct forehead, and there seems to be no reason why she would not have been just capable of some crude kind of articulate speech. … And with that useful right hand, [he assures us that she was right-handed—Ed.] assisted by the more awkward left, she and her kind can do things never done before. Having for a long time wielded big sticks more or less adroitly as clubs, they now apparently are beginning to find that a likely-shaped flint, used as a hand-axe, can inflict a severe wound.[56]

We are also duly informed of how she died—"*She may have been submerged in a drowning struggle*" (p. 29)—and her species' hunting methods—"*The old males in particular may have got into the habit of taking a well-selected flint when out on the*

53. McCann, A.W., *God or Gorilla*, Devin-Adair, New York, p. 1, 1922.
54. Keith, *The Antiquity of Man*, pp. 322–323.
55. Henderson, *Prehistoric Man*, pp. 29–30.
56. Henderson, *Prehistoric Man*, p. 30.

prowl. The young ones would soon copy them" (p. 30). All this from a few skull fragments shown in Figure 3!

Another example of how the scientists went well beyond the evidence is the claim that it is "*generally agreed that the skull belonged to a race of men who lacked the power of speech. A prominent anthropologist ... said that the evidence on that point was convincing, the 'speech centers' in the* [Piltdown Man's] *brain being so feebly developed that brain power was practically non-existent.*"[57] When the fraud was exposed they realized that the owner of the skull could speak quite well.

Another expert wrote that the Nature Conservancy even spent significant taxpayer money to designate the Piltdown site as a national monument. So important was the find that Millar claimed that Dawson would have been knighted for his discovery if it were not for his premature death.[58] Its importance is evident from the fact that "*the three leading lights of British anthropology and paleontology—Arthur Smith Woodward, Grafton Elliot Smith, and Arthur Keith—had staked their careers on the reality of Piltdown.*"[59] Fix claimed that many scientists then regarded Piltdown Man as "*the most important evidence*" of human evolution ever uncovered.[60]

Doubts begin to surface

Although some scientists eventually came to believe the two did not belong together, almost all scientists evidently accepted the orthodox reconstruction of Piltdown Man as genuine. Weidenreich was one of the "*few paleoanthropologists*" who did not accept Piltdown Man as valid.[61] Lubenow added that "*the vast majority of paleoanthropologists worldwide*" accepted Piltdown as legitimate, "*especially after the confirming discoveries at Piltdown II.*"[62]

Figure 3
The skull fragments of Piltdown illustrating the difficulty in accurate reconstruction.

Many leading paleoanthropologists, such as William King Gregory, George MacCurdy, and Aleš Hrdlička, believed Piltdown skull was a genuine human evolutionary link, but that the specific jaw and skull find were from two different Piltdown individuals.[63] To prove the matter one way or the other was difficult, in part because, although human and ape jaws are hinged very differently, the articular condyle—which could have proven if it was ape or human—was missing,

57. *The New York Times*, p. C-1, December 22, 1912.
58. Millar, *The Piltdown Men*, p. 9.
59. Gould, Piltdown revisited, p. 90.
60. Fix, W.R., *The Bone Peddlers: Selling Evolution*, Macmillan, New York, p. 12, 1984.
61. Wolpoff, M. and Caspari, R., *Race and Human Evolution: A Fatal Attraction*, Simon and Schuster. New York, p. 203, 1997.
62. Lubenow, *Bones of Contention*, p. 41.
63. Spencer, *Piltdown*, p. 100.

likely as part of the fraud.[64] Another feature that distinctly separates ape and human mandibles is the chin region, which was also conveniently missing.

A few critical scientists, including Franz Weidenreich and Gerrit Miller, concluded that the jaw was too much like an ape's and that the cranium was far too much like an Anglo-Saxon's. Although these and other scientists had some doubts about certain aspects of the find, no major anthropologist publicly stated that the fossils were an out-and-out fraud until Joseph Sidney Weiner (b. 1915) entered the debate in the early 1950s. The thousands of letters and articles by those who believed the Piltdown fossils were clear evidence of human evolution make fascinating reading today. James Moir, in an article that was often typical of the Piltdown supporters, said of Marcellin Boule's paper critiquing the British eolithic movement that it is the "*most extraordinarily biased statement it has ever been my ill-fortune to read*" and that he does

> not intend to make any reply to the threadbare and foolish arguments he uses to support his case, arguments to which I have replied to a great number of times, and which I do not intend to discuss any further. … both M. Boule and M. Breuil are hopelessly biased. … many weeks before either of these gentlemen visited Suffolk or had seen a single one of my specimens, they had expressed their disbelief … . Their attitude to all the things they saw was careless and almost petulant, and in my opinion quite unscientific. Regarding the capabilities of M M. Boule and Breuil of judging whether a flint has been flaked by nature or by man, I am of the opinion that neither of them is capable of such a judgment. … These are the facts.[65]

It must be noted that Moir wasn't writing as a Piltdown supporter per se, but was defending his own specimen—the Ipswich Skeleton—from his own critics, notably Boule. However, Moir believed his findings would also "*confirm the true age and nature of the curious bone implement from Piltdown.*"[66]

Another response was to the American researcher Gerrit Miller's conclusion that the Piltdown mandible was not human, but rather from a fossil ape (a conclusion that turned out to be true), Woodward called this observation the "*latest ROT from the USA.*"[67] Such *ad hominem* attacks, accompanied by long, detailed, allegedly scientific explanations typified the Piltdown debate for decades. By 1949 the story was already unravelling. One example is

> Piltdown Man, long considered one of mankind's oldest ancestors, is a mere anthropological infant, not more than 10,000 years old, Dr. K.P. Oakley of the British Museum disclosed to the British Association for the

64. Elliott, *The Curious Incident of the Missing Link*, p. 6.
65. Quoted in Spencer, *Piltdown*, pp. 90–91.
66. Spencer, *Piltdown*, p. 90.
67. Spencer, *Piltdown*, p. 94.

> Advancement of Science … . Previously considered to be between 100,000 and 500,000 years old, the jawbone and skull are now proved by analysis of their fluorine content to be definitely of the last interglacial period. Fossil animal bones of known geological age, dating from the Pleistocene or glacial period, unearthed nearby the human bones at Piltdown, England, had the same content of the chemical fluorine picked up from the ground water of the locality.[68]

In fact, the bones were only, at most, a few hundred years old. Nonetheless, after Woodward published a book on fossil man, a "*renewed zest*" about human evolution began. His book, although very technical, served to help trigger a renewal of interest in the Piltdown discoveries and an effort to preserve the excavation site as a historical spot in England. As a result, the small plot of ground was bricked in with the precise spot of the discoveries protected behind thick glass because

> Piltdown had become "*a major event in the unfolding of man's remote past,*" it was declared, and the ground that had yielded the fossils would have great historical value "*for unborn generations.*" When in the spring of 1950 the almost forty-year-old site was thrown open for public viewing, it quickly become a focal point for tourists and school outings. It was in this same year that the first puzzled suspicions, ironically *triggered by a wish to obtain the clinching evidence for authenticity,* [emphasis added—Ed.] began to stir. Late in 1949 the bones were taken from the vault of the Natural History Museum and submitted to a test that had been only recently perfected. The new procedure, it was thought, would settle the vexed question of the jaw-cranium association.[69]

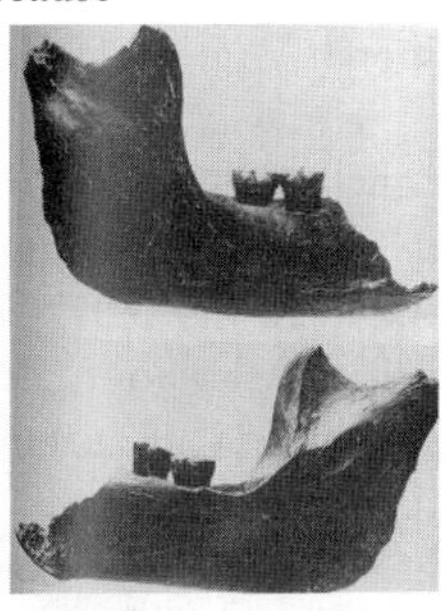

Figure 4
The jaw fragments of Piltdown showing the main focus of the forgery; the jaw and teeth had to be significantly modified to look more human.

Fraud finally proved

Evidently, Oxford anthropologist Joseph S. Weiner was the first scientist to openly suspect that Piltdown was an out and out forgery. Most other scientists were concerned about the *interpretation* of the find, especially the question of whether the jaw and skull went together, *not* if they were a genuine missing link. Weiner's questions originally set in motion the events that led to the retesting and re-evaluation of the Piltdown fossils. Weiner first talked to Le Gros Clark about his concerns. Clark then suggested to British geologist Kenneth Oakley[70] that the skull should be eval-

68. Davis, W., Old Piltdown Man is only about 10,000 years old, *Science News Letter* **56**(12):185, 1949.
69. Walsh, *Unraveling Piltdown*, p. 10.
70. Walsh, *Unraveling Piltdown*, pp. 68–69.

uated using fluorine, nitrogen, and other tests to prove *once and for all* that the find was genuine.[71,72]

Oakley's fluorine-based tests indicated that Piltdown had made a monkey out of almost everyone, concluding that the Piltdown fossils were closer to 10,000 years old, not approximately 100,000 to 300,000 years old as was originally claimed.[73] Modern radiocarbon dating indicates it is only 520 to 720 years old.[74] This finding raised serious questions, not only about its age, but about the whole Piltdown find. It also provided major evidence that led Weiner and others to expose it as a fraud.[75,76]

The skull has now been proven to be from a modern human, evidently an Australian Aborigine or possibly a sufferer of Paget's disease, a hereditary thickening of bone. A similar skull was reported to be missing around 1900 from the Hastings Museum to which Dawson had close connections. The mandible was from a juvenile female orangutan that died about AD 1450.[77,78,79] It was probably part of a collection from Borneo that was reported missing from the British Museum shortly after 1911.

Knowledge of the fragments' true identity illustrates how irresponsible the conclusions about Piltdown were, such as the claim that the "*brain is remarkably under-developed, as one would naturally expect.*"[80] The first rigorous discussion of the hoax was published by Dr Oakley and two scientific collaborators in a 1953 British Museum bulletin. The paper, titled "*The Solution of the Piltdown Problem,*" concluded that the mandible canine teeth had been filed down in an attempt to look like human teeth and to articulate better with the skull. The filing angle was wrong; human teeth wear down flat, apes' teeth do not.

The scientific study also concluded that the skull was stained with potassium bichromate to appear more primitive, and was also impregnated with grains of sand to imitate fossilization. In view of these discoveries, contemporary accounts vividly reveal the tendency to reach broad, sweeping conclusions from a minuscule amount of empirical evidence.

---

71. Oakley, K.P. And Hoskins, C.R., New evidence on the antiquity of Piltdown Man, *Nature* **165**, 379–382, 1950.
72. In 1949 Oakley, who evidently was convinced of the validity of the Piltdown find, read an 1892 paper by the French scientist Carnot. Carnot demonstrated that bones buried in the ground absorb ground fluorine, and that the fluorine content of bone generally *increases with age*. One therefore could obtain an estimate of the age of previously living bone by ascertaining the fluorine content.
73. See example in Osborn, *Men of the Old Stone Age*, p. 145.
74. Lubenow, *Bones of Contention*, p. 42.
75. Gee, H., Box of bones 'clinches' identity of Piltdown paleontology hoaxer, *Nature* **381**(6580):261–262, 1996.
76. Spencer, *Piltdown*, p. xiii.
77. Winslow and Meyer, The perpetrator at Piltdown, p. 33.
78. Spencer, *Piltdown*.
79. British Museum of Natural History, *The Piltdown Man Hoax*.
80. Henderson, *Prehistoric Man*, p. 30.

The Piltdown exposure was covered first in *The Times* of London (November 23, 1953) and the *Manchester Guardian* of November 26, 1953, which called the scientists who perpetrated the hoax "*extraordinarily skillful.*" It soon became obvious that the hoaxer or hoaxers were actually extraordinarily sloppy, "*almost beyond belief.*"[81] The scientific world was stunned by the Piltdown exposure, partly because it proved one of the most important evidences for Darwinism was fraudulent.

The question on which most authors have focused was determining the identity of the culprit. Most of the distinguished paleontologists and archaeologists who originally took part in the Piltdown investigations were considered either perpetrators, or victims, of the hoax. Blame fell first on the discoverer, Charles Dawson. Although his role was difficult to investigate—he had by this time been dead for 37 years—many authorities conclude he was the most likely candidate.[82,83]

Suspicion fell on him for many reasons, such as the fact that he had once been caught trying to stain bones, evidently to make them appear older—as occurred in the case of the Piltdown fossils.[84] His supporters conclude he was only trying to see if the bones could be stained to look older to help determine if his past findings were faked.[85] Dawson also had a long history of questionable finds, some of which have been documented as forgeries.[86] A well-documented 158-page book-length study by Miles Russell likewise concluded that Dawson was the culprit, noting his long history of forgeries and other strong evidence implicating him in the crime.[87]

Arthur Keith was also a prime suspect for several years.[88] Similarly accused was Pierre Teilhard de Chardin, a priest well known for his research on the topic of human evolution. Bowden[89,90] makes an excellent case for de Chardin's guilt. Harvard Professor Stephen Jay Gould once concluded that de Chardin, Dawson and possibly others may have been involved.[91,92,93] In an attempt to show that de

81. Millar, *The Piltdown Men*, p. 228.
82. Weiner, J.S., *The Piltdown Forgery*, Oxford University Press, New York, 2003.
83. Walsh, *Unraveling Piltdown*.
84. Kurtén, *How to Deep-Freeze a Mammoth*, pp. 62–71.
85. Bowden, M., *Ape-men: Fact or Fallacy?* 2nd Edition, Sovereign Publications, Bromley, Kent, UK, Section I, The Piltdown forgery, p. 27, 1977.
86. Russell, M., *Piltdown Man: The Secret Life of Charles Dawson & the World's Greatest Archaeological Hoax*, Tempus Publishing, Gloucestershire, UK, pp. 28–32, 2003.
87. Russell, *The Piltdown Man Hoax*.
88. Spencer, *Piltdown*, pp. 200–201.
89. Bowden, *Ape-men*, p. 27.
90. Bowden, M., The Piltdown hoax—further revelations (appendix 2) in *Science vs. Evolution*, Sovereign Publications, Bromley, Kent, UK, pp. 177–194, 1991.
91. Gould, Piltdown revisited, p. 87.
92. Gould, S., Piltdown in letters, *Natural History* **90**(6):12–30, 1981.
93. Gould, *Hen's Teeth and Horse's Toes*, p. 225.

Chardin was not the culprit, McCulloch[94] wrote an entire monograph pointing out what she believed were the many major flaws in Gould's arguments.

Millar concluded that Sir Grafton Elliot Smith of the British Museum was the fraud's perpetrator.[95] The total number of suspects is now around 40 and includes Woodward.[96,97] Even Sir Arthur Conan Doyle was a suspect (Elliot wrote a monograph attempting to refute this view).[98,99] Spencer wrote that when

> Leakey asked Teilhard what he thought of Weiner's published claim that Dawson had perpetrated the fraud, Louis [Leakey] reported that Teilhard said, "*I know who did the Piltdown hoax and it was not Charles Dawson.*" … Leakey told me that he wanted to publish a book on the Piltdown story, in which he would "*expose*" Teilhard's supposed role in the fraud, but Mary Leakey … said, "*O don't, Louis! You'll only make enemies …* " and Louis said no more on the subject.[100]

Another suspect was Martin A.C. Hinton, who was the British Museum Curator of Zoology from 1936 to 1945.[101,102] A trunk found in the attic of the British Museum that belonged to Hinton contained bones and teeth that were artificially stained in a very similar way to the Piltdown bones.[103] This evidence, along with additional material, caused some people who were close to the case to conclude that the evidence for "*Hinton having been the sole hoaxer is now conclusive.*"[104] Many other investigators, though, still believe the case is unsolved. Nonetheless, the major significance of the hoax is its central importance in understanding the mindset of true believers in evolution.

---

94. McCulloch, W., *Teilhard de Chardin and the Piltdown Hoax*, American Teilhard Association for the Future of Man, New York, 1996.
95. Millar, *The Piltdown Men*.
96. Drawhorn, G., Piltdown: Evidence of Smith-Woodward's Complicity, paper presented at the American Association of Physical Anthropologists meeting, April 1, 1994.
97. Elliott, *The Curious Incident of the Missing Link*, p. 6.
98. Winslow and Meyer, The perpetrator at Piltdown.
99. Elliott, *The Curious Incident of the Missing Link*, p. 6.
100. Spencer, *Piltdown*, p. x.
101. Menon, S., The Piltdown perpetrator, *Discover* **18**(1):34, 1997.
102. Bowden, The Piltdown hoax.
103. Gee, Box of bones 'clinches' identity of Piltdown paleontology hoaxer, pp. 261–262.
104. Gee, Box of bones 'clinches' identity of Piltdown paleontology hoaxer, p. 262.

Figure 5
Aimé Rutot's reconstruction of the Piltdown Man, *Eoanthropus dawsonii*, as part of a museum exhibit on the evolution of man.
Source: Simpson, James, *Man and the Attainment of Immortality*, Doran, New York, p. 99, 1922.

Motivation for the hoax

Several historians have concluded that the most likely motivation for the hoax was to advance the perpetrator's career and scientific reputation. What more important discovery in science could there be than to unearth definitive proof of Darwin's theory of human evolution? Spencer speculates that Dawson's motive was probably related

> to his ambition to become a Fellow of the Royal Society, an honour that marked the pinnacle of scientific achievement. Achieving this accolade was not an easy matter, but it is evident from his later correspondence that he had seen Piltdown as a possible route ... and there is every reason to suppose that, had he lived, he would have been duly elected—an eventuality that would have been based almost entirely on his achievements at Piltdown.[105]

Likewise, Keith's motives, Spencer explains, were similar to Dawson's:

> Dawson's aims were simple: fame and a Fellowship of the Royal Society. Although perhaps more subtle, Keith's motives were, in the final analysis, not much different from those of Dawson ... While there were risks involved, ... there was everything to gain and nothing to lose. Indeed, once the skull was "*launched*" neither Keith nor Dawson could be greatly injured by its demolition. But again, provided they played their cards with care, there was every reason to suppose that this would never happen.[106]

Similar motives are just as likely for many of the other suspects.

Creationists criticized before the hoax was exposed

Darwin skeptics were especially critical of the find, often noting the disagreement that existed among evolutionists concerning the many different interpretations

105. Spencer, *Piltdown*, p. 199.
106. Spencer, *Piltdown*, p. 201.

about Piltdown. Unfortunately, none of the critics had analyzed the find carefully, nor provided a detailed review of it until after the hoax was exposed. One reason why is because very few people had access to the original bones that were carefully guarded by the British Museum. Nonetheless, their insight has proved valid. Typical of the many creationist reviews that avoided making wild stories about the find and stuck to the known facts was the following by Price:

> Considering the fact that these fragments were not all found together or at one time, some of them having been found in the autumn and the rest in the spring of the next year, the various fragments being scattered over an area of several yards, the difficulty of being sure of the real form and size of this skull will be appreciated. As for the geological age of these remains, Keith calls them Pliocene, while Smith Woodward thinks them Pleistocene. Keith thinks the skull is that of a woman.[107]

Assuming much of the information presented in the media about Piltdown was true, Price elsewhere stated he believed that Piltdown Man may be a degenerate human.[108] William Jennings Bryan argued that schools should not teach that Piltdown Man revealed any relationship to anthropoid apes.[109] Plaster casts of Piltdown Man even appeared as evidence for the defence in Scopes' legal challenge to Tennessee's 'anti-evolution law' known as the Butler Act.

A few creationists, such as John Roach Straton, openly denounced Piltdown as a fraud.[110] About this time, creationist Harry Rimmer asserted that the Piltdown hominid consisted mostly of "*plaster of Paris and imagination.*"[111] William Bell Riley referred to it as "*imaginatively created.*"[112] Creationist Professor William Tinkle in his textbook *Fundamentals of Zoology* correctly concluded that the Piltdown skull was a *Homo sapiens* skull but the jaw was from an anthropoid ape.[113]

Probably the most extensive early critical discussions of Piltdown Man were by Catholic biologist George O'Toole[114] and Catholic author Alfred McCann.[115] McCann did an excellent job evaluating the evidence, using journalistic prose to

107. Price, G.M., *The New Geology*, Pacific Press, Mt View, California, p. 699, 1923.
108. Price, G.M., *The Phantom of Organic Evolution*, Fleming H. Revell, New York, p. 110, 1924.
109. Quoted in Larson, *Summer of the Gods*, p. 8.
110. Larson, *Summer of the Gods*, p. 32.
111. Rimmer, H., Monkeyshines: Fakes, Fables, Facts Concerning Evolution, in Edward B.D. (Ed.), *The Antievolution Pamphlets of Harry Rimmer*, Garland, New York, p. 427, 1995.
112. Trollinger, W.V., *The Antievolution Pamphlets of William Bell Riley*, Garland, New York, p. 101, 1995.
113. Tinkle, W.J., *Fundamentals of Zoology*, Zondervan, Grand Rapids, Michigan, p. 425, 1939.
114. O'Toole, G.B., *The Case Against Evolution*, Macmillan, New York, 1929.
115. McCann, *God or Gorilla*, p. 1.

argue that the obviously poorly executed hoax was accepted only because of the powerful desire of Darwinists to find support for human evolution.

McCann, who tracked the Piltdown discovery from its beginning to about 1920, confidently concluded that Piltdown was clearly a "*discredited hoax.*" He also concluded that the skull-cap was human, the jaw was of pongid [ape—Ed.] origin, and that both were assembled deliberately to look like a "*man half way along his journey from simian to the human stage.*"[116] Catholic writer Joseph Mereto[117] wrote that the Piltdown "*skull has been proven to be human and his jawbone that of an ape*", though he gave no evidence for his conclusion.

Professor O'Toole correctly concluded—twenty years before it was finally proven by the scientific community—that

> *Eoanthropus dawsoni* is an invention, not a discovery, an artistic creation, not a specimen. Anyone can combine a simian mandible with a human cranium, and, if the discovery of a connecting link entails no more than this, then there is no reason why evidence of human evolution should not be turned out wholesale.[118]

O'Toole also concluded that Dr Woodward's major error was in his

> failure to discern the obvious disproportion between the mismated cranium and mandible. As a matter of fact, the mandible is older than the skull and belongs to a fossil ape, whereas the cranium is more recent and is conspicuously human. Woodward, however, was blissfully unconscious of this mésalliance. What there is of the lower jaw, he assures us, "*shows the same mineralized condition as the skull*" and "*corresponds sufficiently well in size to be referred to the same individual without hesitation.*"[119]

Many scientists were greatly disappointed when the fraud was exposed. According to Teilhard's biographer, "*the incident cut him quite deeply*" and he had "*trouble believing that Dawson himself perpetrated the fraud.*"[120]

The confidence of leading scientists

The major question is, why did "*so many reputable scientists endorse the now seemingly ludicrous marriage of an orangutan mandible to a palpably modern human*

116. McCann, *God or Gorilla*, p. 1.
117. Mereto, J., *Monkey Craze*, Our Sunday Visitor, Huntington, Indiana, p. 22, 1925.
118. O'Toole, *The Case Against Evolution*, p. 323.
119. O'Toole, *The Case Against Evolution*, p. 322.
120. Lukas, M. and Lukas, E., *Teilhard*, Doubleday, Garden City, New York, p. 330, 1977.

braincase?"[121] That the hoax occurred is less unexpected than the fact that *it was accepted by so many leading scientists for almost half a century*. Statements such as that by MIT Professor of Paleoanthropology Hervey Woodburn Shimer that "*among the most ancient undoubted remains thus far found is Eoanthropus, the 'dawn man'*" were common.[122] Steven Jay Gould concluded that one of the most significant questions is, "*Why did anyone ever accept Piltdown Man in the first place?*"[123] Johanson and Shreeve bluntly asked, "*How could so many trained scientists be so utterly and shamefully fooled?*"[124]

Among the many reasons that exist for its acceptance include the fact that the skull was conveniently "*unwittingly shattered by a workman's pick*" and had to be reassembled without the most critical skull fragments for proper identification, and as is true of most putative human fossils, Darwinistic preconceptions were allowed to influence its reassembly.[125] Gould and many of his colleagues have largely ignored what is probably the best answer to the question of why the Piltdown fossils were accepted for so long: the often blinding desire of some scientists to find evidence for their theory, and often their worldview as well. The lesson here was well expressed by Hawkes—namely, that he found it was shocking to discover how often preconceived ideas have

> affected the investigation of human origins. There is, of course, nothing like a fake for exposing such weaknesses among the experts. For example, to look back over the bold claims and subtle anatomical distinctions made by some of our greatest authorities concerning the recent human skull and modern ape's jaw which together composed "*Piltdown Man,*" rouses either joy or pain according to one's feeling for scientists.[126]

She adds that no reason exists to "*suppose that tendencies to error*" in this academic profession have "*grown very much less*" since then.[127] Extreme confidence in the authenticity of the Piltdown find is frequently found in many pre-1950 evolution writings. In one summary of the status of the support for Piltdown, one scientist concluded that, if the second lower jaw fossil found at Piltdown belonged with the first Piltdown skull,

> as nearly all authorities now believe, it affords a clear case of an ape-like canine belonging in a human jaw. … The human canines may indeed be

121. Spencer, *Piltdown*, p. xvi.
122. Shimer, H.W., *Evolution and Man*, Ginn and Company, New York, p. 166, 1929.
123. Gould, Piltdown revisited, p. 87.
124. Johanson, D. and Shreeve, J., *Lucy's Child: The Discovery of a Human Ancestor*, William Morrow, New York, p. 52, 1989.
125. Baitsell, *The Evolution of Earth and Man*, p. 167.
126. Hawkes, J., Antiquity of man, *Nature* **204**(4962):952–953, 1964.
127. Hawkes, Antiquity of man, p. 952.

> most reasonably regarded as reduced and "*infantilized*" or "*feminized*" derivatives of a primitive anthropoid type, and the process of reduction and infantilization may well have taken place during the millions of years of the Lower Pliocene epoch, at a period when the fossil record of human remains so far discovered is still blank.[128]

Gregory added that the

> great mass of collateral evidence for the derivation of man from primitive anthropoids with well developed but not greatly enlarged canines, has been reviewed lately with great thoroughness by Remane, who finds no justification for the view that man has avoided the primitive anthropoid stage and has been derived from wholly unknown forms with the canine tips not projecting much beyond the level of the premolars.[129]

A common conclusion was that the jaw and cranium *must* have belonged together because the chances of the two being found together accidentally was "*infinitely*" small.[130] The claim that the jaw was so "*absolutely simian*" and the skull was so human, that it must belong to an ape and man respectively, not an ape-like man, was answered by concluding that mathematicians know that "*independent probabilities must be multiplied together*" and that

> the chance is infinitesimal that the only man found in England in a particular geological formation should have left his skull close beside the jaw of the only known ape of the same formation. ... [The] skull and jaw must belong to the same individual; and they point to the existence of a type of man with such characters that he cannot be ancestral to any other known type with the possible exception of the recently discovered Peking man.[131]

The likely possibility that they were planted evidently did not occur to these evolutionists. Among the leading paleontologists that expressed profound confidence in the importance of Piltdown for evolutionary theory was William J. Bryan's nemesis, Henry Fairfield Osborn. He included several chapters devoted largely to Piltdown Man in his important 1928 book on human evolution. The level of confidence that Osborn manifested in his conclusion is clear from his forceful, but ironic, prose:

---

128. Gregory, W., *Our Face from Fish to Man*, G.P. Putnam's Sons, New York, pp. 141–142, 1929.
129. Gregory, *Our Face from Fish to Man*.
130. Gates, R.R., *Human Ancestry from a Genetic Point of View*, Harvard University Press, Cambridge, Massachusetts, p. 239, 1948.
131. Barnes, E.W., *Scientific Theory and Religion*, Cambridge University Press, Cambridge, p. 531, 1933.

> There has been on the part of anthropologists no conspiracy or hasty acceptance of any of these fossil men. The Neanderthal Stone Age man discovered in 1848, the Trinil "*ape-man*" of Java discovered in 1891, the Piltdown Dawn Man discovered in 1911, have had in turn a hard struggle for scientific recognition, lasting … no less than ten years in the case of the Dawn Man of Piltdown.[132]

Osborn added that Arthur Smith Woodward had finally established

> beyond question the authenticity of the Dawn Man of Piltdown. The confirmation of the reality of the Piltdown Man as a veritable "*dawn man*" must be followed by renewed and determined effort to fix more precisely his *geologic antiquity* [original emphasis], about which there has also been a great difference of opinion.[133]

Sir Arthur Keith even stated that the conclusion that the jaw was that of an ape and the skull was that of a human represented a mistake that "*could never have been made if those concerned had studied the comparative anatomy of anthropoid apes.*"[134] Piltdown Man was still being cited in the scientific literature as late as 1945. In a book about British prehistory and the evidence for human evolution, Professor Samuel Edward Winbolt still believed it to be a genuine intermediate fossil, and for this reason favourably quoted Moir who concluded that the

> Piltdown skull and jawbone are among the most important remains of ancient man yet found … . Taking all the known facts into consideration, it appears probable that *Eoanthropus* (Dawn man) represents one of the types of human beings existing at the very beginning of Pleistocene times [omission in original, spelling corrected—Ed.].[135]

Piltdown Man is not an isolated example, but one of many in which the Darwinists' enthusiasm went way beyond the facts. Darwinists today attempt to rationalize the widespread acceptance of the Piltdown fraud by noting that doubters existed from the beginning and that in the end the process of science worked because the hoax was eventually exposed.[136]

'Enthusiastically going beyond the facts' describes most, if not all, of the evolutionists' arguments, including the vestigial organ theory, homology, and the

132. Osborn, H.F., *Man Rises to Parnassus: Critical Epochs in the Prehistory of Man*, Princeton University Press, Princeton, New Jersey, p. 48, 1927.
133. Osborn, *Man Rises to Parnassus*, p. 48.
134. Keith, A., Darwin's theory of man's descent as it stands today, *Science* **66**(1705):201–208, 1927; p. 204.
135. Winbolt, S., *Britain B.C.*, Penguin Books, New York, pp. 15–16, 1945.
136. Blinderman, *The Piltdown Inquest*, p. 239.

ridiculous and long-discredited idea of abiogenesis (life evolving from non-life purely by natural forces, an idea Louis Pasteur, shown in Figure 6, disproved by experiment) which is still adhered to so faithfully by evolutionists even today. These largely discredited claims nonetheless are still often touted in defence of evolutionism, much as Piltdown was.[137] To the chagrin of orthodox Darwinists, dissenters are frequently quoted by various anti-Darwinists. Both today and in the past, the arguments of Piltdown supporters have been thoroughly disproven, including by G.S. Miller Jr, who studied, not the original fossils, but casts, and from his study of the fossils

> came to the conclusion that the jaw and skull could not possibly pertain to the same individual or even the same genus, but that the former was that of a fossil chimpanzee ... despite the fact that fossil anthropoids were heretofore unknown in England. In this conclusion Mr. Miller has had quite a large American following. The matter has, however, been settled beyond question by the finding of a second specimen of the Piltdown Man some two miles distant, consisting of diagnostic cranial fragments associated again with a lower molar of precisely similar character to those in the first jaw, a happening which could hardly occur, according to the law of probabilities, in both of the only known instances if the jaw and skull were not those of the same form.[138]

Figure 6
The French scientist Louis Pasteur, who disproved the theory of Spontaneous Generation.

Much debate, thousands of letters, and hundreds of articles surrounded the Piltdown fossils, but very few scientists questioned the basic finding—as we see in the above quote. Much of the debate was over whether the fossils were from the Pliocene or Pleistocene (both were wrong), if the skull and jaw were from one individual or two (both were wrong), or other such details—not whether the find itself was genuine.[139]

Another significant fact that illustrates the trend today is that the Piltdown hoax even appeared in some texts published *after* it had been exposed. The leading textbook, *Man and his Biological World*, although copyrighted in 1952, years after it was in print and for many years after Piltdown Man was exposed, included a detailed discussion of the find, writing that scientific research has "*practically clinched the argument that the Piltdown and Swanscombe men were very ancient ... probably lived about 500,000 years ago.*"[140]

137. Larson, *Summer of the Gods*, pp. 11–30.
138. Baitsell, *The Evolution of Earth and Man*, p. 168.
139. Spencer, *Piltdown.*
140. Jean, F., Harrah, E., and Herman, F., *Man and his Biological World, Revised Edition*, Ginn and Company, New York, pp. 461–462, 1952.

One egregious example of delayed admission can be found in the 1960 book, *Adam's Ancestors,* by the leading paleontontogist L.S.B. Leakey.[141] The fourth edition was finally corrected, but only by adding a section on the hoax while retaining the original discussion that claimed Piltdown was genuine. The added section, which acknowledged that Piltdown was a fraud, labelled it a "*warning against too easy acceptance of evidence which, in itself, is contrary to all that we know of Biology.*" This example is of special note because Leakey was considered one of the foremost anthropologists ever.

Similarly, examples of long-discredited ideas about origins, such as Haeckel's biogenetic law, are still found in biology and evolution textbooks.[142] Even Piltdown Man is still occasionally used today. The latest example I have come across was in a presentation given on March, 19, 2002, at Michigan State University by Professor Don Weinshank. On slide 16 was "*Eoanthropus dawsoni*" which he stated was one of the "*hominoids … that … lived on this planet in the last four million years*" (page 3 of lecture notes) from which modern humans descended.

Conclusion

The Piltdown case is an excellent example of how social and cultural expectations can powerfully influence scientific opinion. One researcher concluded that an inquest into the Piltdown affair does not

> offer much cheer to those of us who think that science is a legitimate enterprise that has drawn a credible chart of human evolution. Anyone conversant with the Piltdown history will readily, if not eagerly, agree that many of the researchers shaped reality to their heart's desire, protecting their theories, their careers, their reputations, all of which they lugged into the pit with them.[143]

In one of the most insightful assessments of the whole Piltdown affair, Eiseley noted that the level of subjective speculation by many leading authorities about the Piltdown fossil

> can now be viewed historically as a remarkable case history in self-deception. It should serve as an everlasting warning to science that … [scientists] may exhibit irrational bias or give allegiance to theories with only the most tenuous basis in fact. That scientists in the early years of a new discipline should have been easily deceived is not nearly so embarrassing as the rapidity with which they embraced the specimen solely because it fell in with preconceived wishes and could be used to support all manner of convenient

141. Leakey, L.S.B., *Adam's Ancestors*, Harper and Brothers, New York, 1960.
142. Wells, *Icons of Evolution.*
143. Blinderman, *The Piltdown Inquest*, p. 235.

> hypotheses. The enormous bibliography in several languages which grew up around the skull is an ample indication, also, of how much breath can be expended fruitlessly upon ambiguous or dubious materials.[144]

William Fix concluded that what was especially embarrassing for paleontologists is not that one of their own "*should have stooped to manufacturing the evidence, but that so many made so much out of so little.*"[145]

Keith even claimed the exposure caused him to have a "*loss of faith in the testimony of Man.*"[146] The fact that Piltdown Man was proven to be a forgery is somewhat irrelevant now: it has influenced millions of people to accept Darwinism and was even used in the written testimony at the Scopes trial as proof of evolution. What happened was stated eloquently by Pagel:

> Darwin proclaimed a wholly material explanation for species, based on the principle of descent with modification. Lyell had opened the door, and Darwin showed God out. Palaeobiologists flocked to these scientific visions of a world in a constant state of flux and admixture. But instead of finding the slow, smooth and progressive changes Lyell and Darwin had expected, they saw in the fossil records rapid bursts of change, new species appearing seemingly out of nowhere and then remaining unchanged for millions of years—patterns hauntingly reminiscent of creation. But *there was no turning back* [emphasis added], and biologists have for the past century fought over how best to explain the diversity of life.[147]

Millar estimates that some 500 scholarly articles were published about Piltdown during its 40-year lifespan.[148] If references to Piltdown in textbooks and articles about evolution were included, no doubt the count would be in the thousands. Whole chapters were devoted to the find in major anthropology reference books of the day.[149] Since clear evidence existed from the beginning that Piltdown was fraudulent, or at least was not evidence for human evolution, why did it require almost 40 years before it was conclusively exposed? The great German anatomist Professor Schwalbe was forced to abandon the "*missing link*" because it was a fraud, and

> declared that "*the proper restoration of the Piltdown fragments would make them belong not to any preceding stage of man, but to a well-developed, good sized*

144. Eiseley, L., Fossil Man and Human Evolution, in Thomas McKern (Ed.), *Readings in Physical Anthropology*, Prentice-Hall, Englewood Cliffs, New Jersey., p. 111, 1966.
145. Fix, *The Bone Peddlers*, p. 13.
146. Quoted in Williams, T., *A Biographical Dictionary of Scientists*, Wiley-Interscience, New York, p. 286, 1969.
147. Pagel, M., Happy accidents? *Nature* **397**(6721):664–665, 1999; p. 665.
148. Millar, *The Piltdown Men*, p. 10.
149. See Osborn, *Men of the Old Stone Age*, for examples, pp. 130–145.

> *Homo sapiens, the true man of today.*" Why are such facts as these withheld from the young student and from his teacher if truth is really an objective?[150]

The most important lesson of Piltdown, as adroitly summarized by McCann over 90 years ago, was that the affair demonstrated the ease with which evidence linking apes and men can be fabricated even if it requires

> wide stretches of imagination in support of pre-conceived opinions. The materialistic evolutionists, who have misrepresented the Piltdown Man and all that they have sought to make it signify, are careful not to refer to the English authorities in the biological sciences who discussed all the Piltdown remains upon the first report of their discovery to the Geological Society of London, December, 1912. They avoid all mention of the fact that even at that early date … [some] authorities refused to accept the cranium and jaw as belonging to the same individual.[151]

The Piltdown fiasco also documented how easily researchers "*can be manipulated into believing that they actually found just what it was they had been looking for.*"[152] Unfortunately, many Piltdown-type fossils which are not what they claim are still discussed in textbooks today.[153] In fact, Lubenow speculates that if australopithecines had not become

> the preferred evolutionary ancestors of humans, and Piltdown had not become an embarrassment because it no longer fit the scenario, the fraud might still be undiscovered and Piltdown might still be considered a legitimate fossil.[154]

In a survey of the human fossil record, Fix concluded that "*the Piltdown fiasco has happened repeatedly*" and is still being re-enacted today.[155] This is the true lesson of Piltdown.[156] For an excellent review of the difficulties of drawing conclusions from the fossil record and the unethical behavior of many of the leading modern paleoanthropologists today, see Morell.[157] For a few of the many examples of modern-day

150. McCann, *God or Gorilla*, pp. 8–9.
151. McCann, *God or Gorilla*, p. 9.
152. Maienschein, J., Epistemological reflections on the modern human origins debates, chapter 28 in Clark and Willermet (Eds.), *Conceptual Issues in Modern Human Origins Research*, Aldine De Gruyter, New York, p. 415, 1997.
153. See Wells, *Icons of Evolution*, pp. 123–125, 134, 218–219, 321–322.
154. Lubenow, *Bones of Contention*, p. 43.
155. Fix, *The Bone Peddlers*, p. 14.
156. Vere, F., *Lessons of Piltdown*, The Evolution Protest Movement, Hampshire, England, 1959.
157. Morell, V., *Ancestral Passions: The Leakey Family and the Quest for Humankind's Beginnings*, Simon and Schuster, New York, 1995.

cases of hoaxes and frauds in science, see Service,[158] Broad and Wade,[159] Taubes,[160] Kevles,[161] Adler,[162] Kohn,[163] and Joravsky.[164] As Chris Stringer, who works at the museum where the fossils are stored, stated, "*the story has a continuing relevance beyond its allure as a whodunit: it is a warning to scientists to keep their critical guard up, and an example of the (eventual) triumph of the scientific method.*"[165] The same conclusion applies to neo-Darwinian evolution in general. The scientific method must eventually triumph, and remove the dross of evolution from the silver of science.

158. Service, R., Pioneering physics papers under suspicion for data manipulation, *Science* **296**:1376–1377, 2002.
159. Broad, W. and Wade, N., *Betrayers of the Truth: Fraud and Deceit in the Halls of Science*, Simon and Schuster, New York, p. 17, 1982.
160. Taubes, G., *Bad Science: The Short Life and Weird Times of Cold Fusion*, Random House, New York, 1993.
161. Kevles, D.J., *The Baltimore Case; A Trial of Politics, Science, and Character*, W.W. Norton & Company, New York, 1988.
162. Adler, I., *Stories of Hoaxes in the Name of Science*, Collier Books, New York, 1962.
163. Kohn, A., *False Prophets: Fraud and Error in Science and Medicine*, Basil Blackwell Ltd, New York, 1988.
164. Joravsky, D., *The Lysenko Affair*, Harvard University Press, Cambridge, Massachusetts, 1970.
165. Stringer, The 100-year mystery of Piltdown Man, p. 177.

CHAPTER 12

The *Hesperopithecus* debacle: The human-ape link that turned out to be a pig

Introduction

One of the most infamous examples of misidentification in the history of paleo-anthropology was Nebraska Man, formally known as *Hesperopithecus haroldcookii*. Nebraska Man was a fossil discovery that was regarded by leading experts as critically important to documenting evolutionary history. The evidence for this anthropoid was a single tooth that turned out to be a pig's tooth. The discovery and controversy surrounding the fossil find and its importance in history is the focus of this chapter.

The fossil supporters' writings reveal the critical role that preconceptions played in interpreting the limited evidence for their ape-man claims. The Nebraska Man case provides a valuable lesson on the importance of presumptions in interpreting evidence in the human origins field. It also stresses the need for careful evaluation of the empirical evidence for new ideas, and the danger of going beyond what the facts warrant.

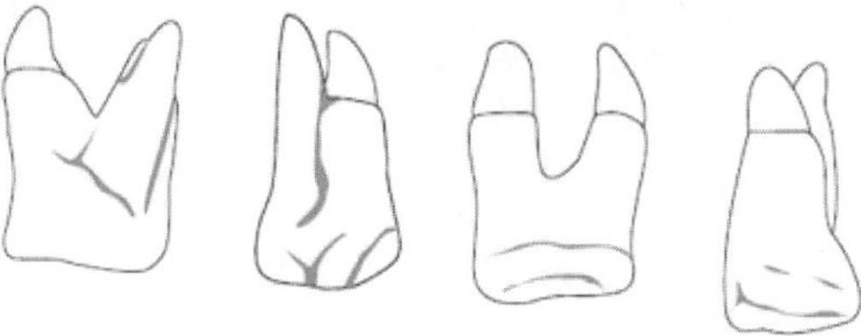

Figure 1
Four different views of the now infamous lone tooth that created all of the controversy.
Source: Professor G. Elliot Smith, Hesperopithecus: The Ape Man of the Western World, *Illustrated London News*, p. 944, 24 June 1922. Drawn from 'Further notes on the molars of *Hesperopithecus* and of *Pithecanthropus*', William, K.G., Hellman, M., Miller, G.S., *Bulletin of the American Museum of Natural History*, **48**:509–530, 1923.

This incident was of special historical importance partly because several prominent paleontologists, including the head of the American Museum of Natural History, Henry Fairfield Osborn, put their weight behind the validity of the find. Certain leading evolutionists argued that the discovery was not only important scientifically, but also serendipitous because it was discovered at the time when evolution was increasingly being attacked by a variety of people. Darwinists even recognized the fossil as having 'comic' aspects because it was discovered in Nebraska where the most well-known anti-evolutionist, William Jennings Bryan, was from.[1,2]

The events surrounding the discovery, as well as statements about the find from internationally prominent anthropologists and evolutionists, are central in assessing the critical influence of belief structures and preconceptions when interpreting empirical data.

Background of the discovery

Nebraska Man was based on a single heavily damaged molar tooth discovered in early 1922 by experienced geologist Harold J. Cook.[3] The 10.5 mm x 11 mm tooth was, in Blinderman's words, "*the answer to American anthropologists' prayers.*"[4] Cook, a consulting geologist in Agate, Nebraska, was also credited with several other fossil discoveries.[5] He unearthed *Hesperopithecus* on the ranch of Harry Ashbrook of Snake Creek, a small town about 640 km (400 miles) west of Omaha, Nebraska.[6]

The find was dug out of a quarry 32km (20 miles) south of Agate on Olcott Hill. This area contained fossils of a fauna type that one of Darwin's most active supporters, Sir Arthur Keith, claimed was "*so Asiatic in its characters that it is necessary to suppose that when these beds were laid down, or before they were deposited, America was united to Asia, thus making it possible for early precursors of man or ape to make their way from the Old World to the New.*"[7]

When Cook discovered his soon-to-become-world-famous tooth, he wrote to the President of the American Museum of Natural History in New York, Henry Fairfield Osborn. Cook, in a letter dated February 25, 1922, stated that he had discovered "*a molar tooth from the Upper, or Hipparion phase of the Snake Creek beds, that very closely approaches the human type. … Inasmuch as you* [and your colleagues]

---

1. Osborn, H.F., *Hesperopithecus*, the anthropoid primate of western Nebraska, *Nature* **110**(2756):281, 1922.
2. Cattell, J.M., An American anthropoid primate, *Scientific Monthly* **14**(6):588–590, June 1922; p. 588.
3. Smith, G.E., *The Evolution of Man: Essays*, Oxford University Press, London, p. 8, 1924.
4. Blinderman, C., The curious case of Nebraska man: his tooth was the answer to American anthropologist's prayers, *Science 85* **6**(6):47–49, 1985.
5. Matthew, W.D. and Cook, H.J, A pliocene fauna from Western Nebraska, *Bulletin of the American Museum of Natural History* **26**:361–414, 1909.
6. Gregory, W.K., and Hellman, M., "Notes on the type of *Hesperopithecus haroldcookii* Osborn", *American Museum Novitates* **53**:1–16, 1923.
7. Keith, A., *The Antiquity of Man, Vol. I and II*, J.B. Lippincott Company, Philadelphia, pp. 474–475, 1927.

are in the best position of any one to accurately determine the relationships of this tooth ... I will be glad to send it on to you."[8]

Osborn received the actual tooth on March 14 and, with what Stephen Jay Gould states was his usual precision,[9] Osborn telegraphed Cook to inform him that the "*tooth just arrived safely. Looks very promising. Will report immediately.*" Osborn concluded that the tooth "*looks one hundred*" percent anthropoid and, after consultation with Dr Matthews concluded that it was "*the last right upper molar tooth of some higher Primate.*"[10]

The crown was "*worn down nearly to the base*", "*the cusps had entirely disappeared*", the roots were broken, and the tooth "*was badly cracked, battered and water-worn.*"[11] Despite its poor condition, Osborn used drawings and casts of other teeth to conclude that the tooth "*was the second right molar of a primate similar to apes and humans, yet distinct from any known species.*"[12] Osborn was so excited over the find that he made casts of the tooth and sent them to 26 institutions in Europe and the United States.[13]

Examinations were also made by other leading scientists, including an authority on dentition and evolution, American Museum of Natural History Scientist William Kane Gregory. Gregory and his colleague, Milo Hellman, concluded that the tooth differed from any known ape molar and resembled modern human teeth, leading to the ape-man speculation.[14,15,16,17,18]

Osborn named the genus *Hesperopithecus* (literally meaning "*ape of the land where the sun sets*") and the species *haroldcookii,* in honor of its discoverer, Harold Cook.[19] Osborn's naming method ultimately set the pattern for other claimed pre-human finds, the most well-known example being *Australopithecus africanus,* which

8. Osborn, H.F., *Hesperopithecus*, the first anthropoid primate found in America, *Science* **55**:463–465, 1922; p.463. Also in *Proceedings of the National Academy of Sciences* **8**(8):245–246, 1922; Also in *American Museum Novitates* 37:1–5, 25 April 1922.
9. Gould, S. J., *Bully for Brontosaurus*, W.W. Norton & Company, New York, p. 434, 1991.
10. Osborn, *Hesperopithecus*, the first anthropoid primate found in America, p. 464.
11. Gregory and Hellman, Notes on the type of *Hesperopithecus ...* , p. 2.
12. Blinderman, The curious case of Nebraska Man, p. 47.
13. Wolf, J. and Mellett, J.S., The role of 'Nebraska Man' in the creation-evolution debate, *Creation Evolution* **5**(2):31–43, 1985; p. 32.
14. Gregory, W.K. and Hellman, M., Further notes on the molars of *Hesperopithecus* and of *Pithecanthropus*, *Bulletin of the American Museum of Natural History* **48**:509–530, 1923.
15. Woodward, A.S., The earliest man? *London Times*, p. 17, May 22, 1922.
16. Smith, G.E., The oldest fossil man? *London Times*, p. 17, May 20, 1922.
17. Smith, G.E., The earliest man, *London Times,* p. 8, May 23, 1922.
18. Smith, G.E., *Hesperopithecus*: the ape-man of the Western world, *The Illustrated London News*, p. 944, June 24, 1922.
19. Osborn, *Hesperopithecus*, the first anthropoid primate found in America, p. 464.

means "*southern ape of Africa.*"[20] After extensive evaluation of the tooth, Gregory and Hellman concluded that the evidence was "*fairly conclusive*" that the tooth was from the "*Lower Pliocene*" and that there "*is no reasonable doubt as to its age.*"[21]

Renowned University of London Professor Grafton Elliot Smith, who was knighted in 1935 for his work, wrote that the tooth "*has been fully confirmed by the investigations of Professor Osborn and Drs Matthew and Gregory, who have an unrivalled experience of the scientific study of mammalian fossilized teeth*", to be a fossil closer to "*the anthropoid-human molar than that of any other mammal known.*"[22]

Smith concluded that "*the specimen was discovered by a geologist of wide experience ... and its identification ...* [was] *made by the most competent authorities on the specific characters of fossilized mammalian teeth.*"[23] Smith also concluded that Osborn, Matthew and Gregory "*have had a wider experience of such material than any other paleontologists*" then alive, and are "*men of exact knowledge and sound judgement.*"[24]

For several years after its discovery, *Hesperopithecus* was believed by some experts to be the oldest known humanoid fossil, both due to its morphology, and because it was found in an estimated 10-million-year-old Miocene fossil bed. Smith wrote in June 1922 that the fossil tooth was either a "*new genus of anthropoid apes or of an extremely primitive member of the human family.*"[25] Smith later wrote that it was part of a "*newly created genus.*"[26] When he received the tooth, Osborn concluded that it looked 100% "*anthropoid ape of America.*"

Gregory and Hellman also concluded that the anatomical, paleontological, and other evidence already accumulated shows that modern humans, "*Pithecanthropus, Hesperopithecus, and the various anthropoids form a natural superfamily group, which may now be named the Hominoidea, in contrast with the Cercopithecoidea, or Old World monkeys.*"[27] Cook argued that the tooth "*appeared to be a fossil human molar*" and "*repeated studies always brought us back to one point ... that the ... tooth must be related to ancestral anthropoid-humanoid stocks*" living over a million years ago.[28]

The tooth's "*very wide root on the inner side, which was similar to the wide root on the inner side of the upper molars of Pithecanthropus and of many teeth of American Indians*" was considered evidence that the tooth was from a creature linking humans with their putative primate ancestors.[29] Smith also concluded that the

---

20. Reader, J., *Missing Links*, Little Brown and Company, Boston, 1981.
21. Gregory and Hellman, Notes on the type of *Hesperopithecus*, p. 13.
22. Smith, *Hesperopithecus*, p. 944.
23. Smith, *Hesperopithecus*, p. 944.
24. Smith, *The Evolution of Man*, p. 7.
25. Smith, *Hesperopithecus*, p. 944.
26. Smith, *The Evolution of Man*, p. 6.
27. Gregory and Hellman, Notes on the type of *Hesperopithecus* ... , p. 14.
28. Cook, H.J., New trails of American man, *Scientific American* **137**(2):114–117, 1927; p. 115.
29. Gregory, W.K., *Hesperopithecus* apparently not an ape nor a man, *Science* **66**(1720):579–581, 1927; p. 580.

> probability is in favour of the view that the tooth found in the Pliocene beds of Nebraska is really that of a primitive member of the Human Family. *Hesperopithecus* is most nearly akin to *Pithecanthropus*; and the fact that the latter was found in what, at the end of the Pliocene Period, was the south-eastern corner of Asia, and the former in North America, which was connected with Eastern Asia by a land bridge enjoying a genial climate, minimizes the difficulty of explaining an identification that at first sight seems to be wholly incredible.[30]

While some scientists concluded that the upper molar resembled that of a man similar to that of an American Indian, others argued that it was a *Homo erectus* tooth similar to Java Man because the wear on its concave surface was "*strikingly similar to the worn-down surface of one of the upper molar teeth*" of primitive Java Man.[31] Disagreements on the interpretation of fossil evidence were not unusual then, and this was true of all of the other alleged ape-man links as well.

The meaning of the discovery

The tooth opened a whole new chapter in geological history that evolutionists hoped would "*throw light on the vexed question of the origin of man.*"[32] Nebraska Man also had great patriotic significance because it was "*the very first evidence after seventy-five years of continuous search in all parts of our great western territory, of a* [higher] *primate of any kind.*"[33] Osborn believed the tooth was evidence of the

> arrival of the anthropoid Primates in North America in Pliocene time. We have been eagerly anticipating some discovery of this kind, but were not prepared for such convincing evidence of the close faunal relationship between eastern Asia and western North America as is revealed by this diminutive specimen.[34]

Osborn was exuberant over the find, which he regarded as the first evidence for anthropoid apes in America and leaned "*toward human affinity, based both on the advice of his colleague, Gregory, and, no doubt, on personal hope and preference.*"[35] He added that his excitement might cool down tomorrow, but his excitement evidently did not cool down until it was exposed as a pig's tooth.[36] Smith College zoologist Harris Wilder concluded that

30. Smith, *The Evolution of Man*, pp. 7–8.
31. Gregory, *Hesperopithecus* apparently not an ape nor a man, p. 580.
32. Cattell, An American Anthropoid Primate, p. 588.
33. Osborn, *Hesperopithecus*, the anthropoid primate of western Nebraska, p. 281.
34. Osborn, *Hesperopithecus*, the first anthropoid primate found in America, p. 463.
35. Gould, *Bully for Brontosaurus*, p. 438.
36. Keith, *The Antiquity of Man*, p. 475.

> Judging from the tooth alone the animal seems to have been about halfway between *Pithecanthropus* and the man of the present day, or perhaps better between *Pithecanthropus* and the man of the Neandertal type, and is assumed to represent a very early migrant from the Old World, passing over land bridges, which then quite possibly existed. It thus revives again a hope, long since abandoned, that the human stem may have had its beginning in the New World.[37]

Grafton Elliot Smith cited the tooth in his textbook as a valid fossil ape-human link and concluded that it was from a primitive member of the human family.[38]

A now famous imaginative drawing of the reconstructed body of *Hesperopithecus haroldcookii* soon appeared in the *Illustrated London News* of June 24, 1922 (Figure 2 on page 195). The two-page spread of Nebraska Man, painted by Amedee Forestier, showed a nude, stooping, primitive-appearing male and female companion complete with a vivid prehistoric background of horses and camels. The text printed under the picture added that the head had "*large muscles from the occipital* [back of the head] *to the back and shoulders*" to counteract the "*weight of the prognathous* [jaws that extended forward] *head and heavy jaw—a simian character.*"[39] The text also admitted that the picture is speculative.

A colleague of Forestier wrote that "*Forestier was especially interested in prehistoric man and loved to bring him to life, not by fictitious imaginings but by the most careful reconstructions based on scientific research.*"[40] A fine tribute to his recently departed friend, though certainly over-generous, as even Osborn and his colleagues at the American Museum were not impressed with Forestier's handiwork and felt that "*such a drawing or 'reconstruction' would doubtless be only a figment of the imagination of no scientific value, and undoubtedly inaccurate.*"[41]

The level of confidence that Osborn had in his conclusion's validity was vividly revealed in his own words:

> The world-wide interest aroused by the discovery in Nebraska of *Hesperopithecus*, "*the ape of the western world*", is in widest possible contrast to the diminutive and insignificant appearance of the single grinding tooth of the right side of the upper jaw, which speaks of the presence of the higher or manlike apes in our western country at a time when the ancient "*Territory of Nebraska*" was in close touch with the animal civilization of Asia and of

37. Wilder, H.H., *The Pedigree of the Human Race*, Henry Holt and Company, New York, p. 157, 1926.
38. Smith, *The Evolution of Man*, pp. 7–9.
39. Forestier, A., The earliest man tracked by a tooth: an "astounding discovery" of human remains in Pliocene strata, *Illustrated London News*, pp. 942–943, June 24, 1922.
40. *The Times*, London, quoted in Gould, *Bully for Brontosaurus*, p. 32.
41. *The New York Times*, quoted in Gould, *Bully for Brontosaurus*, p. 31–32.

western Europe. This *Hesperopithecus* tooth is like the "*still small voice*"; it is by no means easy to hear its sound. Like the hieroglyphics of Egypt, it requires its Rosetta Stone to give the key to interpretation.[42]

Figure 2
The two-page illustration of Nebraska Man painted by Amedee Forestier that appeared in the *Illustrated London News*, pp. 942–943, 24 June 1922. Note the modern horses, camels and a rhinoceros in the background.

Osborn explained that this anthropological 'Rosetta Stone' was a "*comparison with all the similar grinding teeth known, collected from all parts of the world, and described or figured in learned books and illustrations.*"[43] Since evidence of an anthropoid had been found in America, the next question was to explain how it got there. Osborn hypothesized that *Hesperopithecus* had migrated across the Bering Strait land bridge, which he believed had existed during the Miocene Era 10–15 million years ago. Based on the fact that the tooth was discovered in the same stratum as several primitive horses, old world antelopes, hornless rhinos, and other animals dating back to the Miocene era, Osborn also theorized that *Hesperopithecus* must be as ancient as the prehistoric animals unearthed nearby. Osborn then concluded that "*this little tooth speaks volumes of truth*"

consistent with all we have known before, with all that we have found elsewhere. The evidence is strongly supported by many other and more complete fossil specimens that speak of a fresh tide of migration from the Old World

42. Osborn, H.F., The earth speaks to Bryan, *The Forum* **73**:796–803, 1925; p. 800.
43. Osborn, The earth speaks to Bryan, p. 800.

> to the New perhaps a million years ago … we shall not banish this bit of truth because it does not fit in with our preconceived notions and because at present it constitutes infinitesimal but irrefutable evidence that the man-apes wandered over from Asia into North America.[44]

So important was the fossil that it soon became known as the million-dollar tooth. Ironically, the tooth was severely damaged in an accident that occurred while it was being X-rayed:

> The tooth, which had been guarded like so much radium, was taken to a dental laboratory. Professor Gregory handed it to a laboratory assistant and said: "*Now be mighty careful. That tooth is worth a million dollars.*" The laboratory assistant began to tremble all over, the tooth slipped from his fingers, fell to the tiled floor and was shattered. There was boundless consternation for a time. The fragments were recovered and with the help of some cement the tooth was reconstructed and X-rayed. A great library of X-ray photographs of this and other teeth and studies of all kinds went eagerly ahead. It was found that the tooth, its crown being considerably worn, closely resembled a tooth of Pithecanthropus, the Java ape-man.[45]

Also, according to Professor Boule, it was at first speculated that the tooth belonged to a new "*family*" or even a "*superfamily*" of primates.[46]

Although, as noted, several of the most eminent American paleontologists supported the validity of the anthropoid conclusion, some disagreed, especially in Europe.[47] Boule claimed that European paleontologists, in general, greeted the find with "*great skepticism.*"[48] Nationalism, which was involved in most of these early human discoveries, was also very influential in motivating the British acceptance of Piltdown as a valid missing link.[49] Another problem was that Osborn had supported

---

44. Osborn, The earth speaks to Bryan, pp. 800–801.
45. Nebraska ape tooth proved a wild pig's, *New York Times*, 20 February 1928; p. 8.
46. Boule, M. and Vallois, H.V., *Fossil Men: A Textbook of Human Paleontology*, Dryden Press, New York, p. 87, 1957.
47. Boule, M., La Vraie Nature de l'*Hesperopithecus*, *L'Anthropologie* **38**:208–209, 1928.
48. Boule and Vallois, *Fossil Men*, p. 87.
49. Barkan, E. *The Retreat of Scientific Racism: Changing Concepts of Race in Britain and the United States between the World Wars*, Cambridge University Press, New York, pp. 42–43, 1992.

other fossils that turned out to be misidentified.[50,51,52] Regal recounts that one misidentification occurred in the early years of the twentieth century when

> Osborn had begun quietly to formulate an idea about an early human ancestor he would eventually call "*Dawn Man,*" that would cap his work on evolution. Since this creature was a hypothetical construction, he needed some tangible evidence to give it credence.[53]

An earlier Nebraska Man fiasco

In 1906, amateur fossil hunter Richard Gilder found a fossil with "*unusual characteristics*" near Omaha, Nebraska, the site of the later tooth find. When Osborn learned about the discovery, he "*immediately dropped everything and went to Nebraska to view the material firsthand.*"[54,55,56] Soon, Nebraska state geologist Edwin Barbour and University of Nebraska Professor Henry Ward published their conclusions, namely that this new "*Nebraska man*" was "*the earliest type of man known as yet in America.*"[57]

In another article, Barbour argued that the new Nebraska Man fossil was "'*low and savage,' but advanced enough to have religion and veneration of the dead.*"[58] Smithsonian anthropologist Dr Aleš Hrdlička then did a careful investigation, concluding the bones found were not only modern, but were not even fossilized. It was later determined the bones were of an American Indian![59,60] This earlier Nebraska Man fiasco should have been a warning to anthropologists and, at least for Hrdlička, it no doubt was.

50. Osborn, H.F., Discovery of a supposed primitive race of men in Nebraska, *Century Magazine*, pp. 371–375, January, 1907.
51. Osborn, H.F., Evolution and religion, *The New York Times*, section 7, pp. 2, 15, March 5, 1922.
52. Osborn, H.F., Osborn states the case for evolution, *The New York Times*, section 8, p. 1, July 12, 1925.
53. Regal, B., *Henry Fairfield Osborn: Race, and the Search for the Origins of Man*, Ashgate, Burlington, Vermont, p. 93, 2002.
54. Regal, *Henry Fairfield Osborn*, p. 93.
55. Gilder, R., A primitive human type in Nebraska, *Putnam's Monthly*, pp. 407–415, 502–503, January 1907.
56. Ward, H., Peculiarities of the 'Nebraska man', *Putnam's Monthly*, pp. 410–413, January 1907.
57. Barbour, E.H. and Ward, H.B., Preliminary report on the primitive man of Nebraska, *Nebraska Geological Survey*, pp. 319–327, December 22, 1906.
58. Quoted in Regal, *Henry Fairfield Osborn*, p. 95.
59. Regal, *Henry Fairfield Osborn*, p. 95.
60. Hrdlička, A., *Skeletal Remains Suggesting or Attributed to Early Man in North America*, Government Printing Office, Washington, pp. 69–74, 1907.

Opposition to the humanoid interpretation by evolutionists

After evaluating the Nebraska Man tooth, eminent paleontologist Sir Arthur Keith concluded that its wear and crown pattern was not that of a primate, and argued strongly against its being one.[61] To support his conclusion, Keith cited authorities who argued that the tooth was from an animal group that included a bear, and a Professor Schlosser who concluded the tooth was from an extinct horse.[62] MacCurdy relegated the find to a footnote, noting only that the "*teeth are not well preserved, so that the validity of Osborn's determination has not been generally accepted.*"[63]

Other anthropologists, such as the Curator of Geology at the British Museum, Arthur Smith Woodward, pointed out several significant problems with the primate interpretation. Woodward went so far as to conclude that it would be "*difficult for one who has not seen the tooth to understand why Prof. Osborn*" concluded it was a primate:

> The crown may be described as nearly triangular in shape, with bluntly rounded angles, a slightly raised and partially crimped rim surrounding a gently concave surface. The root is very massive, and at a considerable distance below the crown it becomes bifid, the smaller portion extended beneath one margin of the crown, the larger portion beneath and inclined towards the opposite apex.[64]

One major problem Woodward had with the tooth was the irregular indentation between the bifurcation and the crown

> from which Prof. Osborn supposes a third root-fang has been broken away. No stump of this third fang, however, is shown in the drawing. In determining the tooth to be an upper molar, Prof. Osborn regards the edge with the smaller portion of root as external, and the tapering opposite end with the larger portion of root as internal. The hypothetically restored piece of root thus becomes posterior. It is, however, equally reasonable to interpret the so-called external border as anterior and the tapering end as posterior. If, then, the indented lateral portion of the root never bore another fang, the tooth becomes a lower molar.[65]

---

61. Keith, *The Antiquity of Man*, p. 476.
62. Keith, *The Antiquity of Man*, p. 476.
63. MacCurdy, G.G., *Human Origins: A Manual of Prehistory*, D. Appleton, New York, p. 311, 1924.
64. Woodward, A.S., A supposed ancestral man in North America, *Nature* **109**(2745):750, 1922.
65. Woodward, A supposed ancestral man in North America.

Woodward concluded that the general "*appearance and shape of the crown is very suggestive of that of the last molar in the lower jaw of some species ascribed to Hyaenarctos and related genera*" and that there is "*reason to suspect*" that *Hesperopithecus* has "*received an inappropriate name.*"[66] Osborn, though, was adamant, and argued that Woodward's criticism reflected "*too great incredulity*"[67] because in the entire "*history of anthropology no tooth has ever been subjected to such severe cross-examination as this now world famous Hesperopithecus tooth. Every suggestion made by scientific skeptics was weighed and found wanting.*"[68,69]

Gregory and Hellman, who also studied the tooth extensively, concluded that the identification of *Hesperopithecus* as some type of anthropoid ape or human was valid. They felt all other possible identifications had been scientifically shown to be false, including the following:

1. Lower molar of *Hyaenarctos* or allied genus of ursid.
2. A bear's tooth.
3. A molar of an otherwise wholly unknown type of carnivore.
4. An upper or lower molar of a carnivore allied with *Aeloropus.*
5. An upper molar of a gigantic relative of the procyonid carnivore *Potos.*
6. An upper molar of a gigantic relative of South American monkeys such as *Pithecia* and *Lagothrix.*
7. The first upper deciduous premolar of a Pliocene horse.
8. An incus bone of a gigantic mammal.

In the words of Gregory and Hellman, "*We have considered each of these with unbiased minds and compared the type with the various specimens suggested, as well as with many others, but have returned with more confidence to the conclusions set forth above*"—namely that the tooth is some type of anthropoid ape or human.[70]

The method they used to arrive at their conclusion was detailed by Gregory.[71] After noting that the crown had extreme natural wear, he compared the chief characteristics that the *Hesperopithecus* tooth shared with those of man and anthropoid creatures. He was then able to utilize measurements of similar data from chimpanzee and American Indian molars, concluding that the "*Hesperopithecus type on the whole came nearest to the second upper molar of a chimpanzee.*"[72]

66. Woodward, A supposed ancestral man in North America.
67. Osborn, *Hesperopithecus,* the anthropoid primate of western Nebraska, p. 281
68. Osborn, H.F., *Hesperopithecus,* Bulletin of the American Museum of Natural History, February 1925.
69. Quoted in Reader, *Missing Links,* p. 110.
70. Gregory and Hellman, Further notes on the molars … , p. 526.
71. Gregory, *Hesperopithecus* apparently not an ape nor a man.
72. Gregory, *Hesperopithecus* apparently not an ape nor a man.

Of course, as Osborn pointed out,[73] measuring a hard structure such as a tooth, and determining that it physically falls between a chimpanzee and an American Indian, does not prove that the creature from which the tooth came was likewise structurally between these two creatures. Many structures and physiological processes are 'in between' two animals, but the animal of which they are a part may be either much 'higher' or much 'lower' on the 'evolutionary ladder' than either of the animals to which they are being compared.

Osborn and other Nebraska Man supporters decided to silence their critics once and for all by digging up additional evidence. In 1925, they located several objects that they concluded were likely the ancient tools used by Nebraska Man. Two years later, more such objects were found, many that caused them to question earlier claims that the 'tools' were human artifacts. American Museum of Natural History staffer Albert Thomson collected samples from the Snake Creek beds in the summer of 1925, and in 1926 another anthropologist collected many new specimens. All of these finds began to cause an increasing number of anthropologists to doubt the identification of *Hesperopithecus* as an upper molar of an extinct primate.[74]

New teeth discovered

Soon numerous new teeth were uncovered in the same location where the first tooth was found that were morphologically almost identical to the *Hesperopithecus* tooth, except they were in much better condition. For example, the 1927 excavations located several new upper and lower premolar and molar teeth, each of which appeared to belong to *Prosthennops serus*, a peccary or New World pig. Peccaries are members of the *Tayassuidae* family, a new world type of *Suidae.*[75] These findings enabled a more accurate identification.

Gregory eventually was forced to concede that *Hesperopithecus* was not a primate or ape-man, but rather "*an upper premolar of a species of Prosthennops, an extinct genus related to the modern peccaries.*"[76] This conclusion was based primarily on the lower teeth, which the evidence indicated were associated with the upper premolars that previously were determined to be *Hesperopithecus* teeth, yet were "*unquestionably the same or nearly the same as the corresponding lower teeth of Prosthennops.*"[77]

The almost universal conclusion eventually was that the tooth was an upper premolar of a *Prosthennops*. In 1972, Ralph Wetzel discovered a herd of these animals that were very similar to the extinct peccary that had been found in Nebraska by Harold Cook. These animals were *Catagonus wagneri,* a species endemic to South

73. Osborn, Evolution and religion.
74. Reader, *Missing Links*, p. 110.
75. Woodburne, M.O., Systematics, biogeography, and evolution of *Cynorca* and *Dyseohyus* (Tayassuidae), *Bulletin of the American Museum of Natural History* **141**(2):271–356, 1969.
76. Gregory, *Hesperopithecus* apparently not an ape nor a man, p. 580.
77. Gregory, *Hesperopithecus* apparently not an ape nor a man, p. 581.

America.[78,79] The animals were consigned to the species *Catagonus ameghino*, a name first published in 1904.

Although a 1927 *Science* article served as the formal obituary for 'Nebraska Man',[80,81,82] *Hesperopithecus* was cited in textbooks as valid until at least 1945. That year, in a book about British prehistory and the evidence for human evolution, Professor Samuel Edward Winbolt stated that a

> million and a half years ago in Pliocene times came the Bechuanaland man-ape; while later (and higher) branches are represented by the Nebraska man-ape (*Hesperopithecus*) and the Java ape-man (*Pithecanthropus*, 1892–4), perhaps the earliest known human being [spelling corrected—Ed.].[83]

In the revised 1927 edition of his text, Smith added a pasted-in correction that noted new discoveries afford "*no corroboration for any of the three suggestions*" he had made as to the identity of *Hesperopithecus*. Thus, he concludes, it is now "*imperative to omit Hesperopithecus from the discussion of man's ancestry.*" This case, along with Piltdown Man, are excellent examples of the influence of preconceived ideas on scientific conclusions, especially if the evidence is scanty.

The infamous tooth that Bowden calls "*a classic case of excessive imagination*" has now largely been forgotten except by historians of science.[84] It is safely locked in an American Museum of Natural History storage vault. John Reader summarized several contemporary comments about this event:

> "*An ancient and honorable pig no doubt, a pig with a distinguished Greek name,*" commented *The Times* in a leader when the news was released, "*but indubitably porcine.*" *The Times* wondered whether the worshippers who had so eagerly proclaimed themselves made in the image of *Hesperopithecus* were now left desolate; … . Paleontologists had been badly bitten by the Nebraska tooth.[85]

---

78. Wetzel, R., Robert, M., Martin, L. and Myers, P., *Catagonus*, an extinct peccary, alive in Paraguay, *Science* **189**(4200):379–381, 1975; p. 379.
79. Wetzel, R., The extinction of peccaries and a new case of survival, *Annals of the New York Academy of Sciences* **288**:538–544, 1977.
80. Gregory, *Hesperopithecus* apparently not an ape nor a man.
81. Williams, M., Ape tooth proved a wild pig's, *Catholic World* **127**: 306–311, 1928. (With footnote to *The Times*.)
82. Woodward, A.S., *Hesperopithecus* dethroned, only a wild pig, *The London Times*, p. 16, February 21, 1928.
83. Winbolt, S., *Britain B.C.*, Penguin Books, New York, pp. 14–16, 1945.
84. Bowden, M., *Ape-men: Fact or Fallacy?* 2nd Edition, Sovereign Publications, Bromley, Kent, UK, p. 58, 1977.
85. Reader, *Missing Links*, p. 110.

Figure 3
A peccary, also called a javelina or skunk pig, was determined to be the source of the tooth.
Source: Fir0002/Flagstaffotos.

The *London Times* also noted that the zeal for the discovery of our evolutionary ancestors

> has been carried to its highest pitch by that newcomer to the aristocracy of science, the anthropologist. … One of the most notable examples of his skill was given to the world … when a single tooth, which had been dug up in Nebraska, was identified as that of the founder of the family of Man. … From the one surviving molar science drew a complete portrait of the patriarch. He proved to be powerfully built; of homely countenance; a little heavy in the jowl, and not very wide of brow; and … was "*marvelous hairy about the face.*" … What more auspicious beginning for the human family than the union of his daughter and heiress with the *novus homo*, Eoanthropus?[86]

The *London Times* noted that a few daring people contended that a single tooth "*was not quite sufficient evidence*" to obtain the information needed to construct Nebraska Man, but the skeptics were overruled and

86. Anonymous, *Hesperopithecus, The Times* (London), p. 13, February 25, 1928.

> the creative imagination of the artist must be allowed to overlap gulfs that seemed impassable to more pedestrian minds. Let them have faith in comparative morphology, accept their inheritance, recant their heresies, and be reconciled to the communion of the orthodox. And so all might have been well for them and for comparative morphology, if it had not occurred to one of the devotees that *Hesperopithecus* must have possessed other teeth. Accordingly he set out to find them, not being impelled by lack of faith, but moved rather by the pious desire to obtain further hagiological relics.[87]

Williams discussed what he believed may be the significance, for both society generally and religion specifically, of dethroning *Hesperopithecus.* Writing as if he were looking back at the 1928 events a few hundred years later, Williams stated that, in its proper sense, science was a

> disinterested search after demonstrable Facts in all the fields of human thought … [but] became idolized and was set up as a Religion; a popular religion; supposedly one that was the rival and drastic opposite in all respects of the supernatural religion of Christianity. Long before the year 1928 by far the greater part of the Press was devoted to its service. "*Evolution*" was the great shibboleth of this vast popular religion, the end of which was dogmatically asserted.[88]

Noting that the 'descent' of humans from monkeys was a popular test of orthodoxy, Williams concludes that the sole preoccupation of the "*popular science religion*", and

> its fundamental doctrine, was simply that there was (however it happened to be) something called "*matter,*" which was simple in the beginning ("*protoplasm*" was its popular name); which then became somehow or other differentiated; passing into "*higher*" and still "*higher*" forms, till at last the monkey tribe appeared, out of which came man.

Williams added that the "*enormous*" effort by the American Museum of Natural History to establish the tooth as that of an ape-man

> should be studied in their relations to the popular religions of 1928. No newspaper in the world, it may be added, had done more for the spread of the religion of Science than *The Times* … on that historic Monday, February 20, 1928, was simply an isolated bubble of the great wave of mirth which finally did away with so many of the humbugs of an age which so proudly loved to call itself enlightened, but which now appears so pathetically mistaken.[89]

87. *Hesperopithecus, The Times* (London), 1928.
88. Williams, Ape tooth proved a wild pig's, p. 310.
89. Williams, Ape tooth proved a wild pig's, pp. 310–311.

A major concern is, "*How could a worker as careful and methodical as Osborn have made such an egregious error?*"[90] One reason given is "*misidentifications and misallocations of fossil specimens are quite common in the paleontological literature*" but, fortunately, the work of science is

> subject to examination by others in the field and corrections are made in print, usually without fanfare. Some of the misidentifications are extreme: a fossil whale first identified as a giant reptile, rodents misidentified as primates, carnivores as ungulates, ungulates as anteaters. The list is endless, but the public nature of science leads to quick corrections, particularly when the biological group in question is under intense study by a number of competing workers.[91]

Wolf and Mellett's faith in science's self-correcting ability is maybe optimistic, and the 'quick' correction can at times take years, or even decades. Nonetheless, most scientists have faith that truth will prevail in the long run.

The meaning of *Hesperopithecus* today

This case was not a rare aberration but a pattern in the history of paleoanthropology.[92,93] Sir Solly Zuckerman, a leading British scientist, complained a half century ago that there is a tendency for a discoverer of a new primate fossil to attempt to present the find as the major ancestral link between the animals and man and it is "*unlikely that they could all enjoy this distinction.*"[94]

Smith opined that the history of "*the false claims made by over-enthusiastic searchers in different parts of the world*" is both "*interesting and entertaining.*"[95] An example Smith cites is the tooth "*from Nebraska* [that] *gave America the right to claim … (Hesperopithecus) as the earliest known member of the Human Family.*"

These false claims are tragic because they misled science, and wasted enormous amounts of time, energy, and money. The concern over irresponsible conclusions as a result of the *Hesperopithecus* and other debacles existed as early as 1929. Jones concluded that "*almost every new discovery of early Primate remains becomes, for popular*

90. Wolf and Mellett, The role of 'Nebraska Man' … , p. 34.
91. Wolf and Mellett, The role of 'Nebraska Man' … , p. 34.
92. Judson, H.F., *The Great Betrayal: Fraud in Science*, Harcourt, New York, pp. 82–83, 2004.
93. Morell, V., *Ancestral Passions: The Leakey Family and the Quest for Humankind's Beginnings*, Simon and Schuster, New York, 1995.
94. Zuckerman, S., Correlation of change in the evolution of higher primates, in *Evolution as a Process*, Huxley, J., *et al.*, (Eds.), Allen and Unwin, London, p. 301, 1958.
95. Smith, G.E., *et al.*, The Evolution of Man, in *Early Man; His Origin, Development and Culture*, Ernest Benn, London, pp. 20, 1931.

writers, a missing link"—and, after discussing the *Hesperopithecus* case in detail, he added that the same is true for scientific writers.[96] Zuckerman noted that reconstructing the whole animal based on fragments "*has unfortunately too often proved fallacious, as the fate of Hesperopithicus … shows.*"[97]

Identifying a pig's tooth as a higher primate was not the major issue in this case because both pig and peccary cheek teeth are very similar to human teeth. Identification was made more difficult because the specimen was in poor condition, and only when more teeth were found was the error corrected. These facts illustrate the major issue—that difficulties exist in arriving at conclusions in paleoanthropology because very different animals can have many similarities in structures and bone, and fossil teeth are often in poor condition, requiring extreme caution in interpreting evidence.

Many examples of this problem exist in the long history of attempts to document human evolution. This history vividly illustrates Gould's conclusion that, in science, "*no myth deserves a more emphatic death than the idea that science is an inherently impartial and objective enterprise; objectivity has, after all, been battered by everything from Thomas Kuhn to Watergate.*" Gould concluded that the objectivity myth

> continues to thrive among working scientists because it serves us so well. It works within our profession by inspiring our students and sustaining us through inevitable periods of self-doubt; more crucially, it is the hallmark of our effort in public relations—a self-serving statement that enhances the social prestige and political clout of scientists. It also provides the rationale for America's scientific priesthood: the National Academy of Sciences.[98]

Although a leading paleontologist and head of one of the greatest museums in the world, the American Museum of Natural History in New York, Osborn "*promoted … his own beliefs on evolution and human origins with provocative, although scientifically spurious, museum displays.*" He "*tailored the palaeontological evidence to fit these views and values in his voluminous writings and the enormous museum exhibitions and dioramas.*" He was also known as "*an arrogant, bigoted tyrant.*"[99,100,101]

As French paleoanthropologist Marcellin Boule concluded, the Nebraska Man case illustrates the overly vivid imagination of some paleontologists as proven when

96. Jones, F.W., *Man's Place Among the Mammals*, Longmans, Green & Co., New York, pp. 63–67, 1929.
97. Zuckerman, Correlation of change in the evolution of higher primates, p. 314.
98. Gould, S.J., The other scientific method (a review of P. Boffey, *The Brain Bank of America: An inquiry into the politics of science*), *New York Times*, 4 May 1975.
99. Krishtalka, L., Imperious innovator, *Nature* **355**(6359):405–406, 1992; p. 405.
100. See also Osborn, H.F., *Evolution and Religion*, Charles Scribner's Sons, New York, 1923.
101. See also Osborn, H.F., Upper Eocene and Lower Oligocene Titanotheres of Mongolia, *American Museum Novitates* **202**:1–12, 24 November 1925.

the "*Nebraska Ape-Man became a Pig-Man!*"[102] Only when these examples are more widely known can they serve to encourage more careful and objective analyses in science.

102. Boule and Vallois, *Fossil Men*, p. 87; see also Boyle, M.E., *In Search of Our Ancestors: An Attempt to Retrace Man's Origin and Development from Later Ages Back to Their Beginnings*, Little, Brown, and Company, Boston, p. 241, 1928. Nebraska Man was called a very doubtful remain of an ape.

CHAPTER 13

The ape-to-human evolutionary progression: The most common evolution icon is a fraud

Introduction

By far the most famous icon of evolution—seen everywhere from book covers to magazine articles to cartoons—is a drawing showing human body evolution from a primitive, stooping ape-like creature progressing to a modern human. The progression is usually pictured in four to six steps, but as many as 30 are sometimes shown. A review of this, the most published modern pictorial icon of evolution, found that it is largely fraudulent, based on known inaccuracies and false information. It was also determined that this evolutionary icon has racist roots and is an extension of the once common comparisons of ape, Negroid, and Caucasian caricatures found widely in both scientific publications and popular literature.

Darwin proposed that an unbroken evolutionary chain of life stretched from simple molecules (such as ammonia, water, and phosphoric salts) to humans.[1]

The chain analogy gave birth to the idea of missing links in the chain, an analogy still used today to describe the fact that, instead of a chain, what the fossil record shows is many life-form groups with large gaps in the alleged chain between them.[2]

Nonetheless, the so-called 'great chain of evolutionary progress', or 'ladder of evolution' is still presented as fact and Darwinists believe that, given enough time, more fossil discoveries are all that is needed to fill in the many missing links they believe exist. Consequently, every now and then, a 'missing link' discovery is claimed by evolutionists.[3]

The progression chain history

One of the earliest examples of an illustration of the progression was completed by Brooklyn College paleontologist Dr Eric Schlaikjer (see Figure 1 on page 208). His rendition shows 30 links going from fish to amphibians, reptiles, mammals, primates, and, at the top of the evolutionary progression, modern humans.[4]

---

1. Meyer, S., *Signature in the Cell*, Harper One, New York, 2009.
2. Tudge, C. and Young, J., *The Link*, Little Brown, New York, 2009.
3. Tudge and Young, *The Link*.
4. Schlaikjer, E., Scientific theory of evolution traced, *The Star Weekly*, Toronto, magazine section p. 6, February 4, 1939.

Figure 1
An early example of the evolutionary progression by Brooklyn College paleontologist Eric Schlaikjer (from Schlaikjer, Scientific theory of evolution traced).

Note that the progression starts with a vertebrate, a finless fish and that the fish in image 3 has a dorsal fin that disappears in image 4. In image 20 life crawls up into trees and becomes arboreal. Then, in image 25, primates leave the arboreal life and become terrestrial. The evolution of humans shows a monkey in image 26, a stereotypical caveman in image 27 and a modern man in image 28. Unless examined carefully, such illustrations appear to show clear proof of molecules-to-man, or at least fish-to-man evolution. These progression illustrations are very convincing to the uninformed public.

The scenario pictured is very different from that proposed today, but does include some animals still touted as evolutionary links, such as *Seymouria*. The chart depicts the primate common ancestor of humans as a modern ape, and the first human looks very much like a modern man except that he is pictured with an Einstein-like hairstyle and slight Neandertal facial traits. A clear gap is shown to exist between apes and humans. Also, one could line up living animals and produce a progression very close to the one pictured by Dr Schlaikjer. Dumanoski noted that "*the notion of evolution, though in a version quite at odds with*" the modern story,

> served to lend "*scientific*" support to the modern pursuit of progress … In this spirit of progressive evolution, a classic illustration during my school

> days tracing the ascent of humans showed a series of two-legged apes—each less hairy, more upright, and taller than the preceding—that culminates with a modern man striding confidently forward. From the time our remote ancestors stood up on two feet, it suggested, they embarked on an uninterrupted journey of continuous improvement, onward and upward … This march of progress, inevitable and unstoppable, somehow embodied the laws of nature and led inexorably, as one of Spencer's disciples put it, "*from gas to genius.*"[5]

The modern ape-to-human progression

The progression, called the 'ascent of man' in its most recent reincarnation, was first illustrated in *Early Man*, part of Time-Life Books' popular *Nature Library* series and written by University of California, Berkeley, Professor F. Clark Howell (see Figure 2 on page 210). The progression was printed in a 36-inch foldout on pages 41 to 45 in the 1965 edition and reprinted in both the 1968 and 1973 editions. The original chart included 15 pictures that traced human evolution from *Pliopithecus* to *Ramapithecus* to *Homo erectus,* all the way to Cro-Magnon and ending with *Homo sapiens.*

The ascent-of-man series resembles a baby first learning to walk, from crawling to fully upright walking. Lubenow concludes that the human evolution progression

> has been one of the most successful tools ever used to promote human evolution. It constituted powerful visual 'proof' for human evolution that even a small child could grasp. It was a masterpiece of Madison Avenue promotion.[6]

The 'ascent of man' has been prominently displayed in popular books on evolution, biology textbooks, social science classes, and on school bulletin boards for decades. Because of its graphic power, the progression has been "*indelibly etched into the minds of billions of people worldwide.*"[7]

Ironically, the progression was known to be fake when it was first published—the first book that widely circulated it, after noting that only "*fragmentary fossil evidence*" exists for human evolution, openly admitted that the progression was drawn from largely manufactured or distorted evidence. In the author's words: "*Many of the figures shown here have been built up*" from a few fragments, "*a jaw, some teeth … thus are products of educated guessing.*"[8]

---

5. Dumanoski, D., *The End of the Long Summer: Why We Must Remake our Civilization to Survive on a Volatile Earth*, Crown Publishers, New York, p. 98, 2009.
6. Lubenow, M., *Bones of Contention (Revised and Updated): A Creationist Assessment of Human Fossils*, Baker Books, Grand Rapids, Michigan, p. 39, 2004.
7. Lubenow, *Bones of Contention*, p. 39.
8. Howell, F.C. *Early Man*, Time Life Books, New York, p. 41, 1970.

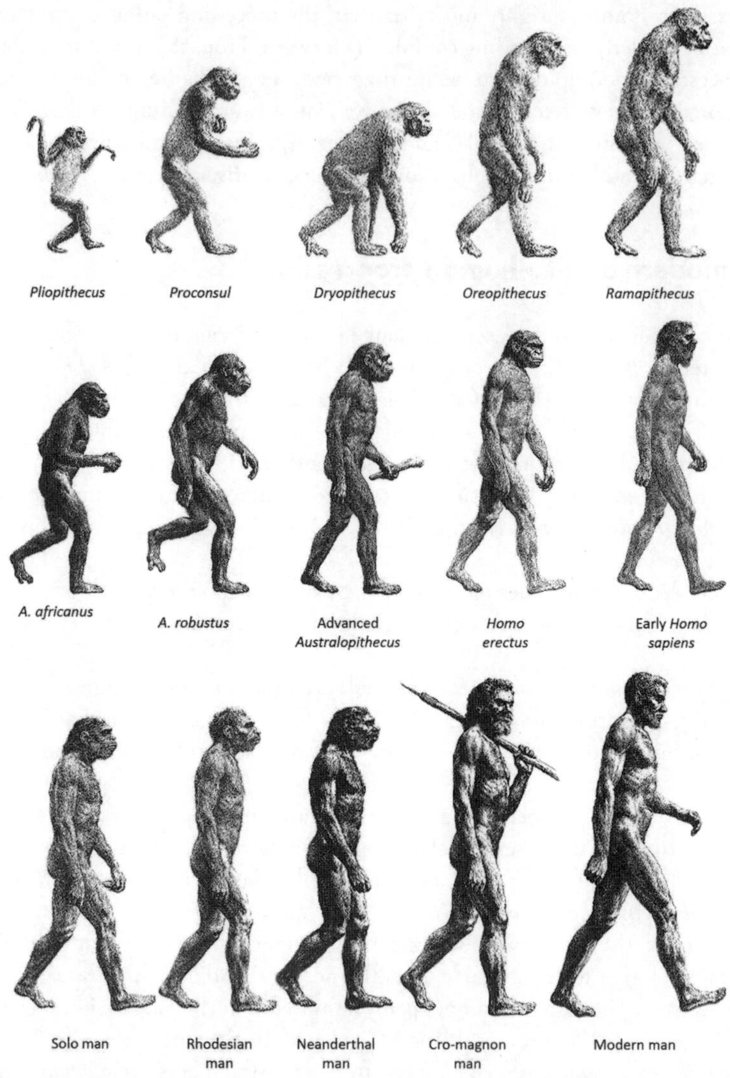

Figure 2
Illustrations from the Time-Life book titled Howell, F.C. *Early Man*, Time Life Books, New York, p. 41, 1970.
Note that from *A. africanus* on the main change, aside from the posture, is the head.

The author added that "*even if later finds should dictate changes*" in the drawing—i.e. even if the drawings are wrong—"*these reconstructions serve a purpose in showing how these creatures might have looked*" (the term *might* is in the original). The progression is also very misleading, even according to orthodox Darwinism, because it implies a single evolutionary line to humans—in contrast to the dominant evolutionary view, which is that human evolution is actually a branching bush.

Below each of the 15 illustrations was a discussion of each picture—information that is rarely added today when the progression is used. Usually the progression starts with an illustration that looks like *Dryopithecus*, adding *A. robustus, Homo erectus*, Neandertal Man, Cro-Magnon Man, and modern man, *Homo sapiens*. Neandertals, even in 1970, were no longer considered part of the *Homo sapiens* evolutionary lineage, but another human race. Both modern humans and Neandertals today are assumed to have evolved from *Homo erectus*.[9] Lubenow stresses that it is "*not that more recent fossil discoveries have revealed that the progression was inaccurate. No, the truth is far worse.*"[10]

A few of the "*far worse*" examples include the fact that the proto-apes pictured were known not to be bipedal, yet are shown in the illustrations as being expertly bipedal. The bipedal apes shown in the evolutionary progression are thought to have lived long before evolutionists believe bipedalism had evolved.[11] The text openly acknowledges this fact, admitting "*although proto-apes and apes were quadrupedal, all are shown here* standing *for purposes of comparison*" [emphasis on the word 'standing' in original].[12]

This admission is actually only partly accurate. Some of the creatures shown in the parade were *physically unable* to stand erect. Furthermore, although the text describes them as "*standing*" they were drawn *walking*. Some of them have one foot in the air, balancing on the other foot as they stride across the page. This confers to them a far more human-like appearance than if they were merely standing. Accurate comparisons require showing their actual normal quadrupedal 'knuckle-walking' gait.

Another problem is the greatly distorted size of the illustrations, showing the *first* link in the progression as a very small animal. With only two exceptions, *Dryopithecus* and 'Solo man', each link in the progression is drawn larger, taller, and progressively standing up straighter. The figures shown become taller as we move towards modern man, not due to fossil or other empirical evidence, but rather as a result of artistic licence that allows the artist to distort the picture to conform to evolutionary theory. They also become progressively *less hairy and lighter in skin colour,* which is also clearly a result of artistic licence. Except for modern humans, no evidence exists allowing anthropologists to determine the amount of body hair for most, if not all, of the fossils. They were given both flesh and hair by the artist.

Furthermore, Howell openly admitted that the first link, *Pliopithecus,* was not even considered to be an evolutionary link to humans in 1965 when the book was first published, but rather was "*classed as an ancestor of the Gibbon line.*"[13] The

9. Hitchcock, L., *The Truth About History*, Barnes & Noble, New York, p. 11, 2007.
10. Lubenow, *Bones of Contention*, p. 39.
11. Lubenow, *Bones of Contention*, p. 40.
12. Lubenow, *Bones of Contention*, p. 40.
13. Howell, *Early Man*, p. 41.

second step, *Proconsul*, even though it is drawn to look more like a modern human, has a picture caption that admits "*proconsul is considered to be a very early ape, the ancestor of the chimpanzee and perhaps of the gorilla.*"[14]

For *Dryopithecus*, Howell admits that the entire animal, although also appearing very human-like but stooped, is known only from "*a few jaws and teeth.*"[15]

The text notes that the fourth step, *Oreopithecus*, is a "*likely side branch* [emphasis added] *on man's family tree*" and not a human evolutionary ancestor.[16]

The text also notes that the next picture, *Ramapithecus*, is "*now thought by some experts to be the oldest of man's ancestors in a direct line.*"[17] Consequently, to conform to the then-orthodox view of evolution, the progression should have begun with *Ramapithecus*, not *Pliopithecus*.

The only evidence given for 'Solo man' is two shin bones and some skull fragments[18] and the text even notes that *A. robustus* "*represents an evolutionary dead end in man's ancestry.*"[19] Of all the inappropriate statements in this illustration, that one is surely the most nonsensical.[20]

Also of note is the fact that from *A. africanus* to modern man, all of the bodies look remarkably similar. Only the heads, most of which are clearly out of place on the bodies, are very different—more apelike as we move backward in time away from modern humans.

Although the text does openly point out many other inaccuracies in the drawings, Lubenow comments that perhaps less than 5% of those who owned this Time-Life book actually read it in its entirety. Conversely, many casual readers have seen the progression, even if they just glanced at the book's illustrations. As a result, the visual image effectively has "*sold the concept of human evolution even though the book revealed that the parade was fictitious.*"[21]

The *National Geographic* progression

The parade achieved even more widespread publicity in a *National Geographic* magazine special dated November 1985.[22] Pages 574 to 577 show the now-familiar progression in a seemingly realistic set of well-made drawings. In several ways, though, this illustration is even less accurate.

14. Howell *Early Man*, p. 41.
15. Howell *Early Man*, p. 42.
16. Howell *Early Man*, p. 42.
17. Howell *Early Man*, p. 42.
18. Howell *Early Man*, p. 44.
19. Howell *Early Man*, p. 43.
20. Substantial rewording in the 1976 edition of this book has resolved some of the more misinformed phrasing, supporting several of my original objections, but the claims it makes in the newer edition stand on evidence no less spurious.
21. Lubenow, *Bones of Contention*, p. 39.
22. Weaver, K., The search for our ancestors, *National Geographic* **168**(5):560–623, 1985.

Beginning with *A. afarensis,* the figures are not walking as they were in the Time-Life book, but are all shown as expert runners, progressively running faster and with more grace, arms swinging as the figures progress towards modern humans. The bodies drawn are all very human, only the heads differ significantly. The first heads in the progression are very apelike; the later heads look very Negroid; and the last head and body is that of a handsome, tanned Caucasian.

Figure 3
The Illustrations from the November 1985 *National Geographic* magazine. Note that from *A. afarensis* to modern man, the bodies are almost identical except that modern man is slightly less hairy. The heads, though, have changed greatly.

The major body differences are the arms, which are comparatively shorter, and the body that is progressively less hairy as it moves forward towards modern humans. The descriptions give no hint of the controversy about the fossils that the illustrations are designed to depict. The text does admit that the artist "*speculated on skin tone and the amount of body hair and its texture*" and that the relationship of the fossils pictured is "*still not fully understood.*"[23]

False implications of the evolutionary progression drawings

The parade implies that evolution from our putative ape-like ancestor that looks much like the chimp, *Pliopithecus,* to modern humans was very straightforward, showing hereditary changes progressively moving forward along a single line from ape-like ancestors to modern humans. As shown graphically by Burenhult,[24] even if the ape-to-human evolution were true, and a progression of some type actually occurred, so much controversy exists about it that a single diagram is grossly misleading.

Burenhult's drawing shows four different models, including those developed by some of the most prominent modern paleontologists, including Donald Johanson, Tim White, Richard Leakey, Colin Groves, and Bernard Wood. Each of these four

23. Weaver, The search for our ancestors, p. 574.
24. Burenhult, G., *People of the Past,* Fog City Press, San Francisco, pp. 50–51, 2003.

family trees is drastically different and, in contrast to the visual parade illustration, shows several offshoots or side branches.

An important fact is that no evidence exists that *any* creature has existed in the past that normally walked bent over, as the progression illustrates and as many other pictures of our putative evolutionary ancestors show.[25] When apes walk on all fours, they 'knuckle walk' and only appear to be bent over. For this reason, it was assumed that, as apes' common ancestor evolved into humans, the stoop slowly became less as we evolved. However, no evidence exists of a creature "*hovering between a two-legged and a four-legged stance*" as the progression shows.[26]

The notion of a 'stooped over' hominid shows ignorance of basic engineering principles. Such a posture places tremendous loads on the lower spine and is sure to rapidly lead to severe back pain and injury. Natural selection would strongly reject such a painful, inefficient posture shown by the creatures evolving slowly from four-footed locomotion into a stooped locomotion!

The more complete progression

A common version of the evolutionary progression is to show the first step involving a fish in water, then a fish crawling out with small legs evolving into a four-legged animal, and lastly, a set of primates similar to the old parade leading to humans. In recent years the parade itself has evolved due to recent fossil finds, more detailed study of the fossil record, and extensive DNA analysis. The radical 'new view' refuting the parade is now being presented in some mass media publications. A *Newsweek* article pictured the parade as the "*old view*" and, next to it, showed the "*new view,*" a complex bush that is very different from the now-famous progression.[27]

Other authors are more blunt, concluding that the "*gradual progression from crouching to standing as shown in the series … is almost certainly wrong,*" even from an evolutionary standpoint.[28] One reason Hitchcock gives for this assessment is that it is now believed that early humans "*were able to walk upright a lot earlier than was thought when the first 'ascent of man' illustrations were published. In fact, like chimpanzees today, our ape ancestors could walk upright on two legs whenever it suited them.*"[29] Hitchcock recommends for this reason that "*it would be best to scrap the* [classic progression] *illustration altogether.*"[30]

---

25. Hitchcock, *The Truth About History*, p. 11.
26. Hitchcock, *The Truth About History*, p. 11.
27. Begley, S., Beyond Stones & Bones, *Newsweek* **149**(12):52–58, 19 March 2007; p. 56.
28. Hitchcock, *The Truth About History*, p. 11.
29. Hitchcock, *The Truth About History*, p. 11.
30. Hitchcock, *The Truth About History*, p.13.

The racist history of the progression

Some version of the progression idea has been a common theme in evolutionary literature since about 1870, usually with obvious racial implications. Often such progressions would show an ape, a black African, then a Caucasian—or an ape, a Neandertal, and modern man. For example, Professor Chapin shows a gorilla, a Neandertal, and modern man, all grossly distorted except the modern man.[31] He pictures Neandertal Man as very apelike, a picture that is today recognized as very inaccurate.[32]

In another example of gross distortion, University of Michigan Professor Winchell illustrated the heads of a 'Female Gorilla' and a 'Female Hottentot' (an African tribal ethnic group) as remarkably similar (see Figure 4 on page 216).[33]

The earliest evolutionary progression drawings show evolution from the most primitive to the most advanced animals starting with a fish, then a bird, then a dog, a monkey, a black African or some other 'primitive human', and the last picture, the most evolved human, is a Caucasian. One common example of the evolutionary progression shows only the head profiles.[34] Such progressions were shown in museum displays, like the American Museum of Natural History display on page 311.

Another common illustration was an evolutionary progression from what purports to be the most primitive human, typically an Aborigine or an African, to the most advanced human, a Caucasian—often appearing Scandinavian. An example is profiles that stress the change in the facial angle from horizontal to vertical, with the black African shown as being the most primitive, and the Swede shown as being the most advanced.[35]

Even modern illustrations show evidence of this racist past. For example, many show the figures as less hairy and the skin colour becoming lighter as evolution progresses.

Despite being widely recognized by academics as involving gross distortions, the progression is nonetheless not only a cultural icon but also a cross-cultural icon. Stephen Jay Gould wrote in reference to the progression, what he calls the *march of progress*, that "*My books are dedicated to debunking this picture of evolution*", adding that it was even used as a book jacket illustration in four translations of his own books, something he said he had no control over.[36]

---

31. Chapin, F.S., *An Introduction to the Study of Social Evolution; The Prehistoric Period*, The Century Co., New York, p. 63, 1915.
32. See frontispiece of Chapin, *An Introduction to the Study of Social Evolution*.
33. Winchell, A., *Preadamites; Or a Demonstration of the Existence of Men Before Adam*, S.C. Griggs. & Company, Chicago, p. 252, 1880.
34. See Haller, J., *Outcasts from Evolution*, University of Illinois Press, Chicago, p. 13, 1971.
35. Haller, *Outcasts from Evolution*, p.12.
36. Gould, S.J., *Wonderful Life: The Burgess Shale and the Nature of Life*, Norton, New York, p. 30, 1989.

The reason it is so universal, Gould notes, is because "*The march of progress is the canonical representation of evolution—the one picture immediately grasped and viscerally understood by all.*"[37] Tim White of the Evolution Research Center at the University of California, Berkeley, firmly condemned the progression in these words:

> The unilineal depiction of human evolution popularized by the familiar iconography of an evolutionary 'march to modern man' has been proven wrong for more than 60 years. However, the cartoon continues to provide a popular straw man for scientists, writers and editors alike.[38]

Yet it is the most popular depiction of evolution, even today. One of the latest examples is the most accepted five steps to modern humans, which shows a very modern male body and a clearly chimp head that slowly morphs into a modern Caucasian male.[39]

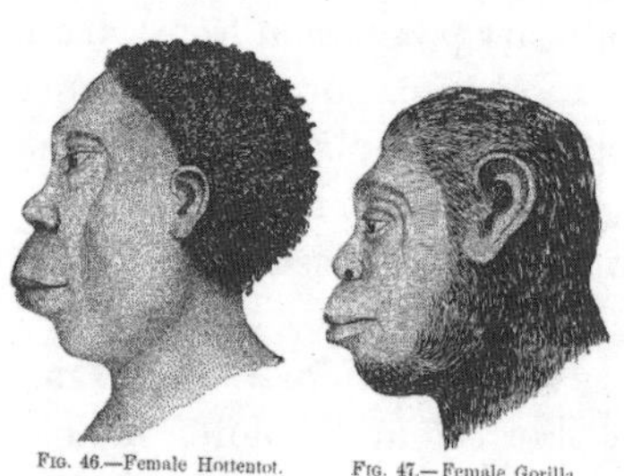

Figure 4
An illustration of an ape and an African (from the Khoisan group, then known as 'Hottentots'). Note they are both distorted to look far more alike than they actually are. From Winchell, A. (Professor of Geology and Paleontology, University of Michigan), *Preadamites; or a Demonstration of The Existence of Men Before Adam; Together with A Study of Their Condition, Antiquity, Racial Affinities, and Progressive Dispersion Over the Earth*, S.C. Griggs and Company, Chicago, 1888.

Summary

As Lubenow concludes, the parade is "*raw propaganda–brilliant propaganda, but raw nonetheless*" and very "*few evolutionists have protested this gross lack of scientific objectivity*" such as shown in the Time-Life book.[40]

Yet, this "*outrageous … raw propaganda*" has no doubt influenced millions of people to accept the Darwinian worldview of human evolution and is, by far, the most popular icon of evolution that is found everywhere in the media today and for

37. Gould, *Wonderful Life*, p. 31.
38. White, T., Paleoanthropology: five's a crowd in our family tree, *Current Biology* **23**(3):R112–R115, 2013; p. R114.
39. Croton, G., *et al.* (Eds) *The Human Body*, Parragon, Bath, UK, pp. 18–19, 2012.
40. Lubenow, *Bones of Contention*, p. 40.

decades. The fact is, the still popular progression illustrations that show a "*single file of marching hominids becoming ever more vertical, tall, and hairless*" is a fiction.[41]

Furthermore, the drawings originally were very racist and still have clear racist implications. Most of the drawings not only show Negro-looking men as primitive humans, but also show the evolution to modern humans as having lighter skin and less hair as they evolved into modern humans. All of the hundreds of progression drawings I have seen were of males; probably a reflection of the fact that, until very recently, evolutionists in general favoured males in their evolutionary constructions.

We now know that the drawings are not only racist, but also clearly false, as is obvious when we compare the drawings to photographs of the animal or race they are supposed to represent. This racism is still very much with us. One study showed that "*Americans of various races still unconsciously dehumanize their fellow black citizens by subtly associating them with apes,*" an association that is no doubt reinforced by the common progression drawings.[42]

This erroneous view is increasingly being debunked by scientists and writers. Professor Shea, in an article titled "*Refuting a Myth about Human Origins,*" documents that the progression illustration was a popular way of 'proving' human evolution.[43] He added that this image implies a steady march of progress from archaic to modern humans in contrast to the research which shows that an "*increasing behavioral and morphological variability*" has occurred historically.

41. Hublin, J.J., An evolutionary odyssey, *Nature* **403**(6768):363–364, 2000; p. 363.
42. Editorial: Racism still runs deep: even the most well-meaning liberal can harbour hidden prejudice, *New Scientist* **197**(2643):5, 2008.
43. Shea, J.J., Refuting a myth about human origins, *American Scientist* **99**(2):128–135, 2011; p. 128.

CHAPTER 14

Human-ape hybridization: The failed attempts to support Darwinism

Introduction

One of the most radical attempts to prove macroevolution was the effort to produce a human-ape hybrid by artificial insemination. All of the bizarre experiments used to produce a viable human-ape hybrid embryo have so far failed. A major goal of this research was an attempt to prove ape-to-human evolution by documenting the putative close relatedness between humans and apes. The most well-known example involved the many attempts by the internationally known Russian scientist, Ilya Ivanov.

Figure 1
Ilya Ivanov specialized in the fields of artificial insemination and the interspecific hybridization of animals. He repeatedly attempted and failed to breed 'Negroes' with primates partly to prove Darwinism.

Justification of the experiment

Several leading scientists in Europe in the early twentieth century seriously discussed crossing anthropoid apes with humans to document macroevolution.[1] Biologists justified this research by "*emphasizing the close biological link*" between apes and humans.[2]

They concluded that successful human-ape hybrids would blur the boundaries between humans and anthropoid apes, supporting an ape-to-human evolutionary descent. The London Zoo mammal curator, Dr Desmond Morris, wrote that "*the scientific interest of such an experiment, if successful, would be tremendous.*"[3]

For this research, putative "*racially inferior people, where the distance between man and the animal was small*" were selected to help ensure that the experiment would be successful.[4]

---

1. Rossiianov, K., Beyond species: Ilya Ivanov and his experiments on cross-breeding humans with anthropoid apes, *Science in Context* **15**(2):277–316, 2002; p. 290.
2. Rossiianov, Beyond species, p. 290.
3. Morris, R. and Morris, D, *Men and Apes*, McGraw-Hill, New York, p. 81, 1966.
4. Rossiianov, Beyond species, p. 290.

Achieving human-ape hybrids was important for Darwinism because Darwin's theory of gradualism required that differences "*between the highest men of the highest races and the lowest savages,*" as well as those between the 'lowest savages' and the highest primate, be biologically "*connected by the finest gradations.*"[5]

Darwin also expected that at some future point, "*not very distant ... the civilized races of man will almost certainly exterminate and replace throughout the world the savage races,*" thus making the gap between humans and apes even greater than it is now.[6] Hybridization of the lowest human and the highest ape would help to vindicate Darwin and serve as powerful evidence of evolution.[7]

Figure 2
An early 20th century photograph of an adult woman and an adult chimp to show the morphology contrast.

Early researchers

Hans Friedenthal, a scientist working in the early 1900s, discussed the possibility of obtaining ape-human hybrids. He incorrectly reasoned that since ape and human blood types were identical (humans can be A, B, AB or O; chimps are blood group A, rarely O, and never B), therefore their gametes must also be very similar.[8]

Hermann Moens, another scientist who planned to do experiments very similar to Ivanov's (described below), was also motivated to prove evolutionary theory and "*solve a mystery that had eluded science for decades, namely, the origins of the human species.*"[9]

He discussed his proposal in detail with the leading European Darwinist, scientist Ernst Haeckel of Germany. Haeckel was very supportive of the idea, and agreed that this research would be very important evidence for human evolution.[10]

Of the many similarities that convinced him that humans and apes could interbreed, none impressed him more than what he incorrectly assumed was the

5. Darwin, C., *The Descent of Man*, John Murray, London, p. 35, 1871.
6. Darwin, *The Descent of Man*, p. 201.
7. Wiker, B., *The Darwin Myth: The Life and Lies of Charles Darwin*, Regnery, Washington, DC, pp. 106, 118, 2009.
8. Friedenthal, H., Über einen experimentellen Nachweis von Blutsverwandtschaft, *Archiv für Anatomie und Physiologie, Physiologische Abteilung* **5/6**:507–508, 1900; in Morris and Morris, *Men and Apes*, p. 312.
9. De Rooy, P., In Search of Perfection: the Creation of a Missing Link, chapter 15 in Corbey and Theunisen (Eds), *Ape, Man, Apeman: Changing Views Since 1600,* Department of Prehistory, Leiden University, Netherlands, p. 195, 1995.
10. Rossiianov, Beyond species, p. 291.

similarity of their blood types that made them "*literally blood relatives.*"[11] His proposal was to

> capture gorillas and chimpanzees in the Congo, and orang utans and gibbons in the Dutch East Indies. The female animals would then be "*artificially fertilized … with human sperm (gorillas and chimpanzees primarily will be fertilized with the sperm of negroes).*" In addition, Moens would attempt to crossbreed the various ape species, and finally, he would investigate a number of diseases, including syphilis, found in these anthropoid apes [emphasis in original]. [12]

Moens published his research idea in detail and even attempted to organize an expedition to complete the fieldwork.[13]

Because he believed in the separate evolutionary origins of the different human races, Haeckel stressed that Negro sperm should be used because he believed they were the human race closest to the apes.[14] Haeckel, therefore, supported Moens' plan to inseminate a female chimpanzee with Negro male sperm.[15]

Many other scientists at this time believed Negroes were biologically very close to apes. They also believed that apes were like "*untalented children with an extreme deficit of attention*" who could be taught human language and even math, music, and other basic skills.[16]

Most importantly, many scientists concluded that a human-ape hybrid would be "*irrefutable vindication of Darwin.*"[17]

Rohleder's human-ape hybridization research

Around 1916, the prominent German scientist and author Hermann Rohleder also proposed research on human-ape hybridization. Rohleder, a pioneer in the field of artificial insemination, had the knowledge required to do the experiments and believed that a "*hybrid would provide the crucial evidence for evolution.*"[18]

His strong interest in this area was demonstrated by the fact that he had published a major 243-page volume of his work in this area.[19] His goal was to

---

11. De Rooy, In Search of Perfection, p. 195.
12. De Rooy, In Search of Perfection, p. 195.
13. Moens, H., *Truth: Experimental Researches about the Descent of Man*, A. Owen, London, 1908.
14. Rossiianov, Beyond species, p. 291.
15. Moens, *Truth*.
16. Rossiianov, Beyond species, p. 292.
17. De Rooy, In Search of Perfection, p. 196.
18. Rossiianov, Beyond species, p. 292.
19. Rohleder, H., Künstliche Zeugung und Anthropogenie, in *Monographien über die Zeugung beim Menschen*, Vol. 6, Georg Thieme, Leipzig, 1918.

"*artificially inseminate apes with the sperm of blacks … The result would be a living reconstruction of a long extinct link between apes and humans.*"[20]

Another researcher, Charles L. Remington, even concluded that "*experimental crosses between separate species are becoming a principal source of biological knowledge of evolutionary relationships.*"[21] He found it ironic that hybridization studies had been completed on a wide variety of animals except for the species that most interests us, *Homo sapiens.* Remington added that *Homo sapiens* hybrid research was required to enable humans to understand both our relationship to other life and the history of our species, adding that the

> very great scientific value of well-performed hybridization experiments emphasizes the high priority that should be given to a thorough study of the interspecific genetics of *Homo* with one or more of the three types of pongids (chimpanzee, gorilla, orang) most similar to *Homo.* Because there is a strong possibility that hybrid analysis will significantly clarify and alter present views of our relationships and our past history, such an analysis will not be neglected much longer.[22]

Remington was evidently unaware of the Russian research discussed below. This research was made possible because, after the 1917 Russian revolution, a radical break with the old Russia resulted, destroying or radically altering its major institutions, including the church and private property. The leaders of the communist revolution also assigned a major role to science in their new society.[23]

This new emphasis on science included a change that opened the door to human-ape hybrid research. Besides attempting to prove evolution, another reason for the scientific importance of *Homo* hybridization experimentation was the value scientists generally gave to learning more about humanity.[24]

Ilya Ivanov's attempts

Professor Ilya Ivanov (1870–1932) was an eminent biologist who achieved considerable success in the field of artificial insemination of horses and other animals. He studied under the famous Russian Nobel Laureate scientist, Ivan Pavlov, graduated

---

20. De Rooy, In Search of Perfection, p. 199.
21. Remington, C.L., An experimental study of man's genetic relationship to great apes by means of interspecific hybridization, pp. 461–464 in: Katz, J., *Experimentation with Human Beings*, New York, Russell Sage Foundation, 1972; p. 461.
22. Remington, An experimental study … , p. 461.
23. Rossiianov, Beyond species, p. 285.
24. Remington, An experimental study … , p. 461.

from Kharkov University in 1896, and became Professor of Animal Husbandry at several leading Russian universities.[25]

Acknowledged as "*one of the greatest authorities on the artificial fecundation of animals,*" he earned an international reputation for his research.[26]

His artificial insemination techniques were so successful that he was able to fertilize as many as 500 mares with the semen from a single stallion. He used his method on a total of 6,804 mares and over a thousand sheep, making him the leader in using artificial insemination on farm animals.[27] His major goal was the improvement of effective breeding of farm stock.

Ivanov also pioneered the use of artificial insemination in an attempt to produce hybrids between various species of mammals and birds, including a zebra and a donkey, a rat and a mouse, a mouse and a guinea pig, and an antelope and a cow.[28] His most radical experiment, though, was his attempt to produce a human-ape hybrid.[29]

He first mentioned the idea of human-ape hybrids in 1910 at a major scientific conference, a goal that became an obsession until he died. In view of how successful Ivanov had been with his animal experiments—and how biologically close Darwinists then regarded apes and humans—Ivanov strongly felt that human-ape hybrids were possible.

Human-ape experiments were supported by some of the most respected scientists of the day, including Professor Hermann Klaatsch and Dr F.G. Crookshank.[30,31] Ivanov had support from both the French and Soviet Academy of Sciences and presented his human-ape hybrid experiment proposal to a supportive World Congress of Zoologists in Graz. Other well-known scientists that supported this research included Dr Oscar Riddle of the Carnegie School of Experimental Evolution and Dr A.L. Herrera of Mexico.[32]

According to a report in The *New York Times*, Charles Smith, President of the American Association for the Advancement of Atheism, claimed that the main opposition was from "*two or three religious publications.*"[33]

---

25. Weiner, D.R., *Models of Nature*, Indiana University Press, Indianapolis, Indiana, p. 74, 1988.
26. Anonymous, Russian admits ape experiments, *The New York Times*, p. 2, June 19, 1926.
27. Rossiianov, Beyond species, p. 282.
28. Rossiianov, Beyond species, p. 284.
29. Pain, S., The forgotten scandal of the Soviet ape-man, *New Scientist*, online edition, August 20, 2008; (2670):48–49, 23 August 2008.
30. Armagnac, A.P., Strange creatures made to order, *Popular Science* **31**(33) September 1937, pp. 28–29.
31. Crookshank, F.G., *The Mongol in Our Midst: A Study of Man and His Three Faces*, E.P. Dutton and Company, New York, 1924.
32. England, H.S., Proposal to cross man and ape, *Evolution* **1**(5):5, 1928.
33. Anonymous, Soviet backs plan to test evolution, *The New York Times*, p. 2, June 17, 1926.

His project begins

Because Ivanov was an internationally respected scientist, he was able to obtain several prominent sponsors for his project, including the polymath Otto Schmidt, editor of the *Great Soviet Encyclopedia,* and chemical engineer Nikolay Gorbunov, an important patron of science and a close friend of Lenin.[34,35]

After Ivanov detailed the rationale behind his idea to the British government, they were anxious to support his theory and, therefore, promised to help raise money for his project. The Soviet government and the Pasteur Institute in Paris were also very supportive.[36,37]

The total funds promised for his project from various sources is estimated to have equalled over a million in today's dollars. The Soviet government contributed the first $10,000, and a number of prominent American science patrons were very supportive of the project. These supporters expected Ivanov's research to provide important "*evidence for a better understanding of the problem of the origin of man.*"[38]

Attorney Howell England established a public subscription fund in America to raise money to do the required human-ape experiments. England named it "*The Edward D. Cope Foundation of Experimental Anthropology*" in honor of the American professor who "*did so much to establish the doctrine of biological evolution.*"[39]

The goal of the Foundation was to produce a "*primitive man by hybridizing the several anthropoids with the different races of man.*"[40] Ivanov was personally very confident that human-ape hybridization was feasible.[41]

One reason for his confidence was he believed the various unconfirmed reports that forced human-ape hybridization had already occurred. However, because "*women raped by ape males are regarded as defiled*" they were treated as social pariahs. For this reason they "*usually disappear without any trace,*" presumably because they were killed or fled.[42]

In the mid-1920s, Ivanov initiated his project to hybridize humans and apes by artificial insemination. Ivanov ignored the obvious racism when discussing his ideas with communist officials but, conversely, he stressed it when discussing his ideas with his Western colleagues. In his notebooks he wrote that Negroes "*treat the apes, and in particular the chimpanzees, as an inferior human race*", presumably projecting

34. Etkind, A., Beyond eugenics: the forgotten scandal of hybridizing humans and apes, *Studies in History and Philosophy of Biological and Biomedical Sciences* **39**(2):205–210, 2008; p. 206.
35. Rossiianov, Beyond species, p. 289.
36. Etkind, Beyond eugenics, p. 205.
37. Rossiianov, Beyond species.
38. Rossiianov, Beyond species, p. 289.
39. Etkind, Beyond eugenics, p. 5.
40. Etkind, Beyond eugenics, p. 5.
41. Rossiianov, Beyond species, p. 289.
42. Ivanov quoted in Rossiianov, Beyond species, p. 297.

his own cultural beliefs of racial superiority over the Negroes onto them.[43] This view of Negroes was common in Russia at this time.[44]

The Pongidae (great apes) were chosen to breed with humans because "*specialists in taxonomy, anatomy, and paleontology are agreed that Homo is more closely related to the Pongidae than to any other kind of primate,* [and] *the ultimate aim of the experiment is to cross Homo with at least one pongid species.*"[45] Remington concluded that the

> gorilla (a *Pongid*) appears to be anatomically and biochemically the most similar to *Homo* and has the best size range, but it has become rare and very expensive and is not ideally suited for breeding in captivity, even of its own kind. By elimination, therefore, *Pan troglodytes* best combines the characteristics of an optimal parent species of the *Homo* hybridization.[46]

Remington gives additional reasons, including the fact that psychologists, anatomists, physiologists, cytologists, and biochemists had a better understanding of *Pan troglodytes* than other primates, allowing the characteristics of an F1 hybrid *Homo sapiens x Pan troglodytes* to "*be compared immediately with both parents without new research on an unknown parent … Should this cross fail, however, it would still be necessary to attempt the Homo x Gorilla cross before concluding that Homo is not hybridizable with any other species.*"[47]

Efforts to support evolution

According to Charles Lee Smith, the objective of Ivanov's experiments was to achieve "*artificial insemination of the human and anthropoid species, to support the doctrine of evolution, by establishing* [the] *close kinship between man and the higher apes.*"[48]

The project was supported by American Association for the Advancement of Atheism members because they saw the experiment as an important "*proof of human evolution*" and, therefore, of atheism.[49]

When applying to the Soviet government for funds, Ivanov emphasized the importance of his research for anti-religious propaganda.[50] The Soviet Commissioner of Agriculture wrote that Ivanov's research would be "*a decisive blow to the religious teaching … of the church.*"[51] Rossiianov reports that the communists

---

43. Rossiianov, Beyond species, p. 297.
44. Blakely, A., *Russia and the Negro: Blacks in Russian History and Thought*, Howard University Press, Washington, DC, 1986.
45. Remington, An experimental study … , p. 462.
46. Remington, An experimental study … , p. 462.
47. Remington, An experimental study … , p. 462.
48. Soviet backs plan to test evolution, *The New York Times*, 1926, p. 2.
49. Etkind, Beyond eugenics, p. 209.
50. Etkind, Beyond eugenics p. 206.
51. Rossiianov, Beyond species, p. 286.

> saw science and technology as their only internal allies in the enlightenment of the Russian people. Darwinism, in particular, had a direct political value for them as a tool in anti-religious propaganda. Muller—one of the first western scientists to visit post-revolutionary Russia—stopped in Moscow and Petrograd in the summer of 1922 and was astonished to learn that the authorities had postponed the publication of a book by Lev Berg, the prominent Russian ichthyologist, because the author expressed there [in] anti-Darwinian views. Muller noted with surprise, that while Darwinism was considered a "*pernicious*" doctrine in the United States, anti-Darwinism came to play a similar role in Russia.[52]

The Russians were pro-Darwin to the extent that they attempted to suppress all publications that were "*opposed to Darwinism*" because non-Darwinians were regarded as subversive to science.[53]

England wrote that the scientists involved in advising the project were "*confident that hybrids can be produced*" and, in the event that they were successful, "*the question of the evolution of man will be established to the satisfaction of the most dogmatic anti-evolutionists.*" Although the "*original idea was that only hybrids from the gorilla would prove fertile*" he concluded that other hybrids could also be produced that were fertile.[54]

The scientific advisors wanted the field researchers to use not only gorillas but also orangutans, chimpanzees, and possibly gibbons in the experiments. Most of the hybrid researchers accepted the polygenetic theory of human evolution (that the different human races evolved separately from different primates), proposing that orangutans should be crossed with humans of the "*yellow race,*" gorillas with humans of the "*black race,*" chimpanzees with the "*white race,*" and gibbons with "*the more brachycephalic peoples of Europe (he probably meant Jews).*"

The scientists concluded these matches would ensure that the hybrids were fertile, "*to demonstrate the close relationship of human and ape stocks.*"[55]

The scientists even concluded that "*it would be possible to produce the complete chain of specimens from the perfect anthropoid to the perfect man*" which Etkind concluded was a "*racist … hybridization project.*"[56]

England wrote that Dr Crookshank of London, who "*has made a minute anatomical study of the three larger anthropoids,*" is convinced from his research that, if orangutans can successfully be

52. Rossiianov, Beyond species, p. 287.
53. Muller, H.J., Observations of biological science in Russia, *The Scientific Monthly* **16**:(5):539–552, 1923; p. 549.
54. Soviet backs plan to test evolution, *The New York Times*, 1926, p. 2.
55. Anonymous, Ape-child? *Time Magazine*, August 16, 1926; p. 16.
56. Etkind, Beyond eugenics, p. 207.

> hybridized with the yellow race, the gorilla with the black race, and the chimpanzee with the white race, all three hybrids will reproduce themselves. In his opinion each species of anthropoid is more closely related to its corresponding human type than it is to either of the other anthropoids. In other words … the chimpanzee has a closer relationship to the white race than to the gorilla or the orang. The gibbon … has its corresponding human type in the more brachycephalic [short- or broad-headed—Ed.] peoples of Europe.[57]

Mr England proposed that the research team should attempt to produce a complete evolutionary chain from the lower apes to humans. Because the scientists involved in the project were in complete accord with Dr Crookshank's polygenetic views of humans, they felt this goal was feasible.

Time magazine opined that, if this experiment failed, evolution would not be invalidated because this "*test of evolution would be decisive only in the event that pregnancy, whether productive of healthy offspring or not, could be induced.*"[58]

A single pregnancy would be enough for the project to be judged successful if the offspring was clearly a hybrid. *Time* concluded that, if the experiment succeeded, "*fresh and final evidence would be established that humans and anthropoids belong to a common genus.*" Furthermore, to more confidently establish human-from-ape evolution as fact, the

> hybrid fertilization would have to be attempted upon females of both species, human and ape. Fully formed, healthy offspring, if they resulted, would not be regarded as "*missing links,*" but as living proof that apes and men are species as closely allied as horses and asses which can be hybridized to produce mules or hinnies. If an ape-man or man-ape hybrid should prove fecund, the relationship of the two parent species would be proved even closer than is now supposed. If no offspring resulted, evolution would by no means fail; the distance of apes and men from a parent stock would merely be demonstrated to be as great or greater than it is now estimated.[59]

The research commences

In 1924, Ivanov completed his first experiment in French Guinea in central Africa at the Kindia research facility. He first attempted to produce human male-chimpanzee female hybrids, and all three attempts failed. Ivanov also tried to use ape males and human females to produce hybrids but, as far as is known, he was unable to complete the experiment.

In November of 1926 Ivanov again attempted to inseminate several African women with chimpanzee sperm in a Congo hospital, evidently without the

57. Soviet backs plan to test evolution, *The New York Times*, 1926.
58. Anonymous, Men and apes, *Time Magazine*, June 28, 1926; p. 22.
59. Men and apes, *Time Magazine*, 1926.

women's knowledge or consent. No record exists to verify if these experiments actually occurred.[60]

The details of the 1927 artificial insemination experiments further document the program's failure.[61] Specifically, in 1927 Ivanov had three female chimpanzees inseminated with human sperm, but failed to obtain a hybrid.[62]

He evidently attempted hybridization experiments on ten more chimps, but these attempts also failed.[63] Post-mortem examination of a chimp that died found no evidence of pregnancy.[64]

One major problem was that in his attempts to replicate his research in Paris, more than half of the 700 chimpanzees purchased from native hunters had died even before they could be shipped to Paris for research and, once in Europe, many more died.[65]

Another problem was, we now know that the chimps he first tried to experiment on were too young—below seven years (the age of chimp pubescence), a mistake that illustrates how little knowledge scientists then had about primates.[66]

Ivanov then repeatedly attempted to do further experiments using artificial insemination on women volunteers with the sperm of a 26-year-old orangutan male, which also failed. If they were successful, the researchers would surely have published their results, which would have received wide publicity. Ivanov never published the results of these experiments in scientific journals, consequently few details of the results are known. Ivanov's detailed laboratory research notes still exist, and thus we have been able to reconstruct some of his findings. Ivanov's funds were by this time rapidly running out, but he felt more funding could easily be obtained if he could achieve a single successful hybrid.[67]

Of note is the fact that all of the difficulties encountered make one very skeptical of the ape-human hybrid possibility when it "*would be a simple matter to inseminate a female ape with human sperm or vice versa.*"[68] Others feel that tissue hybrids should be researched first in order to determine if a full development of a zygote is even possible.[69]

---

60. Rossiianov, Beyond species, pp. 299–300.
61. Rossiianov, Beyond species, pp. 277–311.
62. Rossiianov, Beyond species, pp. 278–279.
63. Rossiianov, Beyond species, p. 296.
64. Rossiianov, Beyond species, p. 300.
65. Rossiianov, Beyond species, p. 293.
66. Rossiianov, Beyond species, p. 293.
67. Rossiianov, Beyond species, p. 296.
68. Morris and Morris, *Men and Apes*, p. 81.
69. Lederberg, J., Experimental genetics and human evolution, *The American Naturalist* **100**(915):519–531, 1966; p. 531.

Ethical problems

To achieve their research goals the scientists were often forced to use deception. Ethical concerns existed from the start of the research, and for this reason Ivanov "*tried to conceal his experiments from the native servants*" that he hired to take care of his subjects, by arranging his experiments on the artificial insemination of apes clandestinely under the guise of a medical exam.[70] Later, Ivanov even attempted to

> inseminate black females with ape sperm without their consent, under the pretext of medical examination in the local hospital. The French governor, however, forbade him from carrying out this part of the project. But Ivanov saw no moral problem here. He angrily reported to his sponsors in the Kremlin about the primitive fears of the blacks and the bourgeois prejudices of the French.[71]

Most of the experimenters involved in the research assumed a very clinical, detached attitude, rarely considering the ethical implications of their hybridization research. Ivanov was described as both brutal and insensitive while carrying out his experiments.

The Soviets were concerned that deceiving the African women could undermine their trust in European scientists and doctors, threatening further scientific research in Africa.[72]

Another ethical issue: If the experiment succeeded, would the hybrid be regarded as human with all the rights of humans?[73] How would people be selected to rear the hybrids? The most serious ethical issues raised were ridiculed by one scientist who, incidentally, was a supporter of the research. He complained that the culture, although very supportive of

> the objective analysis of natural phenomena and the general search for knowledge, is still anthropologically primitive in many respects, and the idea of creating hybrid half-men would be repellent to all but the most academic of scientists. Orthodox religion would also be uneasy, and all kinds of basic taboos would be churned up. The situation would soon get out of hand and man would no doubt end up by proving once again that he is not only a good old-fashioned primate below the belt, but also above the collar. But the truth-seekers need not feel too frustrated—the experiment would almost certainly have failed anyway.[74]

---

70. Rossiianov, Beyond species, p. 297.
71. Etkind, Beyond eugenics, p. 206.
72. Rossiianov, Beyond species, p. 301.
73. Rossiianov, Beyond species, p. 279.
74. Morris and Morris, *Men and Apes*, p. 82.

The Soviet Society of Materialist Biologists, which included many leading Russian biologists, was very supportive of achieving "*scientific control of life and active human interference into human evolution,*" and planned experiments using large numbers of women volunteers and ape sperm.[75]

They hoped to recruit women whose interest was mainly ideological. At least one woman volunteered to be inseminated with ape sperm to aid science.[76] The 'humans are animals' attitude reflected itself in the following proposal:

> Ethically, the scientist might be expected to have the same responsibilities for humane care of these hybrids as for any other experimental mammals. He should also have the same freedom to operate on the hybrids and to sacrifice them for study.[77]

Remington added that the

> contribution of one-half of the genetical material by *Homo* should not make the hybrid subject to the legal protections and obligations of a human in the nation in which the experiment is carried out. However, if a hybrid were successfully backcrossed to *Homo,* the new offspring would of course be 0.75 *Homo*, and very interesting legal and ethical questions would then arise.[78]

As late as 2002, Rossiianov argued that the "*border that separates man from animal is in fact, a product of social and cultural construction*"—not biological—and could easily be bridged by science.[79]

Research after Ivanov

Ivanov died from a stroke on March 20, 1932, ending his quest to produce a human-ape hybrid. Nonetheless, interest remained in various human-ape hybridization research studies for decades after 1932. As late as 1972, some researchers were still pursuing this line of research because some interest still existed in the progress and results of such studies. Some theorists speculated about the benefits of human-ape hybridization, some considering them potentially as important as moon exploration or the first heart transplants.

> The human welfare value of hybridization is not easy to predict. There are dimly perceived biomedical applications that would probably be worth exploring once the initial results of hybridizing Homo were available. There

75. Rossiianov, Beyond species, p. 304.
76. Rossiianov, Beyond species, p. 306.
77. Remington, An experimental study … , pp. 463–464.
78. Remington, An experimental study … , p. 464.
79. Rossiianov, Beyond species, p. 310.

> are even vaguer speculations on the cultural uses of half-human livestock … [said to] deserve some debate by thinkers of various backgrounds.[80]

African folklore referring to human-ape hybridization was also common. For example, Jordan claims, quoting White, that "*orang-outans*" (despite being exclusively found in Asia)

> have been known to carry off negro-boys, girls, and even women, with a view of making them subservient to their wants as slaves, or as objects of brutal passion: and it has been asserted by some that women have had offspring from such connections. This last circumstance is not, however certain. Supposing it to be true, it would be an object of inquiry, whether such offspring would propagate, or prove to be mules [infertile].[81]

Jordan notes that the fact "*White felt it appropriate to call for inquiry into the matter spoke volumes in itself.*"[82]

Although "*hints and rumors from several sources*" existed that human-ape hybridization had occurred in Africa and elsewhere, there exists "*no evidence to back these reports.*"[83] In 1971 Bourne wrote that no reason exists

> from the chromosomal point of view why, for instance, a gorilla mated with a chimpanzee should not produce living babies. And it seems reasonable to suppose in view of the evidence we have had from hybridization of other animals that even the orangutan might hybridize with the gorilla and the chimpanzee.[84]

On this basis, Bourne concluded that human-ape hybridizations were possible.[85] In the end, the research along this line all failed for various reasons and has not been attempted again, at least publicly. We now know the experiments will not be successful for many reasons and, therefore, Ivanov's attempts are today a major embarrassment to Darwinism.

One of many genetic differences between humans and apes (including chimpanzees, gorillas and orangutans) is that humans have 46 chromosomes and apes have 48—and for this and other reasons, the chromosomes would often not pair up properly even if the chimp sperm did result in fertilization. The number of human

---

80. Remington, An experimental study … , p. 462.
81. Jordan, W.D., *White over Black*, The University of North Carolina Press, Chapel Hill, North Carolina, p. 500, 1968.
82. Jordan, *White over Black*, p. 500.
83. Morris and Morris, *Men and Apes*, p. 82.
84. Bourne, G., *The Ape People*, Putnam, New York, p. 261, 1971.
85. Bourne, *The Ape People*, p. 261.

chromosomes was not known for certain until the mid-1950s.[86] The number for chimps was not known until around 1960.[87]

Remington speculated that, for reasons including factors such as the chromosome number, if a hybrid was produced it would be "*largely but perhaps not totally sterile*" unless it was bred with another hybrid.[88]

The ultimate goal behind the human-ape hybridization experiments is still with us. Professor Michael Brooks writes, due to the advance of biological knowledge "*humans are being stripped of their status as 'special' animals,*" in contrast to most world religions that still teach humans are above the rest of the biological world. An example is in the

> Book of Genesis, God gives Man 'dominion over the fish of the sea, and over the fowl of the air, and over the cattle, and over all the earth, and over every creeping thing that creepeth upon the earth.' However, geneticists have shown that the differences between us and other animals are only slight. So far we have identified only three genes that are unique to humans: the rest we share with our compatriots in the animal kingdom. When the catalogue of human genes is complete, the likelihood is that fewer than twenty of our 20,000 or so genes are unique to humans. We have also discovered that other primates have brain cells exactly like those inside our own oversized skulls. It's no surprise, then, that our seemingly unique mental capacities are nothing more than sophisticated versions of tricks that other animals can pull off … it is hard to argue that there is anything biologically special about humans.[89]

In the 1920s, the only criteria scientists had available to determine hybrid potential were external morphological and internal anatomical comparisons—the major genetic differences were unknown. Scientists now know a conservative estimate is that no fewer than 400 million to 900 million base pair differences exist between humans and our putative closest evolutionary relatives, the chimps.[90,91]

Human-ape hybridization experiments are the result of evolutionary thinking, and failed because their basic premise was wrong. Even though scientific progress

86. Tjio, J.H. and Levan, A., The chromosome number of man, *Hereditas* **42**(1–2):1–6, 1956.
87. Young, W.J., Merz, T., Ferguson-Smith, M.A., and Johnston, A.W., Chromosome number of the chimpanzee, *Pan troglodytes*, *Science* **131** (3414): 1672–3, 1960.
88. Remington, An experimental study … , p. 463.
89. Brooks, M., *Free Radicals: The Secret Anarchy of Science*, The Overlook Press, New York, p. 157, 2011.
90. Bergman, J. and Tomkins, J., Is the human genome nearly identical to chimpanzee?—a reassessment of the literature, *J. Creation* **26**(1):54–60, 2012.
91. Tomkins, J. and Bergman. J., Genomic monkey business—estimates of nearly identical human-chimp DNA similarity re-evaluated using omitted data, *J. Creation* **26**(1):94–100, 2012; creation.com/chimp.

has now documented the contrast between the two, nonetheless, some diehard Darwinists ignore the chasm between apes and humans, even erroneously concluding that science

> is closing the gap between humans and other animals so fast, in fact, that some scientists are starting to think that human rights should also apply to other primates. In 1993, a team of eminent scientists published a collection of essays aimed at persuading the United Nations to grant chimps and other higher primates the privileges we know as 'human rights.' *The Great Ape Project* demanded that 'non-human hominids'—chimpanzees, gorillas, orang-utans and bonobos—should enjoy the right to life, freedom and protection from torture. … [These included] Peter Singer and evolutionary biologist Richard Dawkins, who writes in typically witty and provocative style:
>
>> Remember the song, 'I've danced with a man who's danced with a girl, who danced with the Prince of Wales?' We can't quite interbreed with modern chimpanzees, but we'd need only a handful of intermediate types to be able to sing: 'I've bred with a man, who's bred with a girl, who's bred with a chimpanzee.'
>
> Humans, Dawkins says, are not far enough removed from chimpanzees for there to be distinctions between their rights and ours. Stumble across one of those missing intermediates in the wild, he says,
>
>> and our precious systems of norms and ethics would come crashing about our ears. The boundaries with which we segregate our world would be all shot to pieces. Racism would blur with speciesism in obdurate and vicious confusion. Apartheid. … would assume a new and perhaps a more urgent import.[92]

As is obvious from these statements, some scientists are still optimistic that human-ape hybrids are possible, although research has not supported this view. A 1984 study reporting the first successful *in vitro* fertilization of a rhesus monkey baby promoted the technique used as providing a good supply of experimental material for improving human *in vitro* fertilization techniques and for saving wild species on the verge of extinction via surrogate motherhood. Their research apparently did not provide any support for cross-species hybridization in primates.[93]

---

92. Quoted in Brooks, *Free Radicals*, pp. 157–158.
93. Bavister, B., *et al.*, Birth of rhesus monkey infant after *in vitro* fertilization and nonsurgical embryo transfer, *Proceedings of the National Academy of Science USA* **81**(7):2218–2222, 1984.

Racial degeneration

Ironically, at the time these experiments were being attempted, it was widely believed that mixing races produced racial degeneration because, it was assumed, the lower race would always bring down the higher race, a theory called *hybrid degeneracy*. Stepan wrote that the hybrid degeneracy thesis was widely supported by evolutionary biology, adding that

> John Lubbock, Darwin's friend and a prolific writer of popular, evolutionary biology, quoted Darwin as saying that "*crossed races of men are singularly savage and degraded,*" and that "*when two races, both low on the scale are crossed, the progeny seems to be eminently bad.*" Darwin concluded that the "*degraded state of so many half-castes is in part due to reversion to a primitive and savage condition, induced by the act of crossing, as well as to the unfavorable moral conditions under which they generally exist.*"[94]

This is one reason why hybrid researchers usually wanted to breed apes with Negroes, and not Caucasians. The eminent polygenist evolutionist, Professor Carl Vogt, "*distinguished, as did most biologists in the second half of the nineteenth century, between crosses of 'allied' races* [such as negroes and apes] *and 'distant' ones, such as white humans and apes.*"[95]

Typical was Harvard geneticist Edward East who taught that "*crosses between races close to each other were fruitful and healthy … but between distant races the hybrids 'would break apart those compatible physical and mental qualities which have established a smoothly operating whole in each race by hundreds of generations of natural selection'.*"[96]

Stepan added that French anthropologist Armand de Quatrefaces was almost alone among "*leading biologists in Europe* [who] *remained steadfast in his monogenism, consistently maintaining that human races throve* [thrived—Ed.] *by crossing, 'even when separated by profound differences'.*"[97]

Religious opposition to hybrid experiments

The main opposition to ape-human hybrid experiments was from the religious community. De Rooy concluded that this point was central to the debate because the "*only thing which stood in the way* [of ape-human hybridization] *were the stubborn remnants of old-fashioned morality, based on the Christian distinction between soul-less*

94. Stepan, N., Biological degeneration: races and proper places, chapter 5 in Chamberlin, J.E. and Gilman, S.L., *Degeneration: The Dark Side of Progress*, Columbia University Press, New York, p. 110, 1985.
95. Stepan, Biological degeneration, p. 110.
96. Stepan, Biological degeneration, p. 111.
97. Stepan, Biological degeneration, p. 111.

animals and human beings as image bearers of God."[98] De Rooy then quoted in detail the scriptural basis for this opposition.

Moens' main goal for supporting the human-ape hybrid research was to "*wholly replace religion with science.*"[99]

One human-ape hybridization crusader even argued that the "*Christian opposition to his ideas was very gratifying* [because] *it proved to Moens that he belonged to the legion of science, which in the name of Enlightenment and Progress battled against the powers of Darkness,*" referring to the fact that "*Christians were afraid that this evidence would prove the unreliability of the Genesis story*" of creation.[100]

De Rooy and other evolutionists concluded that "*evolutionary theory ... shortened the distance between humans and animals and expanded it between blacks and whites, to the point where blacks and apes together were placed fairly low down in the evolutionary charts.*"[101]

When Ivanov planned to visit the United States to lecture and raise money, his American correspondents warned him about religious objections to his plan. The topic of Ivanov's lectures, wrote England,

> would be sufficient to raise a perfect storm in our fundamentalist press, all insisting that you be deported and not allowed to land. I would suggest that the best time to have you come to America to lecture would be after the first little anthropoid hybrid shall have been born and ready for exhibition. We have enough scientists in the United States to assure you after that, not only a safe entrance into the country but a welcome here.[102]

Edwin E. Slosson was Director of Science Service, which published the popular weekly (now biweekly) *Science News Magazine*, and headed the first American non-commercial organization established to popularize science. He "*was very concerned about fundamentalist attacks on Darwinism in the United States*" and concluded that successful hybridization between different mammal species, especially humans and apes, to obtain new animal species would be opposed by Christians because it was "*the best and most convincing evidence for evolution.*"[103]

When Slosson learned about Ivanov's project, he sent information to American newspapers about Ivanov's effort "*to produce a hybrid between the highest anthropoids and the most primitive of the human race.*"[104] Ivanov observed that the news about his ape-human hybridization experiments

98. De Rooy, In Search of Perfection, p. 201.
99. De Rooy, In Search of Perfection, p. 204.
100. De Rooy, In Search of Perfection, pp. 202, 204.
101. De Rooy, In Search of Perfection, p. 201.
102. England to Ivanov, 24 March 1926, *IP* 414, p. 6; quoted in Rossiianov, Beyond species, p. 295.
103. Quoted in Rossiianov, Beyond species, p. 294.
104. Quoted in Rossiianov, Beyond species, p. 294.

> aroused sympathy in progressive newspapers and even the desire to provide us financial support. At the same time, our research caused a burst of indignation, a shower of abuse and threats [among the religious and conservative population] … This only confirms that our work has not only an exceptional scientific, but also a social significance.[105]

Attempts to use monkeys as an experimental model for studies of early embryonic development in humans is one residue of the belief that humans and lower primates can interbreed. An example is the research on *in vitro* fertilization and non-surgical embryo transfer on monkeys by Bavister *et al.*[106]

Summary

Darwinists have attempted to achieve a human-ape hybrid for over a century to produce clear proof of human evolution. The history of the attempts to produce a human-ape hybrid reveals some of the twentieth century's "*important cultural conventions and hidden assumptions about human nature, species, and social hierarchy.*"[107] Attempts at breeding humans and chimps or other primates were not only unethical and invariably dangerous, but they also reveal much about the mindset behind many failed attempts to prove macroevolution.[108] Of note is the fact that "*there was no discussion about the ethical aspects of the proposed experiment*" by evolutionary scientists.[109] Opposition did exist, though. Bourne concluded that considering

> all the stories about apes and human women one might ask, "*Have there ever been any hybrids between a man and apes or have there ever been hybrids between the apes themselves?*" … There is no real evidence that a successful cross has ever been made between a human and an ape.[110]

This conclusion has been supported by recent genetic research, which will likely be the end of dangerous and unethical attempts to achieve human-ape hybridizations, and other such experiments on humans to prove the evolution of humans and apes from some hypothetical common ancestor.[111]

These misguided and uninformed ideas about biology resulted in shocking attempts to produce a human-ape hybrid, all of which, as far as is known, have failed.

105. Quoted in Rossiianov, Beyond species, p. 302.
106. Bavister *et al.*, Birth of rhesus monkey … .
107. Rossiianov, Beyond species, p. 277.
108. Pain, The forgotten scandal of the Soviet ape-man.
109. Rossiianov, Beyond species, p. 289.
110. Bourne, *The Ape People*, p. 261.
111. Remington, An experimental study … .

CHAPTER 15

Java Man: A creature between apes and humans, an extinct ape, a primitive man, or . . . ?

Introduction

Java Man (some conclude he was actually a she) was historically one of the most important fossil finds used to document human evolution. It was used as evidence of ape-to-human evolution for over a half century and was a prime evidence for evolution in the written testimony submitted at the Scopes trial. The fossils were interpreted as "*a creature intermediate in anatomical type between the living great apes and modern man.*"[1]

Although many evolutionists touted it as definitive proof of human evolution, others debated exactly what it was. Although Java Man was long regarded as either a "*progressive ape or primitive man.*"[2] It is now widely regarded not as a link between apes and humans, but rather merely as another race of humans called *Homo erectus.* This chapter documents that even this conclusion is problematic.

The discovery

The Java Man fossil was discovered by a work crew hired by Eugene Dubois (1858–1940) in August of 1891 near Trinil village. Trinil was a worksite located by the Bengavan River in Java, a city in modern-day Indonesia (see figure 1). Once called *Pithecanthropus erectus* (erect ape-man), the creature is now generally classified as *Homo erectus,* which many evolutionists believe is fully human and an example of normal human variability.[3,4] Other paleontologists disagree and various other conclusions have been postulated.

The find was critical for evolutionists because Dubois presented it to the world as a perfect human-ape transitional link for the reason that it appeared to be evidence

1. Carrington, R., *A Million Years of Man: The Story of Human Development as Part of Nature,* The World Publishing Company, Cleveland, Ohio, p. 83, 1963.
2. Osborn, H.F., *The Hall of the Age of Man*, The American Museum of Natural History, New York, 1938; p. 11.
3. Mehlert, A.W., Homo erectus 'to' modern man: evolution or human variability? *J. Creation* **8**(1):105–116, 1994.
4. Habgood, P., A morphometric investigation into the origin(s) of anatomically modern humans, *British Archaeological Reports,* pp. 6, 10–11, 31 December 2003.

of a creature with traits in between apes and humans (see figure 2). The few Java Man fossils Dubois' team discovered included part of a cranial (skull) cap, a diseased left femur (thigh bone) and two (some accounts list three) teeth—the second-left and third-right upper jaw molars.[5]

Dubois concluded that all four fossils belonged "*to one individual or species, but opinions … differ on this point*" and still differ today.[6] Some of Dubois' contemporaries concluded that the find was actually a human femur and an ape skull—and debate still exists on the identity of the femur. Along with these remains were found those of many animals, including boars, tapirs, deer, and even porcupines.[7]

The two bone fragments found are less than 1% of a complete human skeleton. (Humans have an average of 213 bones.) Also, an entire skeleton is only about 10% of a human body, thus the Java bone fragments equal less than one thousandth of the entire body. Other potential 'pre-human' and human bones were found nearby, but some debate still exists about whether they are the Java Man type.

For example, part of a lower jaw was discovered that some have classified as Java Man.[8] For this and other reasons much debate has existed from day one regarding the exact identity of the bones. In the words of Boule and Vallois, the Trinil material was "*tantalizingly incomplete, and for many scientists it was inadequate as confirmation of Darwin's view of human evolution.*"[9]

This fossil find has, ironically, been largely ignored by creationists. Perloff[10] and Davidson[11] mention Java Man briefly. One of the more comprehensive studies in a creationist periodical[12] is based on an article about Java Man by the late Harvard Professor Stephen Jay Gould. Marvin Lubenow's *Bones of Contention,* originally published in 1992, revised in 2004, has a six-page section on Java Man.[13]

Why the find is important

Although controversy has surrounded the find from day one, it was widely touted as proof positive of human evolution in textbooks and popular books for almost

5. MacCurdy, G.G., *Human Origins: A Manual of Prehistory*, D. Appleton, New York, p. 313, 1924.
6. MacCurdy, *Human Origins*, p. 315.
7. MacCurdy, *Human Origins*, pp. 314–315.
8. MacCurdy, *Human Origins*, p. 313.
9. Boule, M. and Vallois, H.V., *Fossil Men: A Textbook of Human Paleontology*, Dryden Press, New York, p. 3, 1957.
10. Perloff, J., Time Magazine's new ape-man, *Creation Matters* **6**(4):1–4, 2001.
11. Davidson, P., Pithecanthropus IV: a human evolutionary ancestor or an artificial reconstruction? *Creation Research Society Quarterly* **32**(3):174–178, 1995.
12. Anonymous, Who was Java Man? *Creation* **13**(3):22–23, 1991; creation.com/javaman.
13. Lubenow, M., *Bones of Contention (Revised and Updated): A Creationist Assessment of Human Fossils*, Baker Books, Grand Rapids, Michigan, pp. 92–97, 2004.

a century.[14] Java Man also occupies an important place in the history of human evolution partially because it was one of the earliest putative ape-man link fossils ever discovered, and was the most widely reputed human evolution fossil, which for decades was considered by many to be a 'missing link' between apes and humans:

> We learned about him in grade school. They called him the ape-man and told us that he was our evolutionary ancestor. The drawings of that beetle-browed, jaw-jutting fellow were quite convincing. In fact, the vast majority of people who believe in human evolution were probably first sold on it by this convincing salesman. Not only is he the best-known human fossil, he is one of the only human fossils most people know.[15]

Java Man was even considered "*one of the most important discoveries ever made in the quest for human origins*"[16] because it was "*the first concrete proof that man has been subject to evolutionary change.*"[17] For this reason it was also prominently displayed for many years in the American Museum of Natural History Hall of the Age of Man along with Piltdown Man and Neandertal Man.[18]

Evidence used at the Scopes trial

Java Man was also a major piece of evidence, along with Piltdown Man, for Darwinism in the Scopes trial. University of Chicago anthropologist Fay-Cooper Cole testified by written documents at the trial that Darwinists had expected to find evidence in ancient rock strata of earlier human forms that more closely resembled the common ancestor of humans and apes. Cole wrote that, on the island of Java, the labourers that Dubois hired to do the work found what they were looking for in 1891, namely "*an attempt of nature*" to evolve a human. Cole also wrote in his court testimony that the Java Man fossils were "*in many ways intermediate between man and the anthropoids*" and that the

> bones were found in undisturbed strata, forty feet below the surface. … These semihuman bones consisted of a skull cap, a femur, and two molar teeth. The skull was very low with narrow receding forehead and heavy ridges of bone above the eye-sockets, while a bony ridge extended from

14. Gould, S.J., Men of the thirty-third division, in *Eight Little Piggies*, W.W. Norton, New York, pp. 124–137, 1993.
15. Lubenow, *Bones of Contention*, p. 86.
16. Milner, R., *The Encyclopedia of Evolution: Humanity's Search for Its Origins*, Facts on File, New York, p. 148, 1990.
17. Boule and Vallois, *Fossil Men*, p. 2.
18. Osborn, *The Hall of the Age of Man*, p. 11.

> between the eye-brows to the top of the head approaching a condition found in the cranium of the anthropoids.[19]

A measurement evaluation which bolstered its missing link status was that Java Man had a cranial capacity of

> between 850 and 900 cubic centimeters, or a little more than half of that of modern man. On the other hand it is half as much again as that of the adult gorilla, and the special development has taken place in these regions whose high development is typical of the brain of man. Hence in this respect this being seems to stand midway between man and the highest anthropoids. … The thigh bone is straight, indicating an upright posture and ability to run and walk, as in man. … If, as seems probable, these four bones belonged to the same individual, he must have been more man-like than any living ape and at the same time, more ape-like than any human known to us. He is known as *Pithecanthropus erectus* or the erect ape-man.[20]

A problem we recognize today is that cranial size is not an accurate measure of intelligence that can be confidently used to distinguish one human being from another. Nonetheless, Shipman claimed the find was so important that she believed Dubois should be honoured as the father of modern paleoanthropology, and she has attempted to rehabilitate him in her recent book.[21] As will be documented below, other scholars are not so sure.

The discoverer biased from day one

Eugene Dubois was born on January 28, 1858, about a year before Darwin published his *Origin of Species* tome in 1859, and 18 months after the first Neandertal skeleton was unearthed in Germany. Born into a conservative Catholic Dutch family, his parents were very supportive of his education.[22] Dubois' strong interest in science motivated his father to send him to the state technical high school with laboratories of the quality similar to a small university. Some local Catholic families objected to Eugene attending this school because they feared—correctly as it turned out—that he would learn at this school "*ideas as well as facts, including that new evolutionary theory.*"[23] Shipman adds that the village elders were

---

19. Cole, F.C., *World's Most Famous Court Trial*, (written testimony in Scopes trial), National Book Company, Cincinnati, Ohio, p. 236, 1925.
20. Cole, *World's Most Famous Court Trial*, p. 236.
21. Shipman, P., *The Man Who Found the Missing Link: Eugene Dubois and his Life Long Quest to Prove Darwin Right*, Simon and Schuster, New York, 2001.
22. Shipman, *The Man Who Found the Missing Link*, p. 11.
23. Shipman, *The Man Who Found the Missing Link*, p. 19.

> horrified that Jean Joseph Dubois would consider sending his son to such a place. "*He'll lose his religion,*" they predict, nodding their heads with conviction. … "*They'll teach him all those anti-Christian theories, and soon he'll believe them. He's a nice boy, a smart boy, but the mayor will be sorry if he sends his son to such a place!*" In the end, they … fuss so tiresomely that Jean Dubois decides to send Eugéne to the HBS in part to defy them. Eugéne remains impeccably polite and studious, but attending the HBS only accelerates the process of his breaking free of convention. By the end of his first year at Roermond, when he is thirteen, he is starting to question the teachings of the Church. … [and] begins to doubt everything, almost reflexively.[24]

After he graduated from the school at age 19, Dubois entered medical school where he was "*exposed to the exciting ideas of Darwinian biologists.*"[25] His Dutch Catholic upbringing openly conflicted with what he was learning about evolution in school—and evolution won out.[26] Dubois lost his religion as his father's friends predicted and became a life-long opponent of Christianity.

While a student at Jena University, Dubois' major professor was the now infamous Ernst Haeckel, an enthusiastic follower of Darwin. Darwin predicted an evolutionary line between modern humans and their ape-like ancestors, but until the Java Man discovery, no plausible candidates were known.[27] In 1877 only a "*scrap or two of fossil evidence for human ancestors, notably the Neanderthal skullcap from Germany,*" existed.[28]

Neandertal Man, though, was far too similar to modern humans to be a convincing link, requiring more exploration to find the prized proof of human evolution. Even more problematic was the fact that many evolutionists determined that modern humans date back almost 100,000 years, but Neandertal was dated at only 35,000 years before present,[29] a fraction of the former date.

Dubois knew these facts and became infected by a drive to find scientific proof for Darwinism—to find the missing link, *Pithecanthropus.*[30] Finding the missing link "*would be the greatest scientific discovery ever.*"[31] Dubois had a powerful motivation to find this missing link—to disprove theism because he now believed

---

24. Shipman, *The Man Who Found the Missing Link*, p. 19.
25. Milner, *The Encyclopedia of Evolution*, p. 147.
26. Regal, B., *Human Evolution: A Guide to the Debates (Controversies in Science), ABC-CLIO,* Santa Barbara, California, p. 64, 2004.
27. Bowden, M., *Ape-men: Fact or Fallacy?* 2nd Edition, Sovereign Publications, Bromley, Kent, UK, Section I, The Piltdown forgery, p. 26, 1977.
28. Milner, *The Encyclopedia of Evolution*, p. 147.
29. Mellars, P., *The Neanderthal Legacy: An Archaeological Perspective from Western Europe*, Princeton University Press, Princeton, New Jersey, pp. 402–403, 1996.
30. Keith, A., *The Antiquity of Man, Vol. I and II,* J.B. Lippincott Company, Philadelphia, p. 438, 1927.
31. Shipman, *The Man Who Found the Missing Link*, p. 22.

"*there is no truth in religion*"—and he was drawn to prove evolution "*with an almost religious fervor.*"[32]

Although trained as a physician and an anatomist, to find his proof Dubois abandoned both his home and a promising career at the University of Amsterdam. He took his young wife and small children halfway around the world to search for Darwin's missing link in a remote part of Dutch East India (now Indonesia). Many felt his quest was based only on a foolish hunch that he would find the missing link there; he had no concrete evidence that this island would produce any fruitful results.

Dubois arrived at the idea of journeying to faraway Java from several sources, including reading Alfred Russel Wallace's account of the orangutan, a human-like animal that lived on two islands in Sumatra.[33] Ernst Haeckel's theory of Asian human origins was also important in Dubois' conclusion that humans first evolved on, or near, Java.[34]

Haeckel was right about one thing: Java was a very good place to look for fossils. Dubois found literally tonnes of them in Java. He shipped 400 cases of the most interesting ones back to Holland, and his workers found so many bones that they sold large numbers to be ground up and sold for medical nostrums (medicines of very dubious use, at times harmful).[35] The bones commonly found included various fish, reptiles, mammals (elephant, rhinoceros, hippopotamus, tapir, assorted ruminants, monkey), and even mollusks of a type still living in the area.[36] How old these bones were is another topic.

The discovery

It took Dubois' workers more than five years to find the first part of his now famous discovery—a molar tooth that he concluded belonged to an extinct ape. A month later and a metre away a heavily fossilized skull cap was discovered by his workers (see figures 2, 3 and 4). He eventually found another tooth and one diseased femur. Dubois concluded in his 1894 monograph that all of these bones belonged together and that they were the missing link between humans and their ape-like ancestors. However, the fossils "*were not lying together, but had been scattered over a distance of about forty-five feet*" or more.[37]

The distance the fossils were found from each other has produced problems that never have been resolved. Cole assumed that the scattering occurred due to the "*action of the ancient river which deposited them.*"[38] The river theory, though, is

32. Shipman, *The Man Who Found the Missing Link*, pp. 19, 24.
33. Milner, *The Encyclopedia of Evolution*, p. 147.
34. Bowden, *Ape-men*, p. 65.
35. Milner, *The Encyclopedia of Evolution*, p. 147.
36. Boule and Vallois, *Fossil Men*, p. 113.
37. Cole, *World's Most Famous Court Trial*, p. 236.
38. Cole, *World's Most Famous Court Trial*, p. 236.

problematic because water adversely affects bone preservation, lending doubt to the long dates claimed for the bones.

Figure 1
Location of the find on the Bengavan River, near Trinil, Java. Note the conditions in this area do not favour preservation. Preservation requites a very dry hot climate such as in places in Africa.
From Aleš Hrdlička, *The Most Ancient Skeletal Remains of Man*, Second Edition, Government Printing Office, Washington, DC, p. 8 plate 1, 1916.

Another reason for the controversy is that Dubois did not personally find the fossils—untrained convict labourers did, creating problems for the find from the start.[39] As Regal concluded, "*The finds were made under circumstances that would later haunt the entire endeavor and threaten to ruin Dubois's reputation.*"[40] Another major problem was that extensive excavation of the area of his original find turned up no clear evidence of any more Java Man fossils.

Yet another problem was that, although a skilled anatomist, Dubois had no fossil experience or training. His hero, Haeckel, was himself "*not particularly enamored of fossils, insisting that a good naturalist could infer biological relations without them.*"[41] Nonetheless, Haeckel concluded that the Java Man bones belonged "*to a creature which seemed admirably suited for the role of the 'missing link'* ."[42] Despite all the major problems with his find, Dubois naively thought he had, at last, proved the evolution of humans.

39. Gould, Men of the thirty-third division, p. 126.
40. Regal, *Human Evolution*, p. 66.
41. Regal, *Human Evolution*, pp. 64–65.
42. Carrington, *A Million Years of Man*, p. 84.

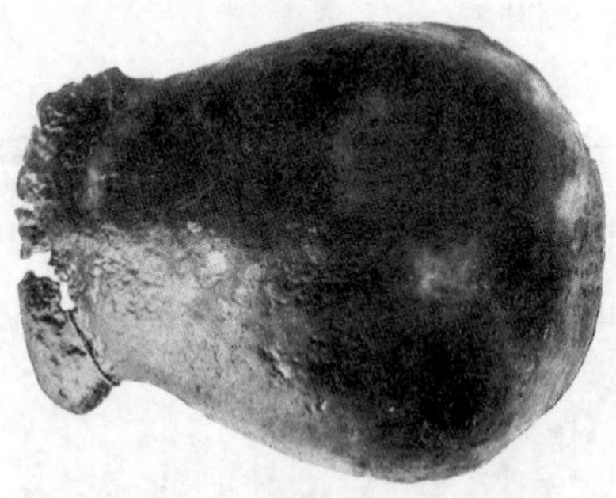

Figure 2
The Java Man skull cap, top view.
Illustration from Aleš Hrdlička, *The Most Ancient Skeletal Remains of Man*, Second Edition, Government Printing Office, Washington, DC, p. 10 plate 2, 1916.

Dubois returns to Europe

Dubois returned to Europe believing that he had found the critical missing link required to prove ape-to-human evolution. His find, though, with good reason generated controversy from the very beginning.[43] Dubois had supporters, but he also "*generated a firestorm of doubt and protest in this perennially contentious field*" of physical anthropology.[44] The outcry against his claims was so great that some claimed that "*in anger as a desperate rearguard defense against a growing and withering attack,*" Dubois locked the bones in a safe (accounts differ—some claim he actually buried them under his own house) for almost twenty-five years.[45] Theunissen concluded that Dubois locked up his bones, not as a desperate defence against critics, but because he was suspicious of others to the point of paranoia.[46] Nonetheless, the fossils "*embroiled their discoverer in bitter controversies for the rest of his life.*"[47]

His colleagues had good reasons to be skeptical, and his many critics are still very skeptical today. Rather than proving evolution, it at best proved the enormous variety of human morphology. A further problem is, despite "*intensive research efforts throughout Indonesia, only Java has yielded fossils of* [putative] *early hominids*" and further attempts at the "*stratigraphic levels that yielded the original Dubois finds* ... [in] *an attempt to recover more Pithecanthropus fossils ... greatly augmented the*

43. Shipman, *The Man Who Found the Missing Link*, p. 11.
44. Gould, Men of the thirty-third division, p. 127.
45. Gould, S., Men of the thirty-third division, *Natural History* **99**(4):12–20, 1990; p. 14.
46. Quoted in Gould, Men of the thirty-third division, p. 130.
47. Milner, *The Encyclopedia of Evolution*, p. 148.

number of fossil mammals but failed to recover any new hominid material."[48] This situation offers yet another parallel with the Piltdown find.

Part of the problem was Dubois' dogmatic attitude about his conclusions. He was "*wedded to his conclusions*" to the degree that he

> dismissed later similar finds made outside Peking, China, in the 1920s and '30s. Oddly, when more *Pithecanthropus* material was unearthed along the Solo River in 1936, Dubois dismissed it too. Anthropologist Ralph Von Koenigswald found most of a young skullcap of what he called Pithecanthropus II (also known as Mojokerto child). Dubois went so far as to accuse Von Koenigswald of either faking the skull or poorly reconstructing it. What is so strange about Dubois is that where others fought to have their finds included in the human family line, he fought to keep his out.[49]

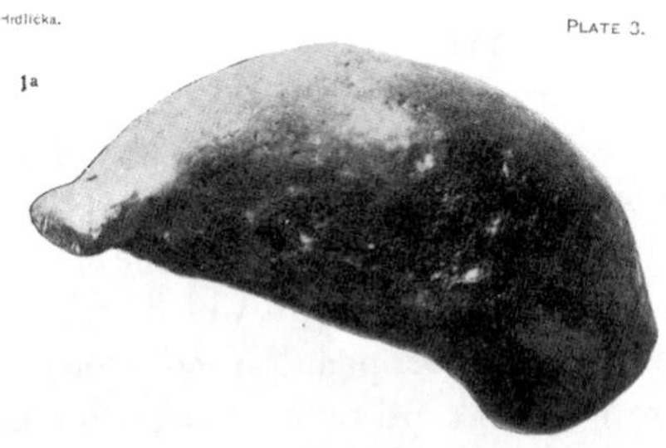

Figure 3
The Java Man skull cap, side view.
From Aleš Hrdlička, *The Most Ancient Skeletal Remains of Man*, Second Edition, Government Printing Office, Washington, DC, p. 10 plate 3, 1916.

Gould concluded that Dubois' arguments in support of his find were "*weakly constructed*" and he was "*willfully blind to opposing evidence.*"[50] In spite of his dogmatic attitude, or possibly due to it, from

> the early 1900s to the early 1920s Dubois remained silent on the issue of his finds. However, when he did finally resume consideration of these finds in the 1920s and 1930s, his views underwent considerable change—ultimately concluding that *Pithecanthropus* was an extinct hylobatid ape.[51]

48. Spencer, F., *History of Physical Anthropology*, Vol. 1, Garland, New York, p. 544, 1997.
49. Regal, *Human Evolution*, p. 67.
50. Gould, Men of the thirty-third division, p. 136.
51. Spencer, *History of Physical Anthropology*, p. 545.

Based on his detailed cranial research work, Dubois eventually argued that his find was of a genus allied to the gibbon family.[52] In his review Gould provides numerous examples of the evidence he believed supported his conclusion. His paper reveals the major difficulty of drawing conclusions from a few bone fragments that have been distorted by the fossilization process. Gould argued that Dubois' last conclusion was not designed to "*demote the greatest discovery of his life*" but rather to exalt it.[53] Gould suggests that Dubois was arguing for *Pithecanthropus* being "*the direct ancestor for all modern humans*", quoting him as saying "*I still believe, now more firmly then ever, that the Pithecanthropus of Trinil is the real 'missing link'.*"[54]

Others argued that Dubois had, in fact, backed down from his original claim in the face of his own scientific research. In my reading of his paper it appears he genuinely felt that his gibbon-like conclusions were correct and he had amassed a fair amount of evidence to support it. Dubois died on December 16, 1940, at age 82, alone, bitter, and an angry man.[55]

The teeth and jaw fragment

The Java Man premolar is morphologically very close to modern human teeth but smaller, "*not unlike a human lower premolar.*"[56] The root tip is bifurcated, a trait sometimes found in modern humans. Furthermore, the buccal and lingual branches are directly opposite, in contrast to apes in which they are located obliquely.[57] Some considered the second-left lower premolar tooth too small to belong with the other molars.[58] A third tooth, a third-right molar, was found 40 km (25 miles) away, and is no longer considered to belong to Java Man but "*might well belong to another individual of the same genus.*"[59]

Commenting on one of the teeth, declared by one scientist to be fully human, MacCurdy says: "*should this prove to be the case, Pithecanthropus could no longer be regarded as a precursor of man*".[60] A jaw fragment was found by G.H.R. von Koenigswald between 1936 and 1940 in the same horizon as the skull cap, but some

52. Dubois, E., "On the fossil human skulls recently discovered in Java and *Pithecanthropus Erectus*," *Man: A Monthly Record of the Anthropological Science* **37**(1):1–7, 1937; pp. 6–7.
53. Gould, Men of the thirty-third division, p. 22.
54. Gould, Men of the thirty-third division, p. 23.
55. Regal, *Human Evolution*, p. 67.
56. MacCurdy, G., *The Coming of Man: Pre-Man and Prehistoric Man*, The University Society, New York, p. 19, 1935.
57. MacCurdy, *The Coming of Man*, p. 19.
58. MacCurdy, *Human Origins*, p. 314.
59. MacCurdy, *Human Origins*, p. 319.
60. MacCurdy, G., Race in the Pacific Area, with Special Reference to the Origin of the American Indians: Antiquity of Occupation, *American Anthropologist*, **17**(4):708–711, 1915.

40 km away.[61] For this and other reasons, the jaw fragment is usually not regarded as likely belonging to the Trinil Java Man type.

The femur

The femur is also controversial for several reasons. A major concern is that it was not found until several months later and at great distance from the skull cap—about 15 m (50 feet). This fact indicates that the skull cap and femur may not belong together or, at the least, makes it difficult to draw this conclusion. Most scientists now conclude the femur is from a modern human because it "*could scarcely be distinguished from our own.*"[62] The femur also has a pathologic lesion of unknown origin near the small trochanter. Assuming the very unlikely conclusion that they belong together, the femur length indicates that the height of Java Man was close to the average male today—from 5 ft 3 in to as much as 5 ft 8 in tall.[63,64]

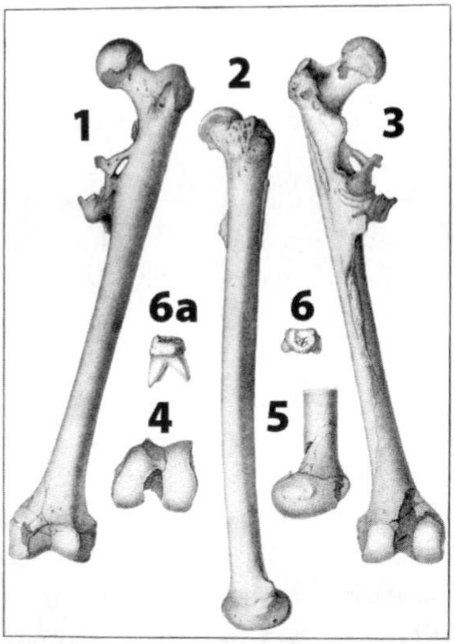

Figure 4
The Java Man femur bone, five views, and tooth, two views. (1) from front (2) from side (3) from behind (4) from below (5) lower end from other side (6) right third upper molar (6a) same tooth from behind.
From Aleš Hrdlička, *The Most Ancient Skeletal Remains of Man*, Second Edition, Government Printing Office, Washington, DC, p. 12 plate 4, 1916.

The femur would also indicate that Java Man walked fully erect, and not like an ape or an intermediate between an ape and human, thus the modern classification for Java Man, *Homo erectus.* One current estimate puts the average *Homo erectus* male at about 62 kg (138 pounds) and 6 ft tall, and the average *Homo erectus* female at about 53 kg (117 pounds) and 5 ft 3 in tall, supporting the *Homo erectus* classification.[65]

61. Theunissen, B, *Eugene Dubois and the Ape-Man from Java*, Kluwer Academic, Dordrecht, The Netherlands, p. 159, 1989.
62. Gould, Men of the thirty-third division, p. 126.
63. Gould, Men of the thirty-third division, p. 23.
64. Boule and Vallois, *Fossil Men*, p. 122.
65. Swisher, C.C. III, Curtis, G.H, and Lewin, R., *Java Man: How Two Geologists' Dramatic Discoveries Changed our Understanding of the Evolutionary Path to Modern Humans*, Scribner, New York, p. 159, 2000.

The skull cap fragment

The skull cap fragment, which looked like a turtle shell, was found about 90 cm (three feet) away from the first find, the tooth. The skull cap was partially encased in a solid rock matrix, requiring its careful removal. Many anthropologists noted that the skull cap was remarkably similar to that of a Neandertal.[66] Since only one skull cap clearly identified as the Java Man type was found at this location, we have no way of knowing how typical the skull is of the putative Java Man type, if it in fact existed.

A major issue in determining the identity of Java Man was the cranial capacity of the skull—a task made difficult because less than 10% of the skull was recovered. The cranial capacity of Java Man was first estimated to be 855 cubic centimetres, and then re-estimated at around 900 cc, or two-thirds that of a modern human adult and somewhat small for a *Homo erectus* skull.[67] Both estimates place the Java Man skull capacity at a level much larger than that of an adult male gorilla, which is 550 cc, but smaller than that of a modern European adult human, about 1350–1400 cc.[68] *Homo erectus* skulls average over 1,000 cc—about 75% of the skull volume of average humans today, but almost twice that of an ape.[69] This value must be adjusted for the average size of *Homo erectus*. Many *Homo erectus* were slightly built compared to modern humans, although evidently, on average, were as tall. *Homo erectus* females probably were shorter than modern human females.

The most well-known picture of the skull cap indicates a small skull and prominent brow ridges similar to the Neandertal, but other pictures, especially a profile, indicate a very different skull shape.[70] If the level of scientific analysis that was completed on the Piltdown Man could also be done on Java Man bones, especially the skull cap, its identity may be more confidently determined.

A major trait of the skull cap was the prominent brow ridges. Louis Leakey and others have regarded brow ridges as specialized traits rather than primitive ones. Prominent brow ridges are also commonly seen in native Australians and a few Africans and Caucasians. It largely reflected frontal sinus size, not cranial capacity.[71] The skull brow ridges typical of the Neandertal type and *H. Sapiens idaltu* also have distinct brow ridges very similar to Java Man. Furthermore, brow ridge size is not consistently reflected in the face morphology of living subjects.[72]

---

66. Lubenow, *Bones of Contention*, p. 95.
67. 1165, p. 14.
68. Gibbons, A., Oldest members of *Homo sapiens* discovered in Africa, *Science* **300** (5626):1641, 2003.
69. Stringer, C. and Andrews, P. *The Complete World of Human Evolution*, Thames and Hudson, New York, p. 138, 2005.
70. Tattersall, I. and Schwartz, J., *Extinct Humans*, Westview Press, p. 150, 2001.
71. Sodera, V., *One Small Speck to Man: The Evolution Myth 2*, Vij Sodera Productions, West Sussex, UK, p. 379, 2003.
72. Sodera, *One Small Speck to Man*, p. 378.

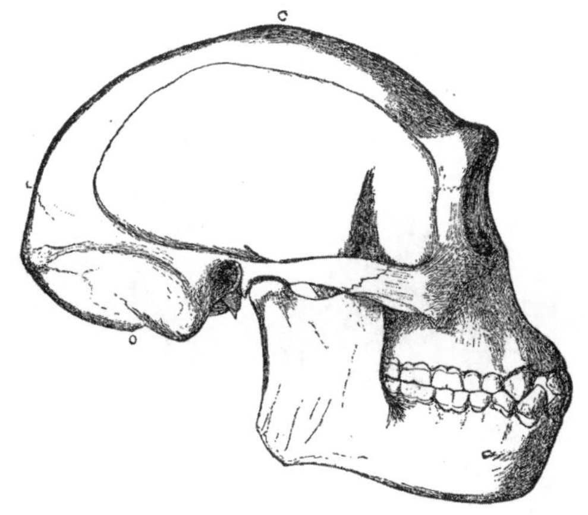

Figure 5
An artist's attempt at the restoration of the skull.
From Aleš Hrdlička, *The Most Ancient Skeletal Remains of Man*, Second Edition, Government Printing Office, Washington, DC, p. 11, 1916.

Do the fossils belong together?

A major problem is, given how far apart from each other they were found, whether the Dubois fossil fragments belong together. The river theory, as noted above, is still very controversial. McCabe deals with the problem by concluding "*it is immaterial whether or not these bones belong to the same individual. If they do not, we have remains of two or three individuals of the same intermediate species.*"[73] The problem, of the difficulty in ascribing the bones to one body, results in all restoration attempts being "*pure flights of fancy*" although some new finds have supported the conclusion that Java Man is a *Homo erectus*.[74]

It is also important to stress that if Java Man were complete and unequivocally morphologically intermediate between humans and some apes, this would support, but not prove, that humans descended from ape-like ancestors. Boule and Vallois note

> that resemblance does not always imply descent. Even if, in the sum of his known characters (poor at the best), *Pithecanthropus* actually forms a structural link between the Great Apes and Man, it does not necessarily follow

73. McCabe, J., *The Story of Evolution*, Small Maynard and Company, Boston, Massachucetts, p. 272, 1912.
74. Boule and Vallois, *Fossil Men*, p. 123.

> that he must be regarded as a genealogical link; and this distinction is not, as has been asserted, merely a question of words.[75]

Figure 6
Photographs of an adult and a juvenile chimpanzee.
From Adolf Naef 1926.

Assuming the femur belongs with the skull cap, Java Man is estimated by some to be closer to 5 ft tall, and not 5 ft 8 in tall as some calculate.[76] If this is true, his cranial capacity would be proportionately close to that of modern humans. Another possibility, rarely considered, is that Java Man, at least the skull top, was from a female, or even a youngster or a short adult. Much depends on whether the femur belongs to the skull cap because, for the cranial estimates to have meaning, comparisons must control for height. If the average size of the Java Man was significantly shorter compared to modern humans, his brain would be estimated at about 1,450 cc, or significantly *above* the modern human average brain volume for the low end of adults of 1130 cm^3 for women and 1260 cm^3 for men.[77]

In the 1920s Dubois revealed for the first time that "*there were four more fossil bones from the area where his material had been discovered.*"[78] The first skeleton, found in mining operations, had been given to him in 1889, which is why he started excavating there the following year. Called Wadjak I, Dubois concluded that the

75. Boule and Vallois, *Fossil Men*, p. 125.
76. Moody, P.A., *Introduction to Evolution,* Harper and Brothers, New York, p. 215, 1953.
77. Cosgrove, K.P., Mazure, C.M. and Staley J.K., Evolving knowledge of sex differences in brain structure, function and chemistry, *Biological Psychiatry* **62**(8):847–855, 2007; p. 848.
78. Brace, C.L. and Montague, A., *Human Evolution: an introduction to biological anthropology*, 2nd edition, Macmillan, New York, p. 204, 1977.

skull (its cranial capacity was 1,550 cc) was from a modern female. Another skull, Wadjak II, likely a male, had a cranial capacity of 1,650 cc.[79]

These findings all raise serious questions about the validity of Java Man as an ape-human link. It is possible that the very human femur belonged to the Wadjak tribe type. Keith concluded that "*the Wadjak race is linked to the negro and original Australian stocks.*"[80] Brace and Montague concluded that they "*looked more like Australian Aborigines than modern Indonesians*", implying that the Wadjak pre-dated the Aborigines.[81] Others argued that these skulls were examples of Java Man, both because of their morphological similarity and their close proximity to Java Man.

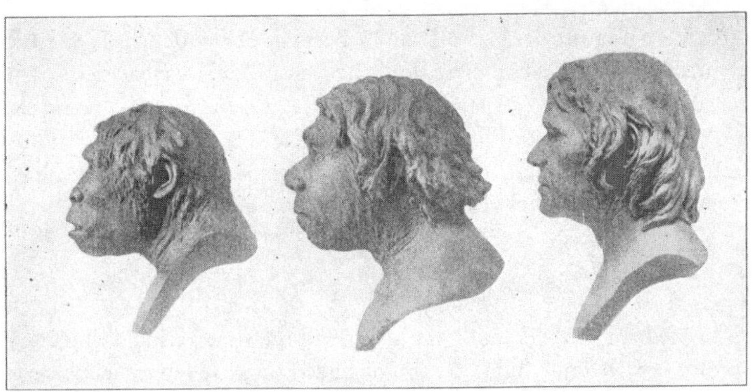

FIG. 258. Three stages in human development

Restorations to suggest the probable appearance of primitive types of human beings. From left to right, *Pithecanthropus erectus* (Java), *Homo neanderthalensis* (Germany), and the "Man of Cro-Magnon," *Homo sapiens* (France). These photographs are of figures molded by Professor J. H. McGregor on the basis of fragments of primitive man discovered from time to time in various parts of the world

Figure 7
From a leading textbook, shows the three evolutionary stages leading to humans. First was Java Man, then Neandertal Man and, last, Cro-Magnon Man looking like a modern white man.
From Gruenberg, page 495

A major question is, although the Wadjak bones (skull and jaw fragments) were evidently discovered by Dubois in 1890, why were they hidden away and inaccessible to other researchers for 26 years after his return from Java?[82] Were these skulls and other fragments far too human and likely to cause serious doubt about Java Man's status as a missing link between humans and apes? Dubois carried the answers to his grave. The reason may be that if the

79. Keith, *The Antiquity of Man*, p. 441.
80. Keith, *The Antiquity of Man*, p. 446.
81. Brace and Montague, *Human Evolution*, pp. 203–204.
82. Keith, *The Antiquity of Man*, pp. 438, 440.

> aborigines of Australia have sprung from the Wadjak type, as Dr. Dubois is inclined to suppose, then evolution has taken a retrograde course, for the average cranial capacity of the male Australian is 1287 c.c.—300 c.c. less than in the Pleistocene people of Java.[83]

The Java Man skull cap also lacked any evidence of the sagittal crest possessed by the largest anthropoid apes, the orang and the gorilla, and the skull convolutions seem to be "*of the human type.*"[84] As of 2003, a total of 23 skulls, teeth and bones from 100 or more *H. erectus*-like individuals have been uncovered in Java. A study of these has supported the conclusion of some that Java Man was simply a human variant like Neandertal Man.

Harvard paleoanthropologist Dan Lieberman concluded from a study of a recently discovered, more complete skull than Java Man (a *Homo erectus* skull also from Java) that it was "*an important find because it is the first H. erectus find with a reasonably complete cranial base, and it looks modern.*"[85] A micro-computerized tomography analysis of the 2001 discovery and its modern-looking traits has added new problems to "*the ongoing controversy surrounding the origin of modern humans.*"[86]

Dating problems

Dubois needed a date that would put his find in the time period of history that he believed apes evolved into humans. He concluded they lived in the Pliocene era 7 to 10 million years ago. Jean, Harrah, and Herman placed Java Man at about 500,000 to 700,000 years ago.[87] Others confidently stated that the skull, teeth and left femur have "*been definitely established as of Middle Pleistocene age.*"[88]

The bone fragments dated by the presence of other fossils indicate that it occupied an era around the middle Pleistocene, usually thought to be about 450,000 to 550,000 years ago. Judging by the associated fauna and flora, some experts placed Java Man at the lower Quaternary instead of the upper Tertiary.[89] Milner notes the find is now dated from 250,000 to 500,000 years old, a window so large that it limits the find's usefulness as a potential transitional form.[90]

---

83. Keith, *The Antiquity of Man*, pp. 443–444.
84. Boule and Vallois, *Fossil Men*, pp. 116, 119.
85. Quoted in Gibbons, A., Java skull offers new view of *Homo erectus*, *Science* **299**(5611):1293, 2003.
86. Baba, H. *et al.*, *Homo erectus* Calvarium from the Pleistocene of Java, *Science* **299**(5611):1384–1388, 2003; p. 1387.
87. Jean, F., Harrah, E., and Herman, F., *Man and his Biological World, Revised Edition*, Ginn and Company, New York, p. 459, 1952.
88. Rogers, J.S., Hubbell, T.H. and Byers, C.F., *Man and the Biological World*, McGraw-Hill, New York, pp. 416–417, 1942.
89. MacCurdy, *Human Origins*, p. 314.
90. Milner, *The Encyclopedia of Evolution*, p. 148.

In spite of these assertions, producing a valid date for Java Man is close to impossible because the major source of information about the fossils is based on fragments that, in turn, were based on their location in the rock stratum in which they were discovered, and exactly where the bones were found is disputed. Furthermore, the different fossils that Dubois' workers found are likely from different dates.

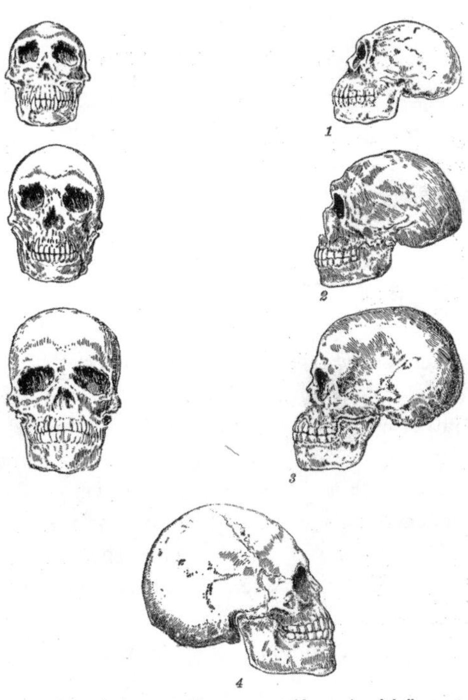

FIG. 256. Ancestors of man represented by remains of skulls

1, *Pithecanthropus erectus*, the "erect ape-man" of Java; 2, the Neanderthal man; 3, the negroid man of Laussel; 4, Nebraska glacial man. These four types represent successive advances in the evolution of the human races, although we must not think of them as a straight series of our ancestors. Compare the size of the brain at different stages of development: Pithecanthropus, 850 cc.; Piltdown, 1300 cc.; Neanderthal, 1600 cc.; modern man, 1500–1800 cc.

Figure 8
An early picture of the now-disproven progression from primitive man to modern man. The numbering shows (1) Java Man (2) Neandertal Man (3) 'Negroid man' (4) Nebraska Man. The caption gives the brain size of *Pithecanthropus* as 850 cc, Piltdown as 1300 cc, Neandertal as 1600 cc and modern man as 1500–1800 cc. Piltdown Man has been proven to be a hoax, Neandertal Man and the 'negroid' skull (3) fully human.
From Gruenberg, 1924, p. 493.

The bones were found in a moist environment, and within a few years or so bone is rapidly damaged in this environment. Deterioration of fossils is caused by water, weather, and temperature. Bone mineral crystals tend to be long and narrow and, as a result, the needle-shaped splinters that form from water trapped in the pore spaces that exist in all bone causes these pores to widen. As they widen, even more water is allowed to enter, forming yet larger crystals.[91] The major causes of deterioration of

91. Calcagno, J.M., *Mechanisms of human dental reduction: A case study from post-Pleistocene Nubia*, Department of Anthropology, University of Kansas, Lawrence, Kansas, 1989.

animal body parts, including bone, all of which were potential problems with Java Man, include:

1. drying and wetting (very important in all semi-arid, arid, and temperate areas, or in humid areas with monsoonal climates);
2. formation of salt crystals during drying (and the analogous formation of ice crystals during freezing); and,
3. freezing and thawing (an important process, especially at high altitudes or for short periods of time).

The Indonesian climate is almost entirely tropical and typically rainforest. The area's relative humidity ranges between 70% and 90%, very poor conditions to preserve fossils. The ideal preservation conditions include a very dry desert with rare rainfall, the opposite of Java, Indonesia. These are yet other major reasons to doubt the veracity of the Java Man finds, especially their age.

Opinions on Java Man today

Java Man is now classified by many experts as *Homo erectus* and not a 'missing link' between man and apes. Lubenow concluded that Java Man, at least the skull cap, is not a missing link, but rather is a true human of the Neandertal type.[92,93] Milner concurred, noting that Java Man is "*considered an early human species, not a 'missing link' between ape and man … Dubois spent most of his life trying to press a wrong conclusion.*"[94] It was concluded as early as the mid-1900s that Java Man was probably in the genus *Homo*. Swisher, Curtis, and Lewin conclude that *Homo erectus* was not apelike and "*every human species that followed erectus was distinctly human.*"[95] They add that "*Homo erectus* was the first human species with a large brain, a large human-shaped (as opposed to ape-shaped) body, and long lower limbs.[96] One history of the status of Java Man notes that Dubois' fossils originally were

> named *Pithecanthropus erectus*, meaning "*erect ape-man.*" For years a controversy as to whether the creature was ape or man raged around these meager fossils. Fortunately he and his fellows are now known from portions of four skulls and some additional bones. One individual, because of large size and massive structure of the teeth and jaws, has been given the name *Pithecanthropus robustus*, which seems to indicate that he belonged to a different *species* from his smaller compatriots. … It seems unlikely that the Java

92. Lubenow, *Bones of Contention*, p. 87.
93. See also Gish, D., *The Fossils Still Say No*, Institute for Creation Research, El Cajon, California, pp. 280–285, 1995.
94. Milner, *The Encyclopedia of Evolution*, p. 148.
95. Swisher *et al.*, *Java Man*, p. 131.
96. Swisher *et al.*, *Java Man*, p. 131.

> men really belonged to separate species or that they should be placed in a separate genus (*Pithecanthropus*) from ourselves (*Homo*).[97]

From these contradictions one researcher concluded:

> The *Homo erectus* type appears to be one of many varieties of humans that have existed historically and still exist today. When all of the early and late *Homo erectus* fossils are measured, there are, in fact, few unequivocal indicators of significant differences between *H. erectus* and *H. sapiens.*[98]

Judging by the drawings of the skull, Johanson and Edey show Java Man to be very close to Neandertals.[99] An American Museum of Natural History publication wrote that disagreements about Java Man

> were plentiful. Some said the skull was that of an idiot, others that it was normal. Some said it was human, others that it was a monkey, a chimpanzee, or a gibbon. The Java Man could speak. The Java Man could not speak. Dubois seems to have had his fill of this, for after a while he retired from the fray, and he took Pithecanthropus with him and locked him up in his house for twenty years.[100]

As late as 1935 only one voice was still "*claiming that Pithecanthropus was not a man at all, but a very large kind of gibbon-like hominid. Sadly, the voice was that of the aged Dubois.*"[101] Dubois "*fought doggedly throughout the rest of his life to maintain that Pithecanthropus was not early man but a giant man-like ape.*"[102]

The one thing that almost all researchers agree on today is that Java Man was not a missing link between apes and humans.

Java Man major evidence of evolution for decades

The enormous controversy documented above did not stop Darwin fundamentalists from touting Java Man as impeccable proof of human evolution. Despite this controversy, Java Man was featured in both textbooks and popular books, often uncritically, as a major evidence of human evolution for several decades. As early as 1912 McCabe claimed the following about Java Man:

---

97. Moody, *Introduction to Evolution,* p. 238.
98. Tattersall, I., Delson, E. and Couvering, J.V. (Eds), *Encyclopedia of Human Evolution and Prehistory*, Garland Publishing, New York, p. 262, 1988.
99. Johanson, D. and Edey, M., *Lucy: The Beginnings of Humankind*, Simon and Schuster, New York, p. 33, 1981.
100. Howells, W., *Mankind So Far*, Doubleday, Garden City, New York, p. 135, 1947.
101. Milner, *The Encyclopedia of Evolution*, p. 148.
102. Boule and Vallois, *Fossil Men*, p. 3.

> Fortunately, although these patriarchal bones are very scanty—two teeth, a thigh-bone, and the skull-cap—we are now in a position to form some idea of the nature of their living owner. They have been subjected to so searching a scrutiny and discussion since they were found in Java in 1891 and 1892 that there is now a general agreement as to their nature. At first some of the experts thought that they were the remains of an abnormally low man, and others that they belonged to an abnormally high ape. The majority held from the start that they belonged to a member of a race almost midway between the highest family of apes and the lowest known tribe of men, and therefore fully merited the name of "*Ape-Man*" (Pithecanthropus). This is now [in 1912] the general view of anthropologists. The Ape-Man of Java was in every respect entitled to that name.[103]

As late as 1945 Java Man was viewed as the precursor of Solo Man, who is postulated to have evolved into the Australian Aborigines.[104] Typical of the uncritical and irresponsible claims about Java Man was the leading biology text by Gruenberg that showed in both its 1919 and 1924 editions (see Figure 8 on page 253) a frontal and side-view drawing of the skull of an ape-man purported to be Java Man that was presented as a documented human ancestor, adding that that they should not be thought of as a straight series of human ancestors.[105,106] He writes that Dubois' find of bones in Java had proven that those who accepted the evolution of plants and animals but "*hesitated to accept the same explanation for the appearance of man upon earth*" are wrong because the Java fossils are a "*very satisfactory*" evidence of the evolution of modern man from prehuman ancestors, concluding it "*probably represents a 'missing link'.*"[107] Gruenberg (figure 8) includes a picture of the progression from ape-man to modern man, which includes Java Man, Neandertal Man, and, lastly, Cro-Magnon Man.[108] He gives no indication of the major problems with the Java Man find documented above.

Professor Winchester, in a text that went through two editions and 14 reprintings, under the subheading "*Earliest Human Remains*" wrote that the Java Man find involved "*three teeth, the top of a skull and a thigh bone*" and never indicated in his discussion any concerns about the validity of the fossils.[109] Jean, Harrah, and

---

103. McCabe, *The Story of Evolution*, p. 271.
104. Andrews, R.C., *Meet Your Ancestors: A Biography of Primitive Man*, Viking Press, New York, endpaper, 1945.
105. Gruenberg, B., *Elementary Biology*, Ginn and Company, Boston, Massachucetts, p. 493, 1919.
106. Gruenberg, B., *Elementary Biology*, Ginn and Company, Boston, Massachusetts, p. 493, 1924.
107. Gruenberg, *Elementary Biology*, 1919, fig. 7, p. 494.
108. Gruenberg, *Elementary Biology*, 1919, p. 494.
109. Winchester, A.M., *Biology and its Relation to Mankind*, D. Van Nostrand, Princeton, New Jersey, p. 851, 1962.

Herman also assumed that all four of the Dubois fossils belong together, writing in 1952 that his "*teeth are of human type, the straightness of the thigh bone indicates that its possessor walked almost as erect as present man*" but admits that the "*skull has been the center of much discussion and controversy.*"[110] In fact, the controversy involved mostly the teeth and the leg bones, not the skull cap.

Rogers, Hubbell and Byers in a leading biology textbook gave a detailed description of Java Man, writing that he was "*5 feet 6 inches in height … of stocky build, and though he stood erect, he was bull-necked, with outthrust head … an extraordinarily ugly, brutish creature …* [and there] *is no telling whether he could speak, and no direct proof that he could use tools.*"[111] This is a good example of conclusions about Java Man going far beyond the evidence.

Bradley concluded from this confusion that, regardless of which theory about Java Man is correct, whatever "*the truth may be, whether he was our granduncle or our grandfather, or just an exalted ape, the Java ape-man breaks down the barrier between ape and man. He is just the sort of creature that should have existed if ape and man share a common ancestor.*"[112]

Some early textbooks, while touting the Java Man remains as "*half a million years old … which possess many of the attributes of 'missing links'*" briefly indicate some problems, such as noting that the "*famous find*" actually consists merely of a skull-cap, since the associated bones proved to be unrelated.[113] Woodruff also wrote that "*the much vaunted Java Man has become overshadowed by newer discoveries*" and then listed Peking Man, Piltdown Man, Heidelberg Man, Neandertal Man and, lastly, Cro-Magnon Man.[114]

One of the most honest discussions in a popular textbook is by Rogers, Hubbell and Byers who stated the Java Man finds are

> without doubt the most famous of all fossils, for they seemed to bridge the gap between man and the higher apes in a most remarkable fashion. They have been intensively studied, and thousands of pages have been written about them. Some students thought that Pithecanthropus was a very primitive and apelike man, others that he was a very advanced and manlike ape, and prolonged controversies raged over his status.[115]

Dubois' survey of the literature, cited below, which was completed before the textbooks cited in this paper were published, illustrates the problem with Java Man that had been outlined decades before. His survey of the conclusions of 19 scientists who

110. Jean *et al.*, *Man and his Biological World*, p. 458.
111. Rogers, J.S., Hubbell, T.H., and Byers, C.F., *Man and the Biological World*, McGraw-Hill, New York, pp. 495–496, 1952.
112. Bradley, J., *Parade of the Living*, Coward-McCann, New York, p. 220, 1930.
113. Woodruff, L.L., *Foundations of Biology*, Macmillan, New York, pp. 608–609, 1948.
114. Woodruff, *Foundations of Biology*, pp. 614.
115. Rogers *et al.*, *Man and the Biological World*, p. 417.

had studied Java Man fossils "*found that five of them judged the remains to be those of an ape; seven judged them to be human; and seven, including Dr Dubois himself, considered them to be intermediate between the ape and man—a sort of 'missing link'*."[116] As noted above, in the end

> Dr. Dubois, after a careful restudy of the whole problem in the spring of 1937, came to the conclusion that *Pithecanthropus* was probably not a man but an ape—a superior sort of gibbon that lived in trees and, although it had a larger brain, neither talked nor thought man-fashion. Dr. Aleš Hrdlička, the late great American anthropologist, on the basis of his study in 1932, believed that we cannot assert that *Pithecanthropus* was a form of early man or a type that eventually evolved into man. He thought that the most we could say from the evidence then available was that this creature was a high primate "*of as yet uncertain ancestry and no known progeny,*" but far advanced "*in what may be termed the humanoid direction.*" On the other hand, Dr. Koeinigswald of Bandoeng, Java, who found some of the new skulls of *Pithecanthropus*, decided after a careful study of the skulls in 1937 that the Java Man is definitely human and perhaps the earliest man that ever walked the earth.[117]

In view of this literature survey of the leading evolutionists that Dubois summarized, it is clear that the numerous claims solemnly cited as fact in the biology textbooks above declaring Java Man to be a link between men and apes, a so-called missing link, were then unwarranted, and likewise today are unwarranted. Fortunately, in newer books about human evolution Java Man is often ignored, although occasionally is at least mentioned.

Java Man an embarrassment today

Java Man is today often ignored in textbooks and reference books on human evolution and, if he is covered at all, is mentioned only briefly, often with no hint of the many major problems with the find. For example, Professor Stanley Rice wrote: "*Java Man was the first human fossil to be found outside of Europe, and the first fossil that could be interpreted as being more primitive than modern humans.*"[118] He adds that Dubois found a skull cap and a thighbone, implying that they were both proven to be *Homo erectus*. In another article he added more details, noting that the femur indicated Java Man walked upright.[119]

Rice does acknowledge that Dubois "*began to doubt that the specimens were really intermediates between apes and human. The more he studied the Southeast gibbon, the*

116. Jean *et al.*, *Man and his Biological World*, p. 458.
117. Jean *et al.*, *Man and his Biological World*, p. 459.
118. Rice, S., *Encyclopedia of Evolution*, Facts on File, New York, p. 188, 2007.
119. Rice, *Encyclopedia of Evolution*, p. 138.

more he came to believe that Java Man was just a large gibbon."[120] As noted above, the claim that Dubois concluded "*Java Man was just a large gibbon*" is not fully accurate.

Tattersall, Delson, and Van Couvering state under the subtopic "*First Discoveries in Asia*" only that Dubois found a skull cap and "*a remarkably complete and modern looking femur*", implying that they were both part of Java Man.[121] Professor Strickberger mentioned only that "*hominid fossils found near the Solo River in Java, dated to less than 250,000 years ago, show brain volumes averaging 1,100 to 1,200 cc. significantly larger than … H. erectus fossils*"[122] found in the same area, yet with 'older' traits, leading to the (speculative) conclusion that it comes from a different source. Notice how very different values are given in the literature for both the reported age and brain size. More typical today is to totally ignore Java Man (and in the case of the leading textbook on evolution by Mark Ridley, the human fossil record as a whole).[123]

Conclusions

Java Man was touted as major evidence of human evolution for decades, a conclusion that, at best, was based on very questionable evidence. Reasons for questioning the validity of Java Man include the difficulty of reconstructing the creature based on only a few bone fragments; the uncertain conditions surrounding its find; the major dating and preservation problems; the problems with the conclusion that all of the bones identified as Java Man were, in fact, part of the same individual; and the many other problems reviewed. All of these problems and more were noted in the literature, but were rarely acknowledged in the over two dozen textbooks intended for high school and college students that were surveyed for this chapter.

Although Java Man is now widely classified as a *Homo erectus,* and not a missing link between humans and our putative ape-like ancestors, it is difficult to come to any firm conclusion about its identity.[124,125,126] The fact that its identification has been so problematic is why its classification included a Neandertal, a creature like or related to a gibbon, an extinct giant ape, a primitive man, and finally a *Homo erectus.* Another problem is the amazing similarity of many fossils used to argue for human evolution, such as the similarity of *Australopithecus* to juvenile chimps, as shown in figure 6. The motivation of its discoverer to find the 'missing link', and the motivations of Darwinists to prove human evolution, all played a part in the

120. Rice, *Encyclopedia of Evolution*, p. 138.
121. Tattersall *et al.*, *Encyclopedia of Human Evolution and Prehistory*, p. 260.
122. Strickberger, M., *Evolution*, Jones and Bartlett, Boston, Massachusetts, p. 479, 2000.
123. Ridley, M., *Evolution*, Blackwell, Cambridge, Massachusetts, 2004.
124. Gibbons, Java skull offers new view of Homo erectus.
125. Gibbons, A., *The First Human*, Doubleday, New York, 2006.
126. Parker, S., *The Dawn of Man: A Fascinating Visual Account of the Emergence and Evolution of Earth's Dominant Species*, Quantum Books, London, 2005.

leading role that Java Man was assigned as proof of this. In short, the evidence is far too problematic to come to any valid conclusion about who Java Man was.

The Java Man case history is only one of many examples of fragmentary evidence and controversy in paleoanthropology that was touted by leading scientists as convincing evidence of human evolution from some ape-like common ancestor. The fact is, "*Most hominid fossils, even though they serve as a basis for endless speculation and elaborate storytelling, are fragments of jaws and scraps of skulls.*"[127] And, as Ann Gibbons concluded, "*Starting with Dutch anatomist Eugene Dubois's discovery of Java Man in Indonesia in 1891, many fossils have been proposed as the missing link, only to be bumped from that spot when an even older and more primitive fossil was found.*"[128]

Acknowledgments

I wish to thank Marvin Lubenow, M.S., Clifford Lillo, M.A., Jody Allen, RN, Wayne Frair, Ph.D., Mary Ann Stuart, M.A, and John UpChurch for their review of earlier drafts of this chapter.

127. Gould, S.J., *The Panda's Thumb*, W.W. Norton, New York, p. 126, 1980.
128. Gibbons, *The First Human*, p. 6.

CHAPTER 16

Two modern fossil forgeries exposed: The *Confuciusornis* and the *Archaeoraptor* fossil forgeries

Introduction

The history of the brief life of the *Confuciusornis* and the *Archaeoraptor* fossil forgeries is reviewed. The claim that these fossils were transitional forms illustrates some of the major difficulties in interpreting the history of life from a few teeth and bone fragments. It also illustrates how easy it is to fool professionals and authorities, although in this case the forgeries were so poorly done that they were exposed within a matter of months. The "*art of faking fossils has a long history*" and is a greater problem today than ever before in history.[1]

A cast of an example of a *Confuciusornis sanctus* fossil in an exhibit in Naturmuseum Senckenberg, Frankfurt-am-Main, Germany. Source: Creative Commons CC0 1.0

The *Confuciusornis*

The lakebeds of Liaoning, China, have produced a large number of Early Cretaceous fossils, including some complete articulated (assembled) skeletons. Many fossils are scattered fragments, and the interpretation of these fossils has caused special problems. The specimens are generally crushed and fragile. Only one side of the skeleton is exposed, the other lies imbedded in the underlying slab and hidden from view. Few Liaoning specimens have been studied in all

1. Stone, R., Altering the past: China's faked fossils problem, *Science* **330**(6012):1740–1741, 2010; p. 1741.

> three dimensions, and knowledge of most Liaoning species is either incomplete or rests upon composite reconstruction.[2]

Dr Timothy Rowe and his associates completed a high-resolution X-ray computerized tomography (CT) study of one specimen of a primitive bird named *Confuciusornis.* The team produced a set of serial CT scan slices from which they were able to create a

> 3-D computer model of the entire skeleton. Manipulation of the model with volumetric rendering software provided anatomical information … to study the down-facing side of the skeleton in considerable detail. And although badly flattened, the opportunity to observe the third dimension helped considerably in interpreting skeletal structure. Preliminary analysis of these new data support [*sic*] the argument that *Confuciusornis* is more closely related to modern birds than to *Archaeopteryx*.[3]

This example of a *Confuciusornis* fossil unearthed in China appeared to be a perfect museum-quality fossil of a bird-dinosaur transitional form until Rowe examined it by cross-section computerized tomography.[4] Scanning revealed it was a forgery built from three separate layers—two (the top and bottom) were constructed from natural material and one (the middle layer) was added by humans. The bottom layer was a piece of shale that was used as the backing on which grout was placed to hold the dozens of separate pieces of rock and bone used to construct the forgery.[5]

The grout contained both air bubbles and metallic inclusions, indicating the grout was a recent addition placed on top of the solid shale layer that lacked fractures. The top layer consisted of one or more other fossils that did not belong to the original fossil, and part of the radius (a bone in the bird's wing) was even upside down! Rowe concluded that the fossil was, without question, a forgery.

Archaeoraptor forgery

When Rowe's work became widely known, soon other fossils were sent to him for examination. One of the most well known was *Archaeoraptor liaoningensis,* commonly called *Archaeoraptor.* This was only one of the latest fossil forgeries used in an attempt to prove Darwinism. Dubbed the evolutionary find of the century, it

2. Rowe, T., Ketcham, R., Guan, J., Alcober, O. and D. Dufeau, High-resolution X-ray CT study of the primitive bird *Confuciusornis*, *Journal of Vertebrate Paleontology* **19**(Supp. 3):72A, 1999.
3. Rowe *et al.*, High-resolution X-ray CT study of the primitive bird *Confuciusornis*, p. 72A.
4. Werner, C., *Evolution: The Grand Experiment Vol. 1*, New Leaf Press, Green Forest, Arkansas, p. 170, 2007.
5. Werner, *Evolution*, pp. 171–172.

was touted as proving that birds evolved from theropod dinosaurs. A superficial evaluation indicated it had the "*appearance of two different animals blended together, just as Darwin predicted.*"[6]

This fossil was discovered in the northeastern province of Liaoning, China, the location of most of the new putative feathered dinosaur species. The find was first announced in October 1998 at a press conference held at the National Geographic Society headquarters in Washington, DC. The announcers included paleontologist Philip J. Currie of the Royal Tyrrell Museum of Paleontology in Drumheller, Alberta, Canada; Stephen Czerkas of the Dinosaur Museum in Blanding, Utah; and Professor Xing Xu of the Institute of Vertebrate Paleontology and Paleoanthropology in Beijing.

The National Geographic Society "*trumpeted the fossil's discovery ... as providing a true missing link in the complex chain that connects dinosaurs to birds.*"[7] The turkey-sized *Archaeoraptor* was also used by certain prominent paleontologists as proof that birds evolved from dinosaurs and provided a "*long-sought key to a mystery of evolution*"—where birds came from.[8]

The *Archaeoraptor liaoningensis* fossil slab now proven to be not only a forgery, but a poorly done forgery.
Source: Wikipedia

The first published documentation of the *Archaeoraptor* find was in a full-colour, well-illustrated feature article in the November 1999 issue of the *National Geographic* magazine.[9] The article touted the fossil as "*a missing link between terrestrial dinosaurs and birds that could fly*" and claimed it was "*the best evidence since* Archaeopteryx" that birds evolved from carnivorous dinosaurs.[10] Rowe *et al.*, wrote that the

> *Archaeoraptor* fossil was announced as a "*missing link*" and purported to be possibly the best evidence since *Archaeopteryx* that birds did, in fact, evolve from certain types of carnivorous dinosaurs. It reportedly came from Early

6. Werner, *Evolution*, p. 174.
7. Simons, L.M., *Archaeoraptor* fossil trail, *National Geographic* **198**(4):128–132, October 2000; p. 128.
8. Simon, *Archaeoraptor* fossil trail, p. 128.
9. Stone, Altering the past, p. 1741.
10. Sloan, C., Feathers for *T. Rex*? *National Geographic* **196**(5):99, 1999.

> Cretaceous beds of China that have produced other spectacular fossils transitional between birds and extinct non-avian dinosaurs.[11]

The find, "*once proclaimed as a key intermediate between carnivorous dinosaurs and birds,*" turned out to be the Piltdown-man forgery story all over again.[12,13,14] It is part of what some now consider an epidemic of fraud in science, especially in the field of evolutionary studies.[15,16,17]

The "*missing link between terrestrial dinosaurs and birds that could actually fly*" had the "*arms of a primitive bird and the tail of a dinosaur*" and was soon touted by the media as a "*true missing link in the complex chain that connects dinosaurs to birds.*"[18] The "*true missing link*" soon "*soared off in a burst of media fame.*"[19]

Suspicions arise early

The fossil soon caused no small sensation. *Nature* reported that, as a result of the find, the "*paleontology community has been rocked by a Chinese 'bird' fossil that may be a new species,*" adding that many observers suspected that the fossil was "*a composite of more than one fossil that was illegally smuggled out of China.*"[20] The importance of the fossil was indicated by the $1.6 million price set on it by the insurer once the experts judged it as "*an important link in dinosaur and bird evolution.*"[21] Nonetheless, suspicions about the fossil arose early. Monastersky wrote that

> Red-faced and downhearted, paleontologists are growing convinced that they have been snookered by a bit of fossil fakery from China. The "*feathered*

11. Rowe, T., Ketcham, R.A., Denison, C., Colbert, M., Xu, X. and Currie, P.J, The *Archaeoraptor* forgery, *Nature* **410**(6828):539–540, 2001; p. 539.
12. Zhou, Z., Clarke, J.A. and Zhang, F., *Archaeoraptor's* better half, *Nature* **420**(6913):285, 2002.
13. Bergman, G., A history of the Piltdown hoax, *Rivista di Biologia/Biology Forum* **96**(3):457–484, 2003.
14. Bergman, J., The history of *Hesperopithecus*: the human-ape link that turned out to be a pig, *Rivista di Biologia/Biology Forum* **99**(2):205–224, 2006.
15. Feder, K.L., *Frauds, Myths, and Mysteries: Science and Pseudoscience in Archaeology*, 6th edition, McGraw Hill, 2008.
16. Chang, K., On scientific fakery and the systems to catch it, *The New York Times Science Times*, pp. 1, 4, 15 October 2002.
17. Rowe *et al.*, The *Archaeoraptor* forgery.
18. Sloan, Feathers for *T. Rex*? p. 100.
19. Chin, G., Disappearing discovery of the year: *Archaeoraptor*, *Science* **290**(5500):2224, 2000.
20. Dalton, R., Feathers fly over Chinese fossil bird's legality and authenticity, *Nature* **403**(6771):689–690, 2000; p. 689.
21. Dalton, Feathers fly over Chinese fossil bird's legality and authenticity, p. 689.

> *dinosaur*" specimen that they recently unveiled to much fanfare apparently combines the tail of a dinosaur with the body of a bird.[22]

The paleontologists had doubts because of their "*concerns about the tail*" due to the fact that the bones connecting it to the body are missing and the slab showed evidence of reworking. The dinosaur-bird evolution supporters had convinced themselves, however, that the two parts belonged together as part of one animal until they could no longer deny the overwhelming evidence against this conclusion.[23]

Professor Xu evaluated the fossil and found a "*strong resemblance*" between the rear half of *Archaeoraptor* and an unnamed dinosaur.[24] High-resolution computerized X-ray tomography evaluations completed by Rowe confirmed Xu's evaluation. Xu now had clear evidence that the fossil consisted of more than two "*unmatched pieces, skillfully pasted over.*" Rowe had completed his examination three months before the *National Geographic* article was published, but *National Geographic* ignored his evidence and published the article anyway.[25] This fact says a great deal about their efforts to defend Darwinism.

The body has now been identified as that of the fossilized fish-eating bird called *Yanornis martini* and the tail as that of the small winged dromaeosaur *Microraptor zhaoianus.*[26] *M. zhaoianus* was a medium-to-large sized animal—all known specimens of *M. zhaoianus* are larger than *Archaeopteryx* except one recently discovered example.[27]

The fossil had evidently been "*badly shattered and put together … deceptively*" by, it appears, amateurs.[28] When carefully examined by X-ray tomography "*it took about five minutes*" to determine that the fossil had been faked.[29] Rowe found that some rock pieces consisted of dense rock, others less dense rock; and some pieces were thin while others were thick.[30] Another problem was that the "*foot bones were exact copies of each other.*"[31]

Rowe determined that a total of 39 rock pieces did not belong to the fossil and 26 fossil bones were from a total of four other animals. The fossil was built from a total of 88 pieces of rock and bone held together by mortar and paint. In the end, the whole story involved "*rampant egos clashing,*" "*misplaced confidence,*" "*wishful*

22. Monastersky, R., All mixed up over birds and dinosaurs, *Science News* **157**:38, 2000.
23. Monastersky, All mixed up over birds and dinosaurs, p. 38.
24. Grant, J., *Corrupted Science: Fraud, Ideology and Politics in Science*, Facts, Figures and Fun, Surrey, UK, p. 78, 2007.
25. Simon, *Archaeoraptor* fossil trail, p. 130.
26. Zhou *et al.*, *Archaeoraptor's* better half, p. 285.
27. Xu, X., Zhou, Z. and Wang, X., The smallest known non-avian theropod dinosaur, *Nature* **408**(6813):705–708, 2000; p. 705.
28. Simons, *Archaeoraptor* fossil trail, p. 130.
29. Dalton. R., Fake bird fossil highlights the problem of illegal trading, *Nature* **404**(6779):696, 2000.
30. Werner, *Evolution*, p. 174.
31. Werner, *Evolution*, p. 174.

thinking," and even a few "*zealots and cranks.*"[32] Simons adds that this case did not reflect well on any of the people involved.[33]

Even the original *National Geographic* article noted that the bird section was part of a bird more advanced than *Archaeopteryx*, the earliest known bird, but the tail was "*strikingly similar to the stiff tails of a family of predatory dinosaurs called dromaeosaurs*" (National Geographic Society press release October 15, 1999). Before the forgery's exposure, the scientist supporters rationalized these major contradictions by claiming that this "*mix of advanced and primitive features is exactly what scientists would expect to find in dinosaurs experimenting with flight.*"

As Chin noted, "*none of these problems sank in at the National Geographic.*"[34] Consequently, they printed their story in spite of the clear evidence that it was a forgery, to their later chagrin. This is only one more example of Darwinism encouraging premature acceptance of published finds, resulting in incorrect conclusions being proclaimed as fact—exactly what happened in the Piltdown and Nebraska Man fiascos.

Paleontologist Philip Currie, a leading proponent of the dinosaur-to-bird evolution theory and a member of the National Geographic scientific team that supported the validity of the find, admitted "*this embarrassment will follow me the rest of my life.*"[35] The editor of *National Geographic* claimed the *Archaeoraptor* article was "*reviewed by six leading paleontologists*" and the staff worked on the story "*for a full year*" to ensure accuracy and high standards of both the facts and the presentation in the magazine.[36] Not one of these six leading experts detected the hoax.

Another problematic issue was that Rowe gave a copy of his report documenting that it was a fake to a *National Geographic* staffer before they published the article. One *National Geographic* staffer told Rowe in response to his evidence of forgery "*all of these Chinese things have been fiddled with.*"[37] Rowe was shocked when *National Geographic* publicly announced that this was a valid fossil. *National Geographic*, finally convinced by the overwhelming evidence that the fossil was a forgery, did retract the article. The original article was 10 pages long, however the retraction was only a few sentences long and printed in the forum section that no doubt few people, in contrast to the original article, saw.

The tip of the iceberg

Archaeoraptor is evidently only the tip of the iceberg—the "*flood of 'improved,' reconfigured and composite*" fossils now in existence, many ending up in the world's museums. This finding has caused major problems in defending various theories

32. Simon, *Archaeoraptor* fossil trail, p. 128.
33. Simon, *Archaeoraptor* fossil trail, p. 128.
34. Chin, Disappearing discovery of the year, p. 2221.
35. Friend, T., The 'missing link' that wasn't, *USA Today* **18**(98):2a, 2000.
36. Allen, W., Fooled, but not foolish, *Nature* **404**(6778):541, 2000.
37. Quoted in Werner, *Evolution*, p. 177.

about evolution.[38] What some describe as a "*flood of sham fossils pouring out of China*" has with good reason caused no small number of people to be skeptical of all new fossil finds from China.[39,40] In December 2009, *Nature* reported the withdrawal of more than 70 papers by Chinese authors whose research was of questionable originality. Evolutionary fossil bird expert Alan Feduccia, referring to the famous 'feathered dinosaur' fossil widely touted by *National Geographic* that turned out to be a fake, stated:

> *Archaeoraptor* is just the tip of the iceberg. *There are scores of fake fossils out there,* and they have cast a dark shadow over the whole field. When you go to these fossil shows, *it's difficult to tell which ones are faked and which ones are not.* I have heard that there is a fake-fossil factory in northeastern China, in Liaoning Province, near the deposits where many of these recent alleged feathered dinosaurs were found.[41]

Paleontologist Jiang Da-yong concluded that the "*fake fossil problem has become very, very serious*" and that "*more than 80% of marine reptile specimens now on display in Chinese museums*" may be fakes or doctored.[42] Another example is when the curator of paleontology at a major museum invited Da-yong to examine some fossils that they intended to purchase for an exhibit. In a review of the collection Da-yong "*identified a dozen specimens … including a 15-meter-long ichthyosaur that was 'totally fake'.*"[43] A major problem is that authentication is difficult because

> High-quality fossil forgeries can fool paleontologists just as easily as forgeries in the art community … Luis Chiappe, an early bird expert at the Natural History Museum of Los Angeles County in California, says that he will "*always be skeptical of any specimen that is so neatly arranged, so well preserved in a single slab with little bone missing.*"[44]

The motivation is often, but not always, money. The Liaoning province economy has significantly benefited because

> local farmers—who vastly outnumber paleontologists—have become better and better at finding fossils and working with intermediaries and dealers

38. Stone, Altering the past, p. 1740.
39. Balter, M., Authenticity of China's fabulous fossils gets new scrutiny, *Science* **340**(6137):1153–1154, 2013; p. 1154.
40. Stone, Altering the past, p. 1740.
41. Feduccia, A., Discover dialogue: ornithologist and evolutionary biologist Alan Feduccia plucking apart the dino-birds, *Discover Magazine* **24**(2):16, 2003.
42. Stone, Altering the past, p. 1740.
43. Stone, Altering the past, p. 1741.
44. Balter, Authenticity of China's fabulous fossils gets new scrutiny, p. 1154.

> to create composites that can be sold for higher prices. "*We can't blame the farmers for this … . It's money.*" … creating composite fossils has become a small-scale industry in fossil-rich areas of China. "*I have personally seen these composite fossils being constructed in workshops or little factories*" across several counties in Gansu province, Deng says. "*In each workshop, there are bones on shelves like parts in factories.*"[45]

He added that some paleontologists have concluded that drastic steps are required, such as every fossil find should be CT-scanned before conclusions about the fossil are published and the scans should be included in the supplementary information provided with the fossil. Balter concluded that this precaution "*has become necessary, at least for high-profile specimens on which major evolutionary claims are being based.*"[46]

Aurornis xui is a well-preserved fossil that reportedly came from China's Tiaojishan Formation. Pascal Godefroit and colleagues believe it represents the earliest branch of dinosaurs from which evolutionists believe birds directly evolved.

From: Godefronit *et al.*, A Jurassic avialan dinosaur from China resolves the early phylogenetic history of birds, *Nature* **498**:359–362, 20 June 2013. Reprinted by permission.

Yet another case

Since *Archaeoraptor* the problem has worsened. Yet another fossil discovery named *Aurornis*, or 'dawn bird', has been called into question. The single specimen, now called *Aurornis xui,* was discovered by a farmer in China's Liaoning Province. It was unidentified until palaeontologist Pascal Godefroit found it last year in the museum at the Fossil and Geology Park in Yizhou. When the

45. Balter, Authenticity of China's fabulous fossils gets new scrutiny, p. 1154.
46. Balter, Authenticity of China's fabulous fossils gets new scrutiny, p. 1154.

> paleontologists unveiled a fossil purporting to be the earliest known bird, media outlets rapidly spread the news. Most relayed the team's contention, published in *Nature*, that the 160-million-year-old fossil from China dubbed *Aurornis* "*resolves*" long-standing controversies about the early evolutionary history of birds.[47]

In the case of *Aurornis*, Balter "*concluded that CT scanning is essential ... Without it, there will always be lingering doubt that the specimen is genuine.*"[48] One major problem is the fossil was not found during the team's excavations, but had been acquired from a fossil dealer, causing concern about the details of the finding and raising the possibility that the fossil could have been altered, or even was a fake. This critical information was not in the main body of the *Nature* paper on the fossil. Furthermore the "*authors acknowledge the possibility that the specimen may be 35 million years younger than reported; they are conducting additional tests to verify its provenance.*"[49] So far, the debate continues.

Conclusions

In the end, the *Archaeoraptor* fiasco was "*a disaster for science.*"[50] In a field based on little solid empirical evidence, many assumptions, and strong personalities, the *Archaeoraptor* affair was not surprising. It also illustrates the conflicts historically common among scientists in the paleontology field.[51] The unprofessional, at times even fraudulent, behaviour of the leading participants in this case is far from what one would expect from highly trained professionals. Holden concluded that a problem in paleontology is the fact that this field naturally excites much interest due to our curiosity about the origins of life, and because conclusions that are

> of emotional significance to many must be drawn from extremely paltry evidence, it is often difficult to separate the personal from the scientific in disputes raging within the field. ... The primary scientific evidence is a pitifully small array of bones ... . One anthropologist has compared the task to that of reconstructing the plot of *War and Peace* with 13 randomly selected pages. Conflicts tend to last longer [than in other fields] because it is so difficult to find conclusive evidence to send a theory packing.[52]

47. Balter, Authenticity of China's fabulous fossils gets new scrutiny, p. 1153.
48. Balter, Authenticity of China's fabulous fossils gets new scrutiny, p. 1154.
49. Balter, Authenticity of China's fabulous fossils gets new scrutiny, p. 1153.
50. Dalton, Feathers fly over Chinese fossil bird's legality and authenticity, p. 690.
51. Chang, On scientific fakery and the systems to catch it.
52. Holden, C., The politics of paleoanthropology, *Science* **213**(4509):737–740, 1981; p. 737.

The fact is, paleontology is an "*unexacting kind of science.*"[53] Tattersall and Schwartz[54] even asked rhetorically if, given the way it is practised by some persons, paleoanthropology should be considered a hard science at all. And, although the whole field of paleontology is more sophisticated today than even just a decade ago, the fact remains that "*modern as the undertaking has become, it continues to be riddled with controversies and dominated by personalities.*"[55]

The unmasking of forgeries in new research is forcing so many revisions in the evolution field that a *Time* magazine senior science editor wrote, as noted above, that, as a former science teacher, many facts about evolution he believed to be true have now been determined to be false. He later reminisced that "*just about everything*" he taught his students in this area has turned out to be wrong.[56]

This is not the first major forgery used to prove evolution, nor, most likely, will it be the last.[57] And unfortunately

> "*Some of these fakes are masterful.*" Kevin Padian, a paleontologist at the University of California (UC), Berkeley says that researchers should be prepared to subject any fossil of uncertain provenance to extra tests, such as computed tomography (CT) scanning, to prove that specimens are genuine.[58]

One conclusion is "*Chinese and Western paleontologists concur that many provincial museums are chock-full of composites, chimeras, and other phony fossils.*"[59] As a result of the number of fraud cases, suspicions exist about all of the specimens found in the

> fabulous fossil fields in northeast China's Liaoning province, where *Aurornis* and dozens of other new species of feathered dinosaurs and early birds have been found over the past 15 years. Some of the country's leading paleontologists have been outspoken about a growing number of fake and composite specimens from Liaoning and other fossil-rich areas of China. … "*This is a big concern,*" says Zhou Zhonghe, director of the Institute of Vertebrate Paleontology and Paleoanthropology (IVPP) in Beijing. "*Illegal and unscientific collecting and commercial trading,*" he says, have flooded the market with

53. Medawar, P., quoted in Hill, A., The gift of Taungs, *Nature* **323**(6085):209, 1986.
54. Tattersall, I. and Schwartz, J.H., Is paleoanthropology science? Naming new fossils and control of access to them, *The Anatomical Record* **269**(6):239–241, 2002.
55. Holden, The politics of paleoanthropology, p. 737.
56. Quoted in Headland, T.N., Revisionism in ecological anthropology, *Current Anthropology* **38**(4):605–630, 1997, p. 605; and Long, E.V., "To our readers", *Time* **143**(11):4, 14 March 1994.
57. Chin, Disappearing discovery of the year.
58. Feduccia, Discover dialogue, p. 1153.
59. Stone, Altering the past, p. 1740.

> fake fossils and caused an "*irretrievable loss*" of crucial information, such as where authentic fossils came from and how old they really are.[60]

Nor is evolutionary biology the only scientific discipline where fraud is a problem. The related area of archaeology, which shares several features with that of paleontology, has also had its share of fraud.[61,62] Even though much progress has been made in these fields in the past century by many dedicated researchers, a major result of the "*flood*" of fake fossils into museums and collections which "*are supposed to enlighten—not con—the public*" has been an erosion of public trust in paleontology,[63] and, it could be added, in evolution. We must wonder how many of the other dino-bird fossils are also forgeries. In conclusion, until paleontologists can find a solution to the fake fossil problem, "*controversies like the one over Aurornis are likely to become more frequent. The flood of fossil fakes … is going to haunt Chinese vertebrate paleontology for the next 100 years.*"[64]

---

60. Balter, Authenticity of China's fabulous fossils gets new scrutiny, p. 1153.
61. Feder, *Frauds, Myths, and Mysteries.*
62. In archaeology, provenance has become an important issue. There are journals that refuse to publish papers on artifacts of uncertain provenance. The antiquities market attracts many unscrupulous people—forgers, thieves, and the like—and researchers must be constantly on guard against deception. If it cannot be verified where the artifact came from, then it must be subjected to a very thorough examination before any interpretation derived from it is given serious consideration. Of course, sometimes even artifacts with provenance of the highest certainty may be rejected to avoid unwelcome implications—particularly so if they happen to confirm some aspect of the biblical record.
63. Stone, Altering the past, p. 1740.
64. Feduccia, Discover dialogue, p. 1154.

CHAPTER 17

Evolutionary throwbacks: Atavisms, another tragic chapter in the history of Darwinism

Introduction

Darwinists once taught that some humans were 'evolutionary throwbacks' which in some ways reverted both physically and mentally to their prehuman origins. This chapter reviews the history of these evolutionary throwbacks that are commonly termed atavisms. Examples of so-called atavisms include tails, extra fingers and nipples, and various other body abnormalities such as considerable body hair. It is concluded that no known biological mechanism can account for atavisms from our past putative evolutionary ancestors. The probable causes of the claimed atavisms include genetic malfunctions, hormonal problems, or diseases. The research reviewed shows why the atavism concept has been discarded like its relatives, the vestigial and nascent organ theories.

History of the theory

Throughout Western history most people have accepted the view that each animal species was specially created in much the same form in which it exists today. Although some ancient philosophers, such as Lucretius, taught that animal species had evolved slowly due to various environmental influences, most natural philosophers believed that biological organisms had changed very little, if at all, throughout most of history.[1]

Long before Darwin published his famous 1859 work, *The Origin of Species*, various evolution theories were discussed by several leading biologists, including some of Darwin's relatives, but Darwin's ideas became the most widely known. Evolution did not receive widespread support until Darwin introduced his evolution theory by natural selection in the mid-1800s. His work, more than any other, caused evolution to gain rapid acceptance and, in turn, influenced almost all other

1. Collier, K., *Cosmogonies of our Fathers*, Octagon Books, New York, 1968.

academic disciplines, even the behavioural sciences.[2,3] One of Darwin's central lines of evidence was the theory of atavisms, the reactivation of long-silent traits that cause the reappearance of one or more long-lost evolutionary ancestral characters.[4,5] In evolutionary theory atavisms are defined as the reappearance of lost traits, physical or behavioural, that were typical of the atavist's remote heritage and not displayed in its recent ancestors.[6]

Atavisms

The term atavism is from the Latin *atavus* signifying an 'ancestor', and *atavus* is a form of *avus*, which means 'a great-great-great-grandfather'. As a biological idea, atavism meant that some individuals reverted in certain ways, both physically and mentally, to an earlier evolutionary type.

The human atavism idea was widely popularized, evidently first by Darwin when he wrote that certain people may be "*reversions to a savage state from which we are not removed by many generations.*"[7] Traits such as supernumerary (extra) nipples, toes, and fingers all were viewed as physical evidence of human atavism.[8] The evolutionary cause of this physical degeneration was never satisfactorily explained by Darwin or anyone else. This problem, though, did not seem to stop it from becoming widely accepted.

Atavistic types

One of the most comprehensive discussions of the various hypothetical atavisms is the work of Yves Delage. Following Delage, Professor Richard Lull divided atavisms into three groups as follows:

(1) ***Family atavism.*** The transmission, within a family, of individual traits in latent conditions for several generations and their sudden reappearance.[9] Examples

2. Papa, E.R., Social sciences, positivism, and political engagement in the European debate on the Italian school of criminal anthropology (18761900), *Critica-Sociologica* **67**:90–113, 1983.
3. Lentini, O., Organicism and social action from Ardigo to Pareto, *Quaderni-di-Sociologia* **29**(2):192–215, 1981.
4. Tintant, H. and Devillers, C., Atavism in present and past; its function in evolution, *Bulletin de la Societe Zoologigue de France Evolution et Zoologie* **120**(4):327–334, 1995.
5. Fryer, G., The case of the one-eyed brine shrimp: are ancient atavisms possible? *Journal of Natural History* **33**(6):791–798, 1999.
6. Verhulst, J., Atavisms in *Homo sapiens*: a Bolkian heterodoxy revisited, *Acta Biotheoretica* **44**(1):59–73, 1996.
7. Darwin, C., *The Descent of Man*, John Murray, London. Reprinted 1896 by D. Appleton and Co., New York, p. 137, 1881.
8. Taylor, I., Walton, P. and Young, J., *The New Criminology: for a social theory of deviance*, Routledge, New York, p. 44, 2013.
9. Lull, R., *Organic Evolution*, Macmillan Co., New York, p. 97, 1932.

include the appearance of a trait such as red hair in a child that has not manifested itself in the parents but in the grandparents, or even in the great-grandparents. This is not a true atavism, but is simply the effects of one or more recessive genes that are expressed in the phenotype as a result of genetic recombinations resulting from two or more recessive allelic gene pairs that occur in one genotype. This phenomenon is familiar to undergraduate genetics students.

(2) ***Race atavism.*** The more or less regular reappearance in a race of characters of another race, from which the first may be derived. Race atavism often refers to traits common to putative earlier 'primitive races' such as the Neandertals in someone of a more 'advanced race'. Race atavism is similar to family atavism except that the concept is concerned only with *specific* characteristics, such as those introduced into the family by miscegenation (inter-racial marriage). An example includes the appearance of an excessive amount of body hair on a person of a nationality that normally does not have much body hair, such as Chinese.[10]

This trait could be due to the presence of genes that entered the family's gene pool as a result of a racial intermarriage that occurred several generations previously. An example is a Chinese child who had an ancestor that married a Pakistani several generations earlier and possesses a trait of this grandparent.

Since division of humans into races is somewhat arbitrary, what could be called a race atavism is somewhat dependent on the observer's subjective judgment. An example Lull used of a race atavism is the "*profuse development of hair on the face and body which occasionally occurs in humans, such as the Russian 'dog man' Adrain Jeftichjew.*"[11] Darwinists claim that the trait comes from our pre-human primate ancestors. Actually, this is not a true race trait because profuse body hair to the degree found on these individuals is not a characteristic of *any* known past race, but is a genetic abnormality known as hirsutism. Some traits classified as race atavisms are actually teratology atavisms (see below).

(3) ***Teratology atavism.*** From *teras* or *tera* (Greek for "*wonder*" or "*monster*"), a teratology atavism is the appearance in a person of abnormal characters which, however, are normal in other supposedly ancestral races. This type of atavist has certain physical characteristics found in modern animals that were assumed to have been common among the atavist's evolutionary ancestors. These traits are abnormal for the race in which they appear, but normal in "*other races supposed to be ancestral.*"[12] This is the only 'true' atavistic type, and is what is referred to both in the literature and this chapter: "*Exemplifying this are the external hind limbs of which a single recorded incidence occurred in a hump back whale taken off Vancouver. The ancestral terrestrial atavus of the whales undoubtedly had these structures, which were gradually lost among other adaptations to aquatic life.*"[13] In other words, their limbs

10. Topping, A., Hairy wild men of China, *Science Digest* **89**(7):64–67, 113, 1981.
11. Lull, *Organic Evolution*, p. 97.
12. Jordan, D. and Kellogg, V., *Evolution and Animal Life*, D. Appleton, New York, p. 166, 1908.
13. Lull, *Organic Evolution*, p. 97.

were assumed to be a genetic throwback to multi-thousands of previous generations when whales were land animals.

Another example Lull[14] suggested was the *fistulae,* the "*permanent abnormal openings of the neck that sometimes occur in the human subject,* [which] *have been considered as relics of the ancient gill-slits of our piscine* [i.e. fish] *ancestry.*"

Sir Charles Lyell even attributed the occasional appearance of extraordinary mental powers in fields as diverse as religion, ethics, philosophy, and the sciences to atavisms—if

> we believe mankind to have risen slowly from a rude and humble starting point, such leaps may have successively introduced not only higher and higher forms or grades of intellect, but at a much remoter period may have cleared at one bound the space which separated the highest stage of the unprogressive intelligence of the inferior animals from the first and lowest form of improvable reason manifested by Man.[15]

Darwin claimed atavisms were evidence for evolution

The concept of atavism was a major line of evidence that Darwin used to support his theory because he believed a "*reversion to a former state of existence*" was the probable cause of certain "*abnormal resemblances*" to apes, such as certain muscular variations found in human subjects. He claimed this could be explained only by the theory that humans are

> descended from some ape-like creature, [as] no valid reason can be assigned why certain muscles should not suddenly reappear after an interval of many thousands of generations in the same manner as with horses, asses, and mules, dark coloured stripes suddenly reappear on the legs and shoulders, after an interval of hundreds, or more probably thousands of generations. These various cases of reversion are … closely related to those of rudimentary organs.[16]

Examples Darwin gives include

> parts which are rudimentary in man, as the os coccyx in both sexes, and the mammae in the male sex are always present; whilst others, such as the supracondyloid foramen, only occasionally appear, and therefore might have been introduced under the head of reversion. These several reversionary structures,

14. Lull, *Organic Evolution*, p. 97.
15. Lyell, C., *Geological Evidences of the Antiquity of Man*, John Murray, London, p. 504, 1863.
16. Darwin, *The Descent of Man*, p. 43.

as well as the strictly rudimentary ones, reveal the descent of man from some lower form in an unmistakable manner.[17]

Human atavistic tails

An example of a 'tail' in a child from India. They are usually surgically removed and generally consist of adipose and connective tissue, central bundles of striated muscle, blood vessels and nerves, and are covered by skin.

The most frequently cited modern example of an atavism is the occasional occurrence of 'tails' in newborn humans. Human tails have been used as a proof for evolution by scientists from Darwin's time[18] to today. Stories "*of tailed men are old and widespread, and tailed races were supposed to reside in almost every country.*"[19] An example Gould gives is "*Struys, a Dutch traveller in Formosa* [Taiwan—Ed.] *in the seventeenth century, describes a wild man … who had a tail more than a foot long, which was covered with red hair like that of a cow.*" He also notes an earlier report from Hibernia [Ireland] about a sighting of a group of people with long tails by Berengarius Carpensis, who, being unable to approach them, did not know if "*the tails were fleshy or cartilaginous.*"

Although hundreds of tailed human cases were reported between 1850 and 1900 "*during the heyday of recapitulation theory and the height of the debates over Darwinism,*" very few cases have been well documented until the latter part of this century.[20] A major problem in understanding the etiology of human tails is that conclusions about them are typically based on very few cases that likely have multiple causes.[21] Gould and Pyle[22] noted that some of the past tail claims were found to be people who wore artificial appendages either for show or, as Andrews notes in the reference below, to exploit others. The well-documented cases have largely disproved the atavistic tail theory.

17. Darwin, *The Descent of Man*, p. 43.
18. Darwin, *The Descent of Man*, p. 29.
19. Gould, G. and Pyle, W., *Anomalies and Curiosities of Medicine*, W.B. Saunders, New York, p. 277, 1896.
20. Ledley, F.D., Evolution and the human tail, *New England Journal of Medicine* **306**(20):1212, 1982.
21. Gish, D.T., Evolution and the human tail, *Impact,* No. 117, 1983.
22. Gould and Pyle, *Anomalies and Curiosities of Medicine*, p. 277.

Due to the difficulty of both researching and verifying these historical accounts—and they vary greatly, both in accuracy and in the extent of their believability—it is difficult to draw conclusions from them. An example that illustrates the credibility problem of these accounts is the following first-hand case history written by a medical doctor who was called on to deliver a baby. When obtaining her history the women stated she had not felt well ever since she had carried some pigs into the house by the tail. After this the event was on her mind, and when she gave birth she discovered her

> son also was blessed with a tail—a nice, well-formed … five-inch tail. … the father, who was chagrined at so unusual an anomaly, requested its immediate amputation, which we reluctantly performed; after which he exclaimed: "*Now, mine pig-boy does better.*" … in conclusion, I am convinced that such mothers can, and do often, transmit their mental impressions to the child *in utero*, thus developing the many so-called mother's marks.[23]

An example of the motivations for false tail reports is provided by Andrews, who wrote in

> 1910, a native was brought to me for inspection. He possessed a blunt bony tail-stump two and one-half inches long. Obviously, it was projection of the coccyx, which, instead of being bent under as usual, continued in a direct line with the spine. A local photographer had retouched and extended the projection in a photograph to a pointed spike six or eight inches long, and sold the pictures to tourists like hotcakes. For years afterward they kept appearing in my mail as indisputable evidence of a "*tribe of people with tails.*"[24]

As early as 1923, Klaatsch reviewed numerous claims of human tails, including one that grew to 7.5 cm (3 in) in six months and another that involved a 6.3 cm (2.5 in) soft tail that developed on a Tamil girl. Klaatsch concluded that babies

> are occasionally born with tails, and these sometimes have nerves, blood vessels, and muscles–in some cases even cartilage or bone. This type of human tail, is, however, scarce and is generally, at most, an inch long projection. 'Soft tails' are more frequently found, and they run to a length of ten inches or more.[25]

23. Berry, J., Baby with a tail, *The Memphis Medical Monthly* **14**:105, 1894.
24. Andrews, R.C., *Meet Your Ancestors: A Biography of Primitive Man*, Viking Press, New York, endpaper, 1945, pp. 15–16.
25. Klaatsch, H., *The Evolution and Progress of Mankind* (edited and enlarged by Adolf Heilborn and translated by Joseph McCabe), Frederick A. Stokes Company Publishers, New York, p. 40, 1923.

Although many tail reports are false or exaggerated, some of the more recent accounts have been verified and studied using the advantages of modern research techniques.[26] A recent human tail controversy was begun by a *New England Journal of Medicine* article[27] that discussed a 3 kg (7 lb) baby born in a Boston hospital with a slender, tapered, 5.5 cm long appendage located on the lower back near the end of the spine.

The report[28] claimed that the tail presented "*a striking confrontation of the reality of evolution. …* [We cannot ignore] *the relation between human beings and their primitive ancestors. The caudal appendage brings this reality to the fore and makes it tangible and inescapable.*"[29] The 'tail' was covered with hair and skin of normal texture and internally consisted of a soft, fibrous fatty core.[30] Although it contained nerves, it was not a true tail since it lacked both bone and cartilage.

The many anomalies that have been falsely labelled tails include a variety of abnormal growths. The putative tail usually develops on the patient's back, but also may be found in other areas in which tails rarely or never appear in lower animals—most commonly in the lumbar gluteal areas. They usually have hair and nerves, but rarely bone, cartilage, or muscle. Ledley noted: "*there are no well-documented cases of caudal appendages containing caudal vertebrae or an increased number of vertebrae in the medical literature, and there is no zoological precedent for a vertebral tail without caudal vertebrae.*"[31]

These finger-like projections, including those mislabelled 'tails,' often are some type of tumour, and many are lipomas. Dr Allford concluded from her review of several pathological examinations of human tails that "*these finger like projections were more than likely fibro-fatty polyps.*"[32]

Embryological studies have also confirmed that most tail examples are some type of tumour or malformation. Furthermore, their location often is too high up on the back to be any type of atavistic tail. Allford further concluded that the

> reason that human tails are never described in medical books of pathology is because they do not exist. What is referred to as tails by some physicians are not true tails but congenital anomalies. In embryonic life, the area that undergoes the most profound growth changes is the nervous system. Because of these changes anomalies frequently result. The finger-like projections, which are found in many areas on the surface of the body, and very commonly in the lumbar gluteal areas, are congenital lipomas. The congenital

26. Gould, S.J., Fascinating tails, *Discover* **3**(9):40–41, 1982.
27. Ledley, Evolution and the human tail, p. 1212.
28. Ledley, Evolution and the human tail, p. 1212.
29. Ledley, Evolution and the human tail, pp. 1212, 1215.
30. Ledley, Evolution and the human tail, p. 1213.
31. Ledley, Evolution and the human tail, p. 1213.
32. Allford, D., *Instant Creation–Not Evolution*, Stein and Day Publishers, New York, p. 37, 1978.

> dermal sinus is frequently found in the lumbosacral area. Its attachment may be directly under the opening of the skin or may go several centimeters deep and be attached to the spinal canal. Frequently these contain hemangiomas or lipomas.[33]

She found no evidence that these tails are able to 'wag' or move, although movement was possible if muscle and nerve extended into these finger-like projections. Interestingly, it is not unusual for tailed animals to develop an *extra* tail. If the presence of one tail is an atavism, the development of two tails would indicate that many animals once normally had two tails in their evolutionary past—a conclusion that lacks any credible evidence. Both of these examples are likely developmental abnormalities, not atavisms.

Many causes and types of human 'tails' exist and, although they are extremely rare (only a few cases or less per decade have been documented worldwide), they are not related to, and often they do not even resemble, animal tails. These cases are not reversions of any sort. It now is known that the body system that undergoes the most profound growth and structural changes during embryonic development is the nervous system. Anomalies are not uncommon, due both to this rapid growth and to the enormous complexity of the nervous system.

Body hair atavisms

A common example often used to prove the existence of atavisms was the extreme body hair condition called *hirsutism*. The importance of this trait was noted by Drimmer in the case of a girl named Krao examined by H. Kaulitz-Jarlow, a member of the Institution Ethnographique during "*the heyday of the controversy over Charles Darwin's theory that man was descended from ape-like creatures …* [when] *his followers were constantly hoping to turn up a creature intermediate between man and the apes. … Krao appeared to be just what they were looking for.*"[34] In his description, Kaulitz-Jarlow emphasized

> those features of Krao that he considered particularly simian. "*Thick, jet-black smooth hair covers her head and reaches far down her back …* [which] *forms a virtual mane on the back of the neck. Her eyes are shadowed by wide, silky, shiny eyebrows. Her pupils are sparkling and dark black.*" Hair … covered her body from the top of her head to her feet. He went on to point out in detail how closely her facial structure resembled that of the gorilla.[35]

He even judged Krao's character as animal-like, noting that she

33. Allford, *Instant Creation*, p. 37.
34. Drimmer, F., *Very Special People*, Amjon Publishers, New York, pp. 162–163, 1973.
35. Drimmer, *Very Special People*, pp. 162–163.

> liked to play and was grateful when attention was paid to her. "*If she is annoyed … her wild nature at once comes to the fore; she throws herself to the ground, screams, kicks, and gives vent to her anger by pulling her hair in a very peculiar way.*" Presumably these were also supposed to be apelike characteristics.[36]

For decades, hirsutism was viewed as compelling evidence for Darwinism.[37] We now know that the condition does not occur because of the inheritance of a specific genotype, but as a result of various abnormal medical conditions, including an increase in androgen production, or hair follicle androgen receptor sensitivity, menstrual irregularity, hormonal malfunction, polycystic ovary syndrome, and problems in embryological development.[38,39,40]

A problem is that no clear distinction between normal body hair and hirsutism exists.[41] One of the most common diagnostic protocols used is the Ferriman-Gallwey method.[42] Another difficulty in researching the cause of hirsutism is both its relative rarity and the fact that it has not been researched extensively because it is primarily a cosmetic problem. Research resources in medicine are usually expended in areas that are more directly relevant to saving lives and reducing physical suffering. Furthermore, only about 6% of all hirsutism cases are diagnosed as idiopathic hirsutism, meaning that the cause is unknown.[43] A common treatment is the administration of various anti-androgens, such as spironolactone, cyproterone

---

36. Drimmer, *Very Special People*, pp. 162–163.
37. Lull, *Organic Evolution*, p. 97.
38. Falsetti, L., Rosina, B., De Fusco, D., Serum levels of 3 alpa-androstanediol glucuronide in hirsute and non-hirsute women, *European Journal of Endocrinology* **138**(4):421–424, 1998.
39. Kaltsas, G.A., Mukherjee, J.J., Jenkins, P.J., Satta, M.A., Islam, N., Monson, J.P., Besser, G.M., Grossman, A.B., Menstrual irregularity in women with acromegaly, *Journal of Clinical Endocrinology & Metabolism* **84**(8):2731–2735, 1999.
40. Vottero, A., Stratakis, C.A., Ghizzoni, L., Longui, C.A., Karl, M., Chrousos, G.P., Androgen receptor-mediated hypersensitivity to androgens in women with nonhyperandrogenic hirsutism: skewing of X-chromosome inactivation, *Journal of Clinical Endocrinology & Metabolism* **84**(3):1091–1095, 1999.
41. Barth, J.H., How hairy are hirsute women? *Clinical Endocrinology* **47**(3):255–260, 1997.
42. Fruzzetti, F., Bersi, C., Parrini, D., Ricci, C. and Genazzani, A.R, Treatment of hirsutism: comparisons between different antiandrogens with central and peripheral effects, *Fertility and Sterility* **71**(3):445–251, 1999.
43. Carmina, E., Prevalence of idiopathic hirsutism, *European Journal of Endocrinology* **139**(4)421–423, 1998.

acetate, and flutamide.[44,45,46] Most other examples used to prove atavism are also all abnormal medical conditions. Darwinists focused on those cases that suited their theory and ignored those that did not. Occasionally, humans and animals are born with two or three heads, but no-one argues from this condition that their ancestors had two or three heads. One well-known class of human deformities are called *sirens* because of their resemblance to the mythological creatures with the same name. This condition is characterized by major structural deformities in the lower extremities that cause the patient to resemble a fish or a snake.[47] Yet, no-one has claimed that siren monsters ever existed in our direct evolutionary family tree.

Mammary gland atavisms

The presence of mammary gland structures that resemble those of lower mammals is another claimed adult human atavism. This condition was once an important line of evidence for evolution because the presence of accessory nipples was believed to "*substantiate the theory that humans have descended from lower forms of animal life.*"[48] They are now recognized as a genetic or developmental abnormality. Supernumerary nipples (*polythelia*) and supernumerary breasts (*polymastia*) are one of the most common developmental anomalies, present in about 1% of all births. They occur in both human females and males.[49,50] The condition is frequently caused by abnormalities that result from genetic disorders and/or developmental diseases. The supernumerary nipples are

> found in pairs or singly, are usually seen on the chest wall beneath the true breast or in the upper abdominal region. Most accessory nipples are in a line with the normal nipples but in a minority of cases they are located on

---

44. Yucelten, D., Mithat, E., Oya, G., Faith, D., Recurrence rate of hirsutism after 3 different antiandrogen therapies, *Journal of American Academy of Dermatology* **41**(1):64–68, 1999. Yucelten, D., Mithat, E., Oya, G., Faith, D., Recurrence rate of hirsutism after 3 different antiandrogen therapies, *Journal of American Academy of Dermatology* **41**(1):64–68, 1999.
45. Faloia, E., Filliponi, S., Mancini, V. Di Marco, S. and Mantero. F., Effect of finasteride in idiopathic hirsuitism, *Journal of Endocrinological Investigation* **21**(10):694–698, 1998.
46. Bayram, F., Muderris. I.I., Sahin,Y. and Kelestimur, F., Finasteride treatment for one year in 35 hirsute patients, *Experimental and Clinical Endocrinology & Diabetes* **107**(3):195–197, 1999.
47. Gould and Pyle, *Anomalies and Curiosities of Medicine*, p. 270.
48. Rothenberg, R., *The Complete Book of Breast Care*, Crown Pub Inc., New York, p. 148, 1975.
49. Leung, W., Heaton, J.P.W. and Morales, A., An uncommon urologic presentation of a supernumerary breast, *Urology* **50**(1):122–124, 1997.
50. Greer, K.E., Supernumerary breasts, *Medical Aspects of Human Sexuality* **11**(5):104, 1977.

> the breast itself or in or near the armpit. Extra nipples occur just as often in males as they do in females. As puberty progresses, the accessory nipple may enlarge somewhat. Sometimes, there is breast tissue beneath the accessory nipple but more often true breast tissue is lacking.[51]

During the seventh week of human embryonic development, the *mammary ridge* first appears. It develops in the thoracic region and becomes breasts in females and nipples in both males and females. Occasionally, more than two nipples develop—a phenomenon cited by evolutionists as evidence of a human relationship to 'lower' mammals because many lower mammals have from six to ten pairs of nipples.[52]

These rudimentary nipples often occur in, or near, the armpits, as is normal in some kinds of bats, or in the inguinal region, as is normal in some whales, but they can occur almost anywhere on the body—even in locations where mammals never have mammary glands, such as on the back, arms, legs, and buttocks.[53]

Allford noted that, during her medical practice, she never saw more than one extra pair of rudimentary nipples. The so-called 'mammary line' that exists in humans often forms a vase-shaped single line. Its top extends from the armpits and narrows as it passes through the normal nipple area, the thinnest part being on the abdomen. To be evidence of evolution a supernumerary breast in humans would have to occur only along the mammary lateral line as it does in lower mammals.

The animal mammary line extends bilaterally from the axillary region to the inguinal ligaments. This arrangement is required if these abnormalities can be considered a throwback to when human females supposedly had a set of teats similar to female dogs. In most cases, though, they do not develop according to this pattern, and the number of added nipples, which often lack breast tissue, usually amounts to only one or two.

This condition is medically classified as a genetic or developmental deformity, and it is consistently treated as such by the medical establishment.[54] Evidence for this view includes the finding that the condition may be sporadic, familial, or associated with other deformities. The polythelia developmental anomaly is a diagnostic indicator of a variety of congenital and hereditary anomalies, including both kidney and urologic malformations.[55]

---

51. Rothenberg, *The Complete Book of Breast Care*, p. 147.
52. Allford, *Instant Creation*, p. 47.
53. Bergman, J., Is the human male nipple vestigial?, *Journal of Creation* **15**(2):38–41, 2001.
54. Rothenberg, *The Complete Book of Breast Care*, p. 148.
55. Urbani, C.E. and Betti, R., Aberrant mammary tissue and nephrourinary malignancy, *Cancer Genetics and Cytogenetics* **87**(1):88–89, 1996.

Polythelia is also a diagnostic indicator of urogenital cancer and several kinds of internal malignancies.[56,57,58] Chromosomal studies have determined that an increased number of X-chromosomes is common in polythelia.[59] All of these findings support the conclusion that polythelia is a disease condition and not an atavism.

A similar, but extremely rare, deformity is the total absence of one or both breasts. This condition affects females more often than males, and generally only one breast is missing.[60] Except for the potential claim that this condition is a throwback to a pre-mammal stage of evolution, no claims can be made regarding how this abnormality supports evolution.

Many other alleged atavisms exist, including excessive hair growth (e.g. the bearded lady), hair colour anomalies (blue, purple, and orange, among others), anomalies of the finger and toe nails, intra-areolar polythelia, growth of deer-like horns out of the head area, abnormal skin elasticity, an ability to move the body in extreme and unusual ways, and a body control level that permits one to move the ears or eyeball via their own muscles so that one literally can pull the eyeball out of its eye socket.

Many of these examples have been demonstrated to be due to disease or genetic/developmental abnormalities.[61] Examples, such as cases of individuals born with what appear to be rudimentary tails, can be selected in an effort to prove that these anomalies are a reversion to previous developmental types, but unless compelling evidence exists otherwise, a consistent interpretation as medical anomalies is required for *all* of these conditions, even those cases where individuals are born with mammary glands on their backs.

A problem occurs when we argue that the occurrence of an inherited genetic trait supports the claim that this trait allegedly existed millions of years ago in the animal's evolutionary history, and has not been expressed during much, or most, of this time. Although Gould referred to horses' extra digits as atavisms, he admitted that they "*had been admired and studied since Caesar's time.*"[62] In this case they are part of the gene pool that, for a variety of reasons, may not be expressed regularly and often skips generations, likely because they were caused by recessive genes, requiring the uncommon event of a zygote receiving a recessive gene from both parents.

Just as one would not call a daughter who has her grandmother's eyes an atavism or an evolutionary throwback, likewise these examples also are not properly termed

---

56. Aslan, D. and Sarikayalar, F., Polythelia: presentation of three cases, *Cocuk Sagligi ve Hastaliklari Dergise* **42**(1):95–102, 1999.
57. Urbani and Betti, Aberrant mammary tissue … , pp. 88–89.
58. Grimshaw, E. and Cohen, P., Supernumerary nipple and seminoma: case report and review of polythelia and genitourinary cancers, *Dermatology Online Journal* 19(1):4.
59. Allford, *Instant Creation*, p. 48.
60. Rothenberg, *The Complete Book of Breast Care*, p. 147.
61. See Baratelli, G.M. and Vischi, S., Unilateral intra-areolar polythelia: a rare anomaly, *Breast* **8**(1):51–52, 1999 for one such case.
62. Gould, S.J., Hen's teeth and horse's toes, *Natural History* **89**(7):24–28, 1980; p. 24.

atavisms. If one insists on using the term atavism, it is necessary to differentiate between the demonstrated property of various traits that simply skipped a generation or two, and the disproven scenario where a woman gives birth to a primitive evolutionary throwback with traits similar to her alleged evolutionary ancestors that lived thousands of years ago.

Other atavistic organs

Other examples of what once were claimed to be atavisms include the supernumerary digits (extra fingers or toes) and both the suppression and hypertrophy of digits that sometimes occurs in humans and animals. Almost all of these cases are now known to be caused by chromosomal mutations or developmental abnormalities. If growth in one region was not suppressed at the precise time in development, an extra appendage could result. Suppression during embryo development can likewise cause the *lack* of a structure. In the case of babies exposed to the drug thalidomide in-utero, the tragic results included complete lack or partial development of an appendage, or even developmental flaws that cause limbs to look like seal flippers.[63]

Atavism and sex

The development of organs that supposedly represent a 'throwback' to a condition found in some hypothetical ancestral type also occurs in humans.[64] Further study, though, usually rules out the atavism hypothesis, such as the case cited by Ducrocq *et al.*[65] An example would be people who are born with a pair of ribs in their neck. Such 'cervical' ribs once were claimed by some evolutionists to be an atavistic throwback to our reptilian ancestry.[66]

Neck ribs normally do not occur in humans, but occur naturally in many living and fossil reptiles. Extra ribs do sometimes occur and, when they do, they develop in only two locations—above and below the normal set. Extra ribs are found either in the neck or lumbar regions, and the same reasoning is true of extra fingers or other supplemental organs—a condition that is not all that rare in humans and animals in general.

63. Fine, R.A., *The Great Drug Deception*, Stein and Day Publishers, New York, p. 168, 1972.
64. Davidheiser, B., *Evolution and Christian Faith*, Presbyterian and Reformed, Nutley, New Jersey, p. 239, 1969.
65. Ducrocq, S., *et al.*, Dental anomalies in Upper Eocene anthracotheriidae: a possible case of inbreeding, *Lethaia* **28**(4):355–360, 1995.
66. Morris, H. (Ed.), *Human Anatomy*, P. Blakiston's, Philadelphia, Pennsylvania, 1899. Later editions dropped the claim.

Interestingly, cervical ribs are *twice* as common in women as in men.[67] The presence of cervical ribs now is widely understood as merely a normal human variation. Occasionally extra ribs, sometimes called gorilla ribs, appear in the lumbar region. This particular anomaly occurs three times more frequently in *men* than women.[68] The logical (albeit absurd) conclusion is that women are more closely related to reptiles than men, and that men are more closely related to gorillas than women.

Some characteristics described as atavistic, such as a hairy breast and greater bodily strength that "*often occur in men, but rarely in women*"[69] are merely examples of sexual dimorphism. Other so-called atavistic characteristics are likely sex linked traits related to the fact that males have an XY chromosome set, and the much shorter Y chromosome cannot fully 'block' deleterious traits on the X chromosome as usually would occur with the female XX chromosome set. Other causes of 'atavistic' traits besides disease include diet problems or hormonal malfunctions that occur during early development.

Atavism and race

The concept of atavism has clear racial implications. An example is the so-called 'Mongolism' condition in which an extra chromosome causes both retardation and the development of certain superficial facial characteristics of this ethnicity. The belief that certain races are 'ancestral' to others, and thus are less evolved than modern Caucasians, was once mainline science.[70,71] The term Mongolism comes from the assumption that this condition is an atavistic throwback to an earlier, less evolved race that, it was once believed, is extinct but similar to the modern mongoloid race. The term 'mongoloid idiot' also has its source in this once-common, but clearly erroneous, belief.[72] Gould wrote that

> the supposed link between degeneracy and racial ranking … has left us at least one legacy—the designation of "*Mongolian idiocy*" or, more blandly, "*mongolism*" for the chromosomal disorder now generally called "*Down's syndrome.*"[73,74]

67. Durham, H.R. (Ed.), *Encyclopedia of Medical Syndromes*, Simon and Schuster, New York, p. 99, 1960.
68. Nordsiek, F., How your bones tell your age, *Science Digest* **47**(5):13–18, 1960.
69. Lull, *Organic Evolution*, p. 136.
70. Down, J.L.H., *Observations on an Ethnic classification of Idiots*, Hospital Reports, London, 1866.
71. Chase, A., *The Legacy of Malthus: the social costs of the new scientific racism*, Alfred A. Knopf, New York, 1980.
72. Stephen Jay Gould, Dr. Down's syndrome, *Natural History* 89:142–148, 1980.
73. Gould, S.J., *The Mismeasure of Man*, W.W. Norton and Co., New York, p. 164, 1996.
74. In 1975, the United States National Institutes of Health standardized the name as Down syndrome, though both Down's and Down remain in common usage.

Gould added that the physician after whom the condition is named, Dr Down,

> argued that many congenital "*idiots*" (a quasi-technical term in his day, not just an epithet) explained anatomical features, absent in their parents but present as defining features of lower races. He found idiots of the "*Ethiopian variety*"—"*white Negroes, although of European descent*" ... others of the Malay type, and "*analogues of the people with shortened foreheads, prominent cheeks, deep-set eyes, and slightly apish nose, originally inhabited the American continent*" ... "*A very large number of congenital idiots are typical Mongols.*"[75]

Down then proceeded to describe

> the features of Down's syndrome in a boy under his charge ... "*obliquely placed*" eyes and slightly yellowish skin. ... he concluded:[76]

> "*The boy's aspect is such that it is difficult to realize that he is the child of Europeans, but so frequently are these characters presented, that there can be no doubt that these ethnic features are the result of degeneration.*" Down even used his ethnic insight to explain the behavior of afflicted children: "*they excel at imitation*"—the trait most frequently cited as typically Mongolian in conventional racist classifications of Down's time.[77]

These beliefs hardly improved race relations in the Western world and, in fact, were a major contributor to the biological racism that developed in the mid-1800s in Europe, the United States, and elsewhere.

The concept of atavism today

Race atavism is still discussed by some scientists as a viable theory for several reasons. As Gould concluded, "*this old—and dangerous—farce keeps reappearing.*"[78] In Northern China, evidence of ambiguous footprints, excretion, and hair samples have been interpreted by scientists as evidence that ape-like atavistic creatures now exist there. According to Topping, "*Chinese scientists now have two theories about these strange creatures. Some believe that the wild men are atavisms—genetic throw-backs to an earlier form of the human species, resulting from chance combinations of ancestral genes. Others say the creatures are actually direct descendants of man's distant ancestor, the great ape, Gigantopithecus.*"[79]

---

75. Gould, *The Mismeasure of Man*, p. 164.
76. Gould, *The Mismeasure of Man*, p. 165.
77. Gould, *The Mismeasure of Man*, p. 165.
78. Gould, S.J., Criminal man revived, *Natural History* **85**(3):16, 1976.
79. Topping, Hairy wild men of China, p. 113.

Objections to the atavism theory

Atavisms, as 'biological throwbacks' to long-lost traits affecting both the appearance and behaviour of the animal, require a biological mechanism to explain their existence. A physical means must exist to carry a complete set of intact genetic instructions from several past stages of human evolution to contemporary humans. This requires a system that utilizes several separate sets of genetic codes—one for the current human and another for some previous stage of evolution.

Because human evolutionary development is believed by most evolutionists to be extremely slow, occurring by almost imperceptible changes from generation to generation, humans would have to store either the genetic code for a certain specific period of human evolution, or the entire code for almost every stage.

The latter would be impossible because Darwinists claim that human evolution requires literally *multi-billions* of separate, small changes. Likewise, no evidence exists for a system that would select only a *certain period* of human evolution, or for certain traits only, and then record this blueprint somewhere in the genome for future use. A set of blueprints must be stored since a set of structures is involved in almost all alleged atavisms. A complex mechanism is also required to store the templates for a certain evolutionary stage, or to store the various sets of plans for traits at different, and clearly distinct, stages of an animal's evolution.

The survival of the fittest concept predicts that selection favours *only* those biological structures that clearly have enabled humans to experience a survival advantage over both other animals, and those individual humans who do not possess the biological structures in question. In almost all cases, the biological structures producing the 'throwback' would confer little or no survival advantage to the animal—tails, extra nipples or ribs, and Mongolian traits—thus would not be selected for. Furthermore, because many alleged atavistic structures are clearly detrimental or fatal, selection would often work *against* their preservation.

Lull concluded that atavistic characteristics "*are such as make their owner more conspicuous and doubtless expose him to dangers from which the more obscure animal would be immune. Hence,* [the continuance of some atavisms] *is opposed to the principle of natural selection, as the results are a handicap and not an aid in the struggle for existence.*"[80] Consequently, if some genetically atavistic characteristics did appear, they would be selected against, thus would no longer appear in the organism.

It is also difficult to imagine how mechanisms for the storage and expression of such biological structures could have evolved by random mutations. Obviously, the structure would be totally useless, or often detrimental, until it evolved or developed to the extent that it was functional and could confer a survival advantage to the animal. Even then, except as a curiosity, most atavisms appear to be useless or worse. Contemporary evolutionary theory concludes that structures which do not confer a

80. Lull, *Organic Evolution*, p. 136.

survival advantage are unlikely to be selected, and consequently are unlikely to be passed on to future generations.

Genetic breeders occasionally claim they have achieved 'reverse evolution' by producing a throwback. German zoologist Heinz Heck spent 30 years in the Munich Zoo labouring to create beasts "*the likes of which have never been seen by living man—a beast, in fact, which had been dead for almost 600 years.*"[81] Heck even attempted to breed a horse back to a tarpan (a miniature horse that allegedly lived during the stone age).[82] In reality, Heck only showed that certain animal traits believed to be extinct can be bred back into existence.

Carpenter described various freak animals, insects and plants that appear to have inherited some of the characteristics of their ancient ancestors. They "*may possess hair in places where their breed has not grown hair in thousands of years*" or possess "*extra toes or feet that their ancestors discarded centuries before.*"[83] Although sometimes referred to as throwbacks or atavisms, these examples actually involve rather minor traits that result from causing a set of conditions that allows genetic traits once common in a population to again increase in number.

One example would be the breeding of horses so that either one, or both, of the side splints are functional—an event that is possible because "*horses have never lost the genetic information for producing side toes. ... What else might their genetic system maintain, normally unexpressed, but able to serve, if activated, as a possible focus for major and rapid evolutionary change? Atavisms reflect the enormous, latent capacity of genetic systems, not primarily the constraints and limitations imposed by an organism's past.*"[84] These, though, are evidently all familial atavisms—similar to a child having a trait such as her great-grandmother's red hair, that the family has not seen in a generation—and are not true atavisms as discussed here.

We also now know that genes are switched on and off, that the various functional components of life are modular, that embryogenesis is controlled by large, complex redundant switching networks, and in most cells most DNA is switched off. Cellular differentiation occurs via rearrangement of the modules and their switching circuits. This model, called 'Facilitated Variation', indicates that some genes can be re-activated.[85] Gene regulation is also controlled by methylation of DNA and histones that blocks transcription, a process called epigenetics that turns genes on and off.

---

81. Carpenter, A., Now they're growing ancestors, *Science Digest* **25**(12):28, 1949; and Heck, H., The breeding-back of the aurochs, *Oryx: The International Journal of Conservation* **1**(3):117–122, 1951.
82. Heck, H., The breeding-back of the tarpan, *Oryx: The International Journal of Conservation* **1**(7):338–342, 1952.
83. Carpenter, Now they're growing ancestors, p. 28.
84. Gould, Hen's teeth and horse's toes, p. 26.
85. Kirschner M. and Gerhart, J., *The Plausibility of Life: Resolving Darwin's Dilemma*, Yale University Press, New Haven, Connecticut, 2005.

Summary

Although atavisms were once presented as proof of evolution by Darwin and then in many textbooks, the subject is generally ignored today. Like vestigial organs, embryological recapitulation, and nascent organs, the whole concept of atavism has largely been abandoned. Almost all of the conditions formerly labelled 'atavistic' are now understood as belonging to the domain of medicine. Atavisms are yet another embarrassing chapter in the history of Darwinian evolution. And, although disproved, the claims regarding atavisms are still very much evident in our culture, and still reflected in modern degeneration theories.[86]

Although the atavism theory ultimately was found to lack empirical support, it was accepted uncritically for decades as an explanation for many biological phenomena that now are known to be caused by genetic, developmental, or medical abnormalities. Unfortunately, this erroneous concept has hindered science, especially medical progress, by misdirecting much energy and resources into non-productive unscientific dead ends.

86. Rothenberg, *The Complete Book of Breast Care*, p. 148.

CHAPTER 18

Why the problem of fraud exists in science today

Introduction

The Piltdown hoax is one of the most famous cases of fraud in all of science.[1] Many Darwinists, though, claim this case is an anomaly, and that fraud in their field is no longer a problem today. However, the cases of fraud or deception in the field of evolution include not only the Piltdown Man but also *Archaeoraptor*, Haeckel's embryos, Ancon sheep, *Bathybius haeckelii*, and *Hesperopithecus* (Nebraska Man)—the missing link that turned out to be a pig—plus the Tasaday tribe claims, the peppered moth, and the midwife toad fraud controversy, to name a few well-known examples.[2,3,4,5,6,7,8]

The fact is, fraud as a whole in science is now "*a serious, deeply rooted problem*" that affects no small number of contemporary scientific research studies, especially in the field of evolution.[9] Scientists recently have been forced by several events to recognize this problem and attempt to deal with it.[10] The published literature and the interviews I completed of my fellow faculty at a medical school consistently confirmed the extent of the problem of fraud in science. This present brief review has highlighted only a few of the thousands of known cases.

Most identified cases of modern-day fraud are in the life sciences. In the biomedical field alone, 127 new misconduct cases were lodged with the Office of Research Integrity in 2001 alone.[11] This was the third consecutive rise in the number of cases

1. Millar, R., *The Piltdown Men*, St Martin's Press, New York, 1972.
2. Simons, L.M., *Archaeoraptor* fossil trail, *National Geographic* **198**(4):128–132, October 2000.
3. Hooper, J., *Of Moths and Men: An Evolutionary Tale—The Untold Story of Science and the Peppered Moth*, Norton, New York, 2002.
4. Talent, J., The case of the peripatetic fossils, *Nature* **338**(6217):613–615, 1989.
5. Wells, J., Haeckel's embryos & evolution, *The American Biology Teacher* **61**(5):345–349, 1999.
6. Koestler, A., *The Case of the Midwife Toad*, Random House, New York, 1972.
7. Pennisi, E., Haeckel's embryos: fraud rediscovered, *Science* **277**(5331):1435, 1997.
8. Mazur, S., *The Altenberg 16: An Exposé of the Evolution Industry,* North Atlantic Books, Berkeley, California, 2010.
9. Roman, M., When good scientists turn bad, *Discover* **9**(4):58, 1988.
10. Abbott, A., Science comes to terms with the lessons of fraud, *Nature* **398**(6722):13–17, 1999; p. 13.
11. Check, E., Sitting in judgment, *Nature* **419**(6905):332–333, 2002; p. 332.

since 1998.[12] This concern is not of mere academic interest, but also profoundly affects human health and life.[13,14] Much more than money and prestige are at stake, because fraud is "*potentially deadly*" in the field of medicine, and researchers are openly "*playing with lives.*"[15] Dangerous drugs are approved on the basis of questionable studies. Fraudulent research impedes and misleads researchers, and wastes billions of dollars that could be used for more productive, or at least honest, research.[16] As a result of the modern fraud epidemic, a *Nature* editorial concluded that the days are over

> when scientific frauds could be dismissed as the work of the mad rather than the bad. The unhappily extensive record of misconduct suggests that many fraudsters believe their faked results, so attempts at replication by others represent no perceived threat.[17]

Or, they believe that no-one will attempt to replicate their work, at least for some time, because much science work is not replicated. Fortunately, although it may take years, medical research is more likely to be replicated than other areas of science because of its importance for human health. One result of the pandemic of fraud is retraction. Retraction involves pulling published articles from online journals, and publishing a notice of retraction in print journals. Although only a small percent of the millions of papers published, hundreds of cases occur each decade. Given all of the cases of fraud estimated to exist, printing retractions is relatively uncommon.[18] That said, the FAQ page of *Retraction Watch*, a blog launched in 2010 which endeavours to track research integrity and document occurrences of retraction in peer-reviewed scientific journals, states "*although we didn't predict this, it's been a struggle to even keep up with retractions as they happen.*"[19] "*Retractions for all reasons, from honest error to plagiarism to the outright faking of data, are on the rise.*"[20]

---

12. Check, Sitting in judgment, p. 332.
13. Kohn, A., *False Prophets: Fraud and Error in Science and Medicine*, Basil Blackwell Ltd, New York, 1988.
14. Crewdson, J., *Science Fictions; a scientific mystery, a massive cover-up, and the dark legacy of Robert Gallo*, Little Brown, New York, 2002.
15. Roman, When good scientists turn bad, p. 52.
16. Begley, C.G. and Ellis, L.M., Raise standards for preclinical cancer research, *Nature* **483**(7391):531–533, 2012.
17. *Nature* **419**(6905):417, 2002
18. Williams, P. and Wager, E., Exploring why and how journal editors retract articles: findings from a qualitative study, *Science and Engineering Ethics* **19**(1):1–11, 2013.
19. Retraction Watch, retractionwatch.com/the-retraction-watch-faq, accessed 6th June 2015.
20. Marcus, A., and Oransky, I., Retractions are coming thick and fast: it's time for publishers to act, *The Guardian,* theguardian.com, 14 July 2014.

The fraud problem is worldwide and has been reported in the United States, Britain, France, Germany, India, Japan, Poland, Sweden, and Australia.[21] Judson claims the French are "*massively skillful at cover-up, with the consequence that, in the rare instance when the lid is pried off, the stench of corruption shakes governments.*"[22]

In Australia, misconduct allegations have created such a problem that the issue was raised in the Australian Parliament, and researchers have called for an "*office of research integrity.*"[23] The accused include some of the greatest modern biologists, and the problem exists at Harvard, Cornell, Princeton, Baylor, and other major universities. In a study of 2,047 retracted biomedical and life science research articles, Fang *et al.* found 67.4% were retracted due to misconduct, including evidence of fraud.[24] They also found that the number of retracted articles due to fraud has increased about tenfold since 1975.

Their analysis revealed that the world's leading scientific journals were hit especially hard.[25] Leading journal *Science* had 70 articles retracted, *PNAS* a total of 69, *The Journal of Biological Chemistry* 54, and *Nature* 44.[26] Furthermore, many of the retracted articles were widely cited and are still being cited today. A study by Wakefield published in the *Lancet* has been cited 758 times, a study by Reyes in *Blood* 740 times, and a study by Fukuhara in *Science* 686 times.[27]

Many of the retracted studies commonly cited were in *Nature*, *Science*, and other leading science journals. Many of the authors of retracted papers taught at Harvard, Yale, Berkeley and other leading universities. The authors of the retracted articles were from 56 nations, with the United States, Germany, Japan and China accounting for three-quarters of all retractions due to fraud.

One typical example of fraud is the widely quoted immunological research studies related to kidney transplantation by Zoltan Lucas (M.D. Johns Hopkins and Ph.D. in biochemistry from Massachusetts Institute of Technology) that were found to contain fraudulent data.[28] Dr Lucas was then an Associate Professor of Surgery at Stanford University. His graduate student, Randall Morris, discovered that Lucas had written reports on research that Morris knew was never done. Morris knew this because he was involved in the research! The studies were published in highly reputable journals and, no doubt, many other researchers relied on the results for their work.

---

21. Judson, H.F., *The Great Betrayal: Fraud in Science*, Harcourt, New York, p. 132, 2004.
22. Judson, *The Great Betrayal*, p. 133.
23. Dennis, C., Misconduct row fuels calls for reform, *Nature* **427**(6976):666, 2004.
24. Fang, F.C., Steen, G. and Casadevall, A., Misconduct accounts for the majority of retracted scientific publications, *Proceedings of the National Academy of Science* **109**(42):17028–17033, 2012; p. 17028.
25. Fang, F.C., Casadevall, A., and Morrison R.P., Retracted science and the retraction index, *Infection and Immunity* **79**(10): 3855–3859, October 2011.
26. Fang *et al.*, Misconduct … , p. 17031.
27. Fang *et al.*, Misconduct … , p. 17032.
28. Kohn, *False Prophets*, pp. 104–110.

A report titled *Integrity in Scientific Research,* completed under the auspices of the US Department of Health and Human Services Office of Research Integrity, concluded that much more could, and should, be done about the problem of "*faking data*" and the lack of integrity common in science research.[29] The problem is so common that researchers who maintain a clean record are sometimes given special recognition, as was Italian scientist Franco Rasetti: "*Today, we hear a great deal about scientific fraud, and commissions and committees on scientific ethics abound. For Rasetti, scientific honesty was axiomatic and automatic.*"[30]

Fraud not just exists, but is *epidemic* to the extent that one study about the problem concluded that "*science bears little resemblance to its conventional portrait.*"[31] Although more common among researchers working alone, "*fakery still abounds*" even in group projects watched over by peer review.[32] A *Nature* editorial noted that many fraud cases involved not just young struggling researchers, but experienced well-published scientists.[33] This *Nature* editorial concluded

> that the dozen or so proven cases of falsification that have cropped up in the past five years have occurred in some of the world's most distinguished research institutions—Cornell, Harvard, Sloan-Kettering, Yale and so on—and have been blamed on people who are acknowledged by their colleagues to have been intellectually outstanding. The pressure to publish may explain much dull literature, but cannot of itself account for fraud.[34]

The fraud ranges from fudging data to plagiarizing large sections from other articles. Molecular biologist Carolyn Price, while peer-reviewing grant applications, noted that one looked "*suspiciously familiar.*" She discovered that sections in the one she was reviewing were plagiarized from her own grant application submitted earlier in the year.[35] A *Nature* editorial concluded that plagiarism was growing, especially in molecular biology.[36] To trap plagiarizers, some researchers have even added incorrect information in their papers, and corrected it just prior to publication.[37] And the problem likely will get worse. We can expect misconduct to occur more often in the future—in particular in biomedicine, where great pressure to publish exists.[38]

---

29. Kaiser, J., Research integrity: U.S. universities urged to do a better job, *Science* **297**(5580):321, 2002.
30. Kerwin, L., Obituary: Franco Rasetti (1901–2001), *Nature* **415**(6872):597, 2002.
31. Broad, W. and Wade, N., *Betrayers of the Truth: Fraud and Deceit in the Halls of Science*, Simon and Schuster, New York, p. 8, 1982.
32. Roman, When good scientists turn bad, p. 53.
33. Anonymous, Is science really a pack of lies? *Nature* **303**(5916):361–362, 1983; p. 361.
34. Anonymous, Is science really a pack of lies? p. 361.
35. Dalton, R., Peers under pressure, *Nature* **413**(6852):102–104, 2001.
36. Anonymous, Bad peer reviewers, *Nature* **413**(6852):93, 2001.
37. Dalton, Peers under pressure, p. 104.
38. Abbott, A. and Schwarz, H., Dubious data remain in print two years after misconduct inquiry, *Nature* **418**(6894):113, 2002.

Recent cases illustrate the seriousness of the problem

Medicine and biology have been hit very hard by fraud: one study found 94 cancer scientific papers likely contained manipulated data.[39] Two years later, many of the papers were still not retracted, confirming the conclusion that "*even when scientific misconduct is proven, no reliable mechanism exists to remove bad information from the literature.*"[40]

Dr John Darsee of Harvard University Medical School was proven to be involved in fabricating data that formed the basis of his over 100 publications over a period of about three years. In this study the researchers found what can only be described as "*bizarre*" data that could not be valid, including numerous blatant internal contradictions and numerical discrepancies.[41] This case illustrates how a few people can produce an enormous number of fraudulent publications.

Investigators also found scores of errors or discrepancies that were so blatant they should easily have been discovered by the reviewers—such as a 17-year-old male who had 4 children aged 8, 7, 5, and 4! A total of 47 co-authors were involved, all of whom were at either Harvard or Emory University. The study also concluded that both the co-authors and reviewers who evaluated the papers were grossly deficient. Harvard's response was questionable, with delays that some felt were an attempt to cover up the scandal.[42] An extensive National Institutes of Health (NIH) report "*scathingly*" criticized Harvard and the head of Darsee's lab, cardiologist Eugene Braunwald, was placed on one year probation.[43] Following the NIH investigation, Harvard retracted 30 of Darsee's papers and a review of Darsee's earlier work at Emory University led to the retraction of an additional 52 papers.

Yet another case of fraud involved Nobel laureate immunologist David Baltimore of Rockefeller University. Evidently he was not personally responsible, but did defend a disputed paper he and six co-authors published in *Cell* when he was at Massachusetts Institute of Technology. Margot O'Toole claimed that scientists spent years researching the case and "*unanimously concluded that fraud had been committed.*"[44] The case probably did more than any other to uncover how common deceptive behavior actually is among scientists.

One paper that "*overturned a widely accepted theory on cell signaling*" was retracted only "*15 months after it was published. The retraction has rocked the cell-biology community and … has effectively ended the career of Siu-Kwong Chan, one of the paper's*

39. Abbott and Schwarz, Dubious data … , p. 113.
40. Abbott and Schwarz, Dubious data … , p. 113.
41. Stewart, W.W. and Feder, N., The integrity of the scientific literature, *Nature* **325**(6101):207–216, 1987.
42. Judson, *The Great Betrayal*, pp. 115–116.
43. Judson, *The Great Betrayal*, p. 116.
44. Kevles, D.J. *The Baltimore Case: A Trial of Politics, Science, and Character*, Norton, New York, p. 370, 1998.

co-authors."[45] In the retraction, Struhl claimed that Chan admitted misreporting or failing to perform crucial experiments described in the original paper.[46]

> Struhl discovered a problem when he repeated some of Chan's experiments. When he didn't get the same results as Chan, Struhl says that he confronted his former postdoc, who had by this time moved to the Albert Einstein College of Medicine in the Bronx. "*When confronted with this discrepancy, S.-K. Chan informed me that most of the results ... were either not performed or gave different results than presented in the paper,*" Struhl wrote in the retraction. "*I therefore withdraw this paper and the conclusions it reports.*"[47]

The pair had worked on the project for five years before publishing their results in October 2002.

Another case involved Mark Spector, a "*brilliant, charming, and multiply talented*" scientist at Cornell who studied the biochemical interactions of sodium-potassium ATPase.[48] With his mentor, Efraim Racker, he wrote and presented several papers at conferences. The problem was Spector was too good—what normally required 20 years of work took him only two.[49] It turned out he spiked his experiments. Spector was fired and his manuscripts withdrawn.

How common is deceit in science?

Broad and Wade conclude that deceit in science has not been the exception but the *trend* from the beginnings of science until today. The percentage depends on how we define fraudulent, and whether we include unconscious fudging (experimental 'error' or bias). Even if we replicate an experiment and find that the results do not conform to those of the original study, it is still difficult to 'prove' deceit because dishonesty in science can often easily be covered up. If a scientist claims certain results were produced, unless one's laboratory assistant testifies that the data were fudged, the most one can prove is that, for some reason, replication consistently failed to support the original result. Those who study the problem agree that fraud is epidemic, and efforts to downgrade the problem, as done by the editor of *Science,* are "*egregiously foolish.*"[50]

45. Check, E., Retraction signals end of cell-biology debate, *Nature* **427**, 574; 2004.
46. Struhl G., Retraction: Evidence that armadillo transduces wingless by mediating nuclear export or cytosolic activation of pangolin, *Cell* 116(3):481, 2004.
47. Check, Retraction signals end of cell-biology debate, p. 574.
48. Judson, *The Great Betrayal*, p. 122.
49. Judson, *The Great Betrayal*, p. 124.
50. Judson, *The Great Betrayal*, p. 132.

Reasons why deceit is so common

The present system of science actually encourages deceit. Careers are at stake, as are jobs, grants, tenure, and, literally, one's livelihood.[51] This problem is expressed in the saying that a professor must publish or perish (meaning that he will be denied tenure, which often ends an academic career). As Broad and Wade note, "*grants and contracts from the Federal government ... dry up quickly unless evidence of immediate and continuing success is forthcoming.*"[52] The motivation to publish, to make a name for oneself, to secure prestigious prizes, or be asked to join a scientific society, all entice dishonesty.

Broad and Wade's disturbing conclusion is corruption and deceit are just as common in science as in any other human undertaking because scientists "*are not different from other people. In donning the white coat at the laboratory door, they do not step aside from the passions, ambitions, and failings that animate those in other walks of life.*"[53]

The fact is, "*science has its pathogenic side*" including a "*lust for power*" and "*greed*" that affects

> scientists as well as anyone else. Anyone who has worked in the laboratory, on a university campus, or read the history of science is well aware of the overweening pride, jealousy and competition that can infect those working in the same field. In the effort to "*succeed,*" some scientists have "*cooked*" their data; that is, they have adjusted the actual results to fit what they were supposed to get.[54]

Zabilka notes that some research fields have been

> especially prone to falsified research data because of the large amounts of money available for research. To keep those grants coming, scientists have, on occasion, resorted to falsified results. The selling of personal philosophy as popular exposition of science as Carl Sagan and John G. Taylor have done is another example. The need for moral and intellectual integrity on both sides of this debate is apparent.[55]

Fraud does not always involve making up data, but most often involves alterations, ignoring certain results, and fudging the data enough to change a close, but non-statistically significant result into a statistically significant difference, meaning that

51. Dalton, Peers under pressure, p. 104.
52. Broad and Wade, *Betrayers of the Truth*, p. 36.
53. Broad and Wade, *Betrayers of the Truth*, p. 19.
54. Zabilka, I.L., *Scientific Malpractice; The Creation/Evolution Debate*, Bristol Books, Lexington, Kentucky, p. 138, 1992.
55. Zabilka, *Scientific Malpractice*, p. 138.

the finding is very unlikely to be due purely to chance. Whether or not intentional deceit is involved is not easy to determine. Dishonesty cannot easily be disentangled from normal human mistakes, sloppiness, gullibility, or technical incompetence. Vested interests operate to prove one's pet theories, causing researchers to don blinders that impede them from seeing what they don't want to see. Once theories are established, they are not overturned easily, often regardless of the amount of new information that may contradict the now hallowed 'written-in-stone' theory.

Among the other reasons for deceit include the fact that comprehensive *theories* are the goal of science, not a collection of isolated facts. Because it is sometimes difficult to force facts to conform to one's theories, such as in situations where there are many anomalies, a strong temptation exists to ignore facts that don't agree with one's theories. The desire to earn respect from one's peers (and, ideally, to become eminent) has, from the earliest days of science, brought with it a temptation to distort, ignore evidence, play loose with the facts, and even lie.[56]

Fraud in science was historically common

The "*scientific community long has been plagued by allegations of fraud and misconduct.*"[57] Chang notes that the

> recent scandals at Bell Labs and Lawrence Berkeley National Laboratory are nothing new. The history of science is replete with researchers who have falsified data in their eagerness to make a name for themselves or prove a cherished theory or simply cut corners. A rogues' gallery could go back at least as far as the second century AD.[58]

If science is normally self-correcting, why do we have so many historical examples of erroneous work that remained uncorrected for many decades, sometimes centuries, even among some of the leading lights of science such as Ptolemy, Galileo, and Newton?[59,60,61,62] Reasons may include a critic's work having been suppressed or having failed to gain the needed publicity, or the critics themselves may have been discredited for questioning a science luminary.

56. Broad and Wade, *Betrayers of the Truth*, p. 24.
57. Roman, When good scientists turn bad, p. 52.
58. Chang, K., On scientific fakery and the systems to catch it, *The New York Times Science Times*, pp. 1, 4, 15 October 2002; p. 1.
59. Broad and Wade, *Betrayers of the Truth*, p. 24.
60. Brooks, M., *Free Radicals: The Secret Anarchy of Science*, The Overlook Press, New York, p. 7, 2011.
61. Grant, J., *Discarded Science: Ideas that Seemed Good at the Time*, AAPPL Artists' and Photographers' Press Limited, Wisley, Surrey, UK, 2006.
62. Grant, J., *Corrupted Science: Fraud, Ideology and Politics in Science*, Facts, Figures and Fun, Surrey, UK, 2007.

Due to the time that has elapsed, it is now often difficult to gather evidence to prove or disprove modern (and hotly disputed) allegations of fraud or plagiarism against Ptolemy, Galileo, Newton, Darwin, Dalton (the chemist who discovered the laws of chemical combination and proved the existence of different types of atoms), Mendel, Kekule (credited with discovery of the benzene ring) and Millikan (the first person to measure the electrical charge of the sub-atomic particle called an electron), to name some relatively recent claims.[63,64]

Some cases of deceit have been uncovered by reviewing a researcher's original notes. In many of these cases, data that supported the researcher's theory were selected for publication and data that did not were ignored. Robert Millikan ended up with a Nobel Prize, while his challenger, whose oil-drop experiments to measure the electron's charge were more accurate, ended up disillusioned.[65]

Ignoring failures

Because the primary means of scientific communication is through the print medium, a tendency exists to record *only* the work of those few people who have successfully contributed to supporting a theory in science, and to ignore the many non-significant findings.[66] Researchers, both deliberately and subconsciously, commonly tout the facts that support their theory, and modify or ignore those that do not. An example of fraud that was more deliberate is the case of Dr Glueck. Only one month after the National Institute of Mental Health announced its decision in another case, the scientific

> community was shaken by yet another scandal. For 22 years internist Charles Glueck had risen steadily through the hierarchy of science. Since graduating from medical school in 1964, he had published nearly 400 papers at the furious rate of close to 17 a year. For his leading-edge research on cholesterol and heart disease Glueck had won the University of Cincinnati's prestigious Rieveschl Award in 1980. As head of the lipid unit and the General Clinical Research Center at the university, Glueck was one of the most powerful and heavily funded scientists on staff. But last July the National Institutes of Health found that a paper of Glueck's published in the August 1986 issue of the journal *Pediatrics* was riddled with inconsistencies and errors … the paper was utterly shoddy science, its conclusions empty.[67]

One wonders how Glueck got a paper "*riddled with inconsistencies and errors*" past the peer reviewers.

63. Judson, *The Great Betrayal.*
64. Adler, I., *Stories of Hoaxes in the Name of Science*, Collier Books, New York, 1962.
65. Kohn, *False Prophets*, pp. 57–62.
66. Broad and Wade, *Betrayers of the Truth*, p. 35.
67. Roman, When good scientists turn bad, p. 57.

Problems with peer preview

The scientific enterprise is touted by its advocates as being self-correcting by peer review, a process that a *Nature* editorial noted depends on trust.[68] The fact is, as is clear in the Glueck case, peer review often does not function as it should. A study of peer review published in *Nature* found that not only did it often not work, but it is "*getting worse.*"[69]

One major case involved the French twin brothers, Grichka and Igor Bogdanov, who duped several

> journals by tying together a nonsensical string of trendy terms and mathematical equations in papers that slipped through the peer-review process. "*I hear that two brothers have managed to publish 3 meaningless papers … as a hoax—and even get Ph.D. degrees in physics from Bourgogne University in the process!*" … In the end, the case turned out to be far more complex than a hoax, and it exposed potentially wide cracks in how theoretical physicists judge one another's work. "*It's an interesting case study in how stuff that is basically nonsense is easily gotten past referees these days,*" says Peter G. Woit, a theoretical physicist … at Columbia University. "*There really was a serious failure of the refereeing here.*"[70]

The exaggerated claims about peer review ensuring quality science are a myth. The former editor-in-chief of *Science,* Donald Kennedy, admitted that "*peer review has never been expected to detect scientific fraud*" and concluded that this defence may be partly valid, but the anomalies in some fraudulent papers published in *Science* and *Nature*

> were hardly subtle: in one, he used the same curve to represent the behaviours of different materials … Both journals stress that papers are chosen on technical merit and reviewers for their technical skills. Should not the manuscript editors or reviewers have remarked on these discrepancies? These papers were, after all, making claims of huge importance to industry and academia.[71]

One problem is that the journal refereeing system is controlled by a closed, elite group of scientists who often exercise censorship that, at times, can be pernicious to

68. Anonymous, Peer review reviewed, *Nature* **417**(6885):103, 2002.
69. Anonymous, Bad peer reviewers, p. 93.
70. Monastersky, R., The emperor's new science; French TV stars rock the world of theoretical physics, *The Chronicle of Higher Education* **49**(12):A16–A18, November 15, 2002; p. A16.
71. Anderson, A., Conduct unbecoming: it's the biggest scandal ever to hit physics, *New Scientist* 176(2363):3, 2002.

the extreme. The elitism problem in science results in ideas becoming accepted more because of who said them, instead of the merits of what was said. Poor ideas "*get accepted because their proponents are members of the elite*" and, as a result, "*good ideas may be ignored because their advocates may have poor standing in the social structure of science.*"[72] The elite both perpetuate their own ideas and create the next group of elites. As a result, the next group of elites tend to be those that agree with the ideas of the previous elites. Thus, elites and ideas are both uncritically perpetuated. In an attempt to resist fads, they also tend to resist change and progress.

Another problem is that reviewers may attempt to block a rival's publication or, at the least, delay it until the reviewer's own paper has been published, to give him or her priority.[73] The result of this is that foul play by reviewers has

> obviously had major implications for tenure, patent rights and so on. No wonder, then, that some are tempted to seek a legal solution to some of the injustices that the peer-review system has enabled the less scrupulous to perform.[74]

A major problem that results from the epidemic of fraud is that it produces an "*enormous waste of scientists' time, and the absolute, ineluctable bias against innovation.*"[75]A *Nature* editorial concluded that most

> researchers agree that peer review is the least imperfect way of upholding the quality of scientific publications. But those who administer it also have to cope with, and attempt to solve, the problems that peer review gives rise to. One such problem is misconduct. The peer-review process depends on trust, and the great majority of reviewers are trustworthy, but there are occasions when that trust has been abused by a referee.[76]

The editorial noted that one of the worst cases *Nature* has encountered involved a referee who "*obstructed a paper, and used its information indirectly to obtain materials from the author*" to complete a competing study of his own, which he published, thereby scooping the original.[77]

> There have also been cases of "*fabricated*" peer reviews, in which friends or colleagues are suggested as reviewers, or even unscrupulous third parties who favourably review papers for a fee. A recent article by *The Washington*

72. Broad and Wade, *Betrayers of the Truth*, p. 98.
73. Dalton, Peers under pressure, p. 104.
74. Donovan, S.K., Peers under review, *Nature* **413**(6857):669, 2001.
75. Roy, R. and Ashburn, J.R., The perils of peer review, *Nature* **414**(6862):393–394, 2001; p. 394.
76. Anonymous, Bad peer reviewers, p. 93.
77. Anonymous, Bad peer reviewers, p. 93.

> *Post* claims that a major publisher, *BioMed Central*, has had to retract 43 papers on the discovery of a "*fake peer review racket affecting many more publications.*"[78]

A major problem in the editorial review process is the lack of reliability. To improve this "*flawed system,*" some recommend that the process must be more open so that interested people can judge the paper as well as the reviewer's comments.[79] Several studies support the conclusion that chance, such as who reviews the paper, is critical in determining if a paper is published. Some online journals allow comments on provisional articles, such as *arXiv* for the physics and mathematics communities.

One study selected "*high quality*" articles that had been published two or three years earlier and resubmitted them with the authors' names and affiliations changed to the *very same journals* that previously had published them. Only 18% of the resubmitted articles were recommended for publication; the rest were rejected by the very same journals that previously had published the articles![80] Other studies found that when the results of a study agreed with the reviewer's philosophical position, the likelihood of acceptance was much higher.

The peer review required for grant funding, to determine which applicant is awarded research money, also has a major influence in what research is done. The case of astronomer Halton Arp who had to leave the United States to be able to do his scientific work is an example. In-vogue research is funded, and research which has implications that contradict a prevailing scientific belief structure, such as Darwinism, is far less apt to be funded. Dalton noted that, despite the widely acknowledged problems of peer review,

> no serious alternative has yet been proposed. "*It is easy to say the system is flawed; it is harder to say how to improve it,*" … One tweak to the process—asking reviewers to sign their reviews—has been experimented with. The idea is that, if reviewers are obliged to identify themselves, it will improve transparency and discourage anyone who might be tempted to abuse the process under the cloak of anonymity.[81]

In response to this suggestion, Roy and Ashburn write that

> *Nature* should not repeat the old canards such as "*despite the problems thrown up by peer review, no serious alternative has yet been proposed.*" Nonsense. They have not only been proposed but have been in regular use worldwide for a

78. Barbash, F., Major publisher retracts 43 scientific papers amid wider fake peer-review scandal, *The Washington Post,* 27th March 2015.
79. Gura, T., Peer review, unmasked, *Nature* **416**:258–260, 2002; p. 258.
80. Broad and Wade, *Betrayers of the Truth*, pp. 102–103.
81. Dalton, Peers under pressure, p. 103.

> very long time. The users include the world's largest research agency, the U.S. Department of Defense, and industrial research worldwide.[82]

There exist "*lots of flaws in the publishing system*" largely because "*peer review doesn't guarantee quality.*"[83] Some ways to reduce the problems include to publish the names of the reviewers and give them credit as well. Another is to publish clear and strict acceptance policies and ensure that, if a paper does not meet these, it will not be reviewed until it does.

Is science self-correcting?

The assumption that science is self-correcting was evaluated by a Food and Drug Administration study. The study concluded that one well-known case is

> just the tip of the fraud and misconduct iceberg. Investigators at the FDA run across so much shoddy research that they have quippy terms like "*Dr. Schlockmeister*" for a bad scientist, and "*graphite statistics*" for data that flow from the tip of a pencil. Every year, as a quality-control measure, the FDA conducts investigations of key studies of researchers involved in getting new drugs to the agency for approval. "*This is the last stop for drugs before they go to the public,*" explains Alan Lisook, who heads the FDA investigations. "*You'd think we'd get some of the cleanest science around.*"

He continues, adding that

> in 1986, when he analyzed the investigations of the previous ten years, Lisook compiled some shocking numbers: Nearly 200 studies contained so many flaws that the efficacy of the drug itself could be called into question. Some 40 studies exhibited not simple oversights but recklessness or outright fraud. In those ten years the FDA banned more than 60 scientists from testing experimental drugs, after finding that they had falsified data or engaged in inept research.[84]

The difficulty of correcting problematic research, either by retraction or correction is illustrated by a problematic study related to Darwin's theory of sexual selection. The study, directed by Rutgers University evolutionary biologist Robert Trivers, has inspired at least ten related publications.[85] Reich writes that few "*researchers have tried harder than Robert Trivers to retract one of their own papers.*" Originally

82. Roy and Ashburn, The perils of peer review, p. 394.
83. Muir, H., Twins raise ruckus, *New Scientist* **176**(2369):6, 2002.
84. Abbott, Science comes to terms with the lessons of fraud, p. 55.
85. Reich, E.S., Symmetry study deemed a fraud, *Nature* **297**(7448):170–171, 2013; p. 171.

published in a cover story article in a 2005 issue of *Nature,* Trivers has evidence that the study had been faked by one of his co-authors, William Brown, then a postdoctoral researcher, who insists the data is valid. Professor Trivers is so confident that the study is invalid that he has published an entire book about the dispute, yet it has not been resolved and may never be.[86]

The major problem with fraud is the problem of science itself, namely scientists "*see their own profession in terms of the powerfully appealing ideal that the philosophers and sociologists have constructed. Like all believers, they tend to interpret what they see of the world in terms of what the faith says is there.*"[87] And, unfortunately, science is a "*complex process in which the observer can see almost anything he wants provided he narrows his vision sufficiently.*"[88]

James Randi has concluded that scientists are among the *easiest* to fool with magic tricks because they see what they are led to see.[89] Most scientists believe passionately in their work and the theories they are trying to prove. While this passion may enable the scientist to sustain the effort necessary to produce results, it also may colour, and even distort, those results.

Many examples exist to support the conclusion that researchers' propensity for self-delusion is particularly strong, especially when examining ideas and data that impugn on their core belief structure. The fact is, all human observers have a strong tendency to see what they expect to see.[90] Nowhere is this more evident than in the admittedly highly emotional field of evolution.

The effect of experimental perceptions on the part of the researchers was researched by Robert Rosenthal in a now-classic set of experiments.[91] In one of these studies Rosenthal asked researchers to test what he said were "*maze bright*" and "*maze dull*" rats. The rats were actually randomly divided into two groups and *none* was specially trained. The 'maze bright' rats were then 'rated' as superior by researchers when, in fact, they were not. The experimenters saw what they wanted (or expected) to see; the phenomenon is now called the 'expectancy effect'. Perhaps unconsciously, the researchers may have pressed the stopwatch button a fraction of a second too early for the 'maze bright' rats and a fraction of a second later for the 'maze dull' rats. Other experiments have produced similar results.

---

86. Trivers, R., *The Anatomy of a Fraud: Symmetry and Dance*, TPZ Publishers, New York, 2009.
87. Broad and Wade, *Betrayers of the Truth*, p. 79.
88. Broad and Wade, *Betrayers of the Truth*, pp. 217–218.
89. Randi, J., *Flim Flam!: psychics, ESP, unicorns, and other delusions*, Prometheus, Buffalo, New York, p. 7, 1982.
90. Broad and Wade, *Betrayers of the Truth*, p. 114.
91. Rosenthal, R., *Experimenter Effects in Behavioral Research*, Irvington, New York, pp. 171, 459, 1976.

Replication: another myth

Replication is an important tool for exposing fraudulent research, but replication often is not carried out for many reasons. One reason is that replication requires the original experimenter to delineate the exact protocol used for an experiment, and experiments often are not, or cannot, be perfectly described in detail. The descriptions published by the experimenters are often detailed, but incomplete.

The now-classic study reported by Leroy Wolins involved a request for raw data sent to 37 authors of published research. Wolins found that, of the 32 who replied, 21 reported that their data had been "*misplaced, lost or inadvertently destroyed.*"[92] One might have supposed that "*something so precious as raw scientific data would have been kept in less accident-prone conditions.*"[93] And of the nine sets of data that were sent to the researchers, seven were analyzed and, of these, three contained "*gross*" errors, causing Broad and Wade to conclude that the "*implications of the Wolins study are almost too awesome to digest.*"[94]

The study also found that fewer than one in four scientists was willing to provide the raw data without self-serving conditions, and nearly half of the studies analyzed had gross statistical errors. Missing data are so common it is called the Andrea Doria phenomenon—the notes went down with the ship.[95]

This is hardly the behaviour of a "*rational, self-correcting, self-policing community of scholars.*"[96] While Broad and Wade may be too harsh, their criticisms clearly have much validity. Several other studies produced essentially the same conclusions. As a result, the "*notion of replication, in the sense of repeating an experiment in order to test its validity, is a myth, a theoretical construct dreamed up by the philosophers and sociologists of science.*"[97]

Kohn concludes that fraud will eventually be discovered if the implications of the results are sufficiently important, but its discovery may take a decade or longer.[98] Another problem is that the epidemic of fraud has resulted in a rash of lawsuits, large demands on the time of researchers to investigate fraud charges of peers, as well as hiring full-time college faculty and others just to investigate the many fraud charges now surfacing.[99] Some biomedicine misconduct investigators "*now work in teams backed up by federally funded experts.*"[100]

---

92. Wolins, L., Responsibility for raw data, *American Psychologist* **17**(9):657–658, 1962; p. 657.
93. Broad and Wade, *Betrayers of the Truth*, p. 78.
94. Broad and Wade, *Betrayers of the Truth*, p. 78.
95. Roman, When good scientists turn bad, p. 57.
96. Broad and Wade, *Betrayers of the Truth*, p. 78.
97. Broad and Wade, *Betrayers of the Truth*, p. 77.
98. Kohn, *False Prophets*, p. 112.
99. Check, Sitting in judgment, pp. 332–333.
100. Check, Sitting in judgment, p. 332.

Furthermore, unknown variables may interfere: research may work out one way with a specific strain of mice and a slightly different way with another strain. Many researchers have the expertise to replicate only experiments that are specifically in their field. Also, most researchers lack the time, money, and motivation to replicate the work of others because replication is not original science, and is mostly arduous work with few potential rewards. Science rewards originality, and being second usually wins few rewards. For these and other reasons, replications of most studies often are not completed.

One study by C. Glenn Begley attempted to replicate 53 'landmark' studies published in the leading science journals from reputable labs. Begley sought to double-check the findings before trying to build on them for drug development. He found 47 of the 53 studies could not be replicated for various reasons.[101] The inability to reproduce important scientific research has become a major concern of scientists today for good reason.[102]

Another reason for the publication of erroneous, selective, or irreproducible data is the fact that the

> academic system and peer-review process tolerates and perhaps even inadvertently encourages such conduct. To obtain funding, a job, promotion or tenure, researchers need a strong publication record, often including a first-authored high-impact publication. Journal editors, reviewers and grant-review committees often look for a scientific finding that is simple, clear and complete—a 'perfect' story. It is therefore tempting for investigators to submit selected data sets for publication, or even to massage data to fit the underlying hypothesis.[103]

Begley and Ellis also observed that "*journals and grant reviewers must allow for the presentation of imperfect stories, and recognize and reward reproducible results, so that scientists feel less pressure to tell an impossibly perfect story to advance their careers.*"[104]

Separating fraud and mistakes

In a study of mistakes in the field where it matters most, health and medicine, De Lacey *et al.* assessed the accuracy of quotations and references in the six leading medical journals, including *Lancet* and the *New England Journal of Medicine.* They found that the original author was misquoted in 15% of all references, and that

101. Begley and Ellis, Raise standards for preclinical cancer research.
102. Abrahamson, C., A fine mess we're in: majority of cancer preclinical research findings not replicable, candidaabrahamson.wordpress.com, 25 April 2014.
103. Begley and Ellis, Raise standards for preclinical cancer research, p. 533.
104. Begley and Ellis, Raise standards for preclinical cancer research, p. 533.

> most of the errors would have misled readers. Errors in citation of references occurred in 24%, of which 8% were major errors—that is, they prevented immediate identification of the source of the reference. Inaccurate quotations and citations are displeasing for the original author, misleading for the reader, and mean that untruths become "*accepted fact.*"[105]

Several studies have concluded that scientists are "*sloppy reporters*" because many do not bother to read the original papers that they cite.[106] Mikhail Simkin and Vwani Roychowdhury of the University of California, Los Angeles, while studying how information is spread, noticed from examining a citation database that reference errors were "*fairly common.*" They also found that many of the citation mistakes are *identical*, suggesting that many scientists simply copied a reference from another paper rather than consulting the original sources.

To determine how common this problem is, Simkin and Roychowdhury evaluated the citation data for a famous 1973 scientific paper

> cited in other papers 4300 times, with 196 citations containing misprints in the volume, page or year. But despite the fact that a billion different versions of erroneous reference are possible, they counted only 45. The most popular mistake appeared 78 times. The pattern suggests that 45 scientists, who might well have read the paper, made an error when they cited it. Then 151 others copied their misprints without reading the original. So for at least 77 per cent of the 196 misprinted citations, no one read the paper.[107]

The researchers found similar patterns for the dozen other high-profile papers they investigated.

Another study on the evolution of antibiotic resistance, led by Peter Davey at the University of Dundee, concluded that "*many researchers fail to meet even the minimum standards required to make their research useful.*" Davey concluded that "*seventy percent of what is published is a waste of time*" to read. When Davey's team reviewed the papers, they found that only 26% of them met what they determined were *minimum* research criteria.[108]

The problem of separating fraud from honest mistakes and errors is no easy task. The existence of cold fusion is widely considered to have been refuted, and many conclude that both fraud and mistakes were clearly involved in the early positive

105. De Lacey, G., Record, C. and Wade, J., How accurate are quotations and references in medical journals? *British Medical Journal* **291**(6499):884–886, 1985; p. 884.
106. Muir, H., Misprinted citations finger scientists who fail to do their homework, *New Scientist* **176**(2373):12, 2002.
107. Muir, Misprinted citations finger scientists who fail to do their homework, p. 12.
108. Tuma, R., Sloppy studies 'wasting time', *New Scientist* **176**(2364):23, 2002.

results.[109,110,111] Cold fusion is a classic case where replication was attempted because the implications of the research were enormous.

Science is clearly *not* what the public commonly believes it to be, and scientists do not always behave properly. Plagiarism, even "*blatant*" plagiarism at major universities such as Cambridge, is an "*increasing problem,*" which scientists are often complacent about.[112,113,114]

The fact is, science is not always self-policing, and scholars do not always read the scientific literature carefully. And, significantly, science often is not a very objective process: dogma and prejudice, when suitably whitewashed, creep into science just as easily as they do into most other human enterprises, often more easily because the entry of dogma is unexpected in science compared to politics and religion.

The fact is, experimental evidence alone is all too commonly not enough to overturn an older theory. No matter how valid, new results can often be explained away. The classic example is the Hungarian physician, Ignaz Semmelweis, who discovered that childbed fever, which typically caused 10–30% mortality in hospitals throughout Europe, could largely be abolished if doctors washed their hands in a chlorine solution before examining the mothers.

The mortality rate in his own clinic dropped from 18% to zero after requiring this practice. This compelling evidence, though, failed to convince his superiors, despite the fact that doctors who were not using this simple germicidal technique were still losing the same number of patients as Semmelweis did before his innovation.[115]

His procedure, while simple and obvious to us today, went contrary to the whole theory of medicine existing in his day. His fellow doctors, as is true of scientists today, did not accept a new idea easily. Semmelweis was eventually dismissed from the clinic, and spent the last years of his life trying to convince European doctors of his system's effectiveness.[116] They simply could not accept the fact that they had unwittingly caused so many patients to die from their own unwashed hands.

109. Peat, F.D., *Cold Fusion; The Making of a Scientific Controversy*, Contemporary Books, Chicago, 1990.
110. Taubes, G., *Bad Science: The Short Life and Weird Times of Cold Fusion*, Random House, New York, 1993.
111. Close, F., *Too Hot to Handle; The Race for Cold Fusion*, Princeton University Press, Princeton, New Jersey, 1991.
112. Stenflo, L., Intelligent plagiarists are the most dangerous: How should we tackle the increasing problem of researchers rewriting others' results? *Nature* **427**(6977):777, 2004.
113. Giles, J., Plagiarism in Cambridge physics lab prompts calls for guidelines, *Nature* **427**(6969):3, 2004.
114. Campbell, P., Complacency about misconduct, *Nature* **427**:1, 2004.
115. Nuland, S., *The Doctors' Plague: Germs, Childbed Fever, and the Strange Story of Ignác Semmelweis*, Norton, New York, 2003.
116. Carter, K.C., and Carter, B., *Childbed Fever: A Scientific Biography of Ignaz Semmelweis*, Transaction Publishers, Piscataway, New Jersey, 2005.

One reason for Semmelweis's failure to convince his contemporaries was that he was not an effective propagandist. The results of research, no matter how good, will not be implemented until a convincing communicator comes along to advertise them. A brilliant scientist must also be, it seems, a brilliant communicator, or at least a good one.

In frustration, after 20 years of trying, Semmelweis ended up in a mental hospital, his ideas forgotten until Joseph Lister again took up his battle. This time, Semmelweis was fully vindicated. The claim that science fundamentally differs from other belief systems because it rests on reason alone is false.[117] This claim must be modified in light of what historians have to say about scientists' resistance to scientific ideas, and their tendency to reject ideas based on the prism of their own theories. History shows that the "*community of scientists is often ready to swallow whole the dogma served up to them, as long as it is palatable and has the right measure of scientific reasoning ... objectivity often fails to resist infiltration by dogma.*"[118]

One method of discrediting unpopular theories, especially those involving biological origins, is to label them 'non-science' and the competing theories 'science'. Sociologists have for years explored the pernicious effects of labelling via dichotomizing concepts. This method places a broad positive term on half of the artificial dichotomy, and a broad negative term on the other half. The appropriate response to any science controversy is to argue each proposition solely on its merits, using only the tools of science.

In their exploration of fraud in science, Broad and Wade conclude that the term 'science' is often a label used to imply that something is true or false. In their words, the conventional wisdom concludes that

> science is a strictly logical process, objectivity is the essence of the scientist's attitude to his work, and scientific claims are rigorously checked by peer scrutiny and the replication of experiments. From this self-verifying system, error of all sorts is speedily and inexorably cast out.[119]

The authors then show why this common belief about science is false. The results of their investigation can help us to understand the activity of science from a far more realistic standpoint than is common today. They demonstrate that the supposedly 'fail-safe' mechanisms of scientific inquiry often do *not* correct the frauds they claim have now become an 'epidemic' in modern science. The idea of being 'first', the need to obtain research grants, trips to exotic places for conferences, and the lure of money and prestige, lead many scientists to abandon any lofty ideals they may have once had as a neophyte scientist. To repeat in Brooks' words:

---

117. Broad and Wade, *Betrayers of the Truth*, p. 140.
118. Broad and Wade, *Betrayers of the Truth*, p. 193.
119. Broad and Wade, *Betrayers of the Truth*, p. 7.

> scientists take drugs, they follow crazy dreams, they experiment on themselves and on one another, and occasionally they die in the process. They fight—sometimes physically, but mostly in intellectual battles. They try to entrap one another, standing in their colleagues' way to block progress and maintain the lead. They break all the rules of polite society, trampling on the sacred, showing a total disregard for authority.[120]

Furthermore, they even

> commit fraud or deceive or manipulate others ... conjure up seemingly ridiculous ideas, then fight tooth and nail to show that the ideas are not only far from ridiculous, but exactly how things really are ... . Science is peppered with successes that defy rational explanation and failures that seem even more illogical ... . This is not the 'wacky' science, the crazy things that happen on the fringes of research. This is the mainstream. These anarchies are behind many of the Nobel Prizes of the last few decades ... . It really does seem that, in science, anything goes. And this is no modern phenomenon. Science has always been this way.[121]

Conclusions

The reasons for this serious problem in science include the drive for money, tenure, promotions, grant renewals, professional rivalry, and the need to prove one's own theories and ideas. Another factor is the rejection of Christianity and moral absolutes, which has resulted in a collapse of the moral foundation that is critical in controlling fraud. Some claim the problem is so serious that possibly the majority of published research claims are false.[122]

Fraud is especially a problem in attempts to support Darwinism and, especially in this field, it tends to take decades to root out fraud. Hundreds of well-documented cases of fraud have been discussed in the literature.[123] Unfortunately, except for replication, which is uncommon in many fields, fraud in science often is very difficult to detect. Usually, it is lab assistants and colleagues who uncover fraud, and they are often unwilling to report it because doing so could cost them friends, tarnish their reputation, and result in retaliation. Roman claims that "*snitching on*

120. Brooks, *Free Radicals*, p. 6.
121. Brooks, *Free Radicals*, p. 6.
122. Ioannidis, J.P.A., Why most published research findings are false, *PLoS Medicine* **2**(8):696–701, 2005.
123. For examples see Kohn, *False Prophets*, Broad and Wade, *Betrayers of the Truth*, Adler, *Stories of Hoaxes in the Name of Science*, and Abbott, Science comes to terms with the lessons of fraud.

an esteemed colleague could only mean trouble", and "*Unfortunately researchers like Sprague* [who did just that—Ed.] *are rare.*"[124]

As a result, fraud in science is a serious problem.[125,126,127] Biological research is one of the chief fields of concern, and some conclude that it is possible that as many as 2% to 5% of all researchers in this field are less than fully honest. Indeed, probably many researchers have quoted data that are fraudulent, or at least inaccurate. Few extensive research investigations on fraud under the present system exist, and the cases unearthed probably represent only the tip of the proverbial iceberg. This problem is one of several major reasons why Darwinism's conclusions are suspect.

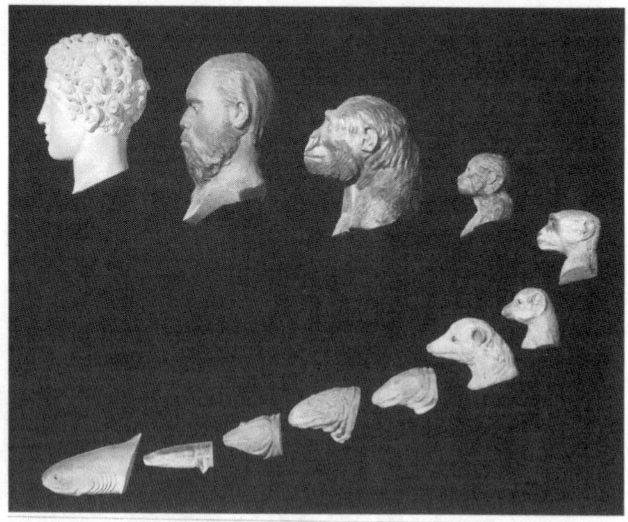

This picture of evolution, now totally discredited, was once located in The American Museum of Natural History in the 1930s. This "outmoded embarrassment was trashed" only in the 1960s. Milner noted: "Widespread racism resulted in placing a black man one rung below a European ... represented by a Greek God" (from Richard Milner, *Darwin's Universe*, University of California Press, Berkeley, p. 366, 2009).

124. Roman, When good scientists turn bad, p. 58.
125. Grant, *Discarded Science*.
126. Grant, *Corrupted Science*.
127. Broad and Wade, *Betrayers of the Truth*.

CHAPTER 19

Conclusions

The Darwinian revolution is over. Victory was claimed, and yielded, long ago. The ongoing challenge for Darwinists is how to maintain the upper hand without having the legitimate means of doing so—a plausible mechanism. In answer to this challenge they have adopted what we might call 'the respectable bully' approach:

1. The first step is to maintain a respectable appearance of scientific enterprise by repeating the mantra that discarding old theories in favour of new ones is a normal part of science. This is indeed legitimate if a new theory performs better than an old theory, but it is not a normal part of science if old theories are discarded because they never did work, but neither do the new ones!
2. The second step is to take an aggressive stand against 'unbelievers' by ridiculing them in class, marking down their grades, denying tenure and sacking them if they manage to get so far as a staff position.

But, the public might say, scientists are decent people, aren't they? Surely they will do what is right in the long run. As we have seen in the last chapter, fraud is epidemic among scientists just as it is in all other walks of life.

Are we justified in calling the dominance of Darwinism in society today 'culpable fraud'? In physics, Copernicus, Galileo, Newton, Kelvin, Maxwell, Einstein and many others have revolutionized our understanding of matter and energy. As each new theory explains more than the old one did (Newton's laws are still valid in our everyday life) we can agree that physics is indeed a science with high 'truth content'. But Darwinism's ongoing failure to find a cause, together with the blunders, frauds and forgeries described in this book, make a clear case of modern-day pretence. Darwinists have no known mechanism by which a microbe could evolve into a human. Natural selection can only prune what exists, and neither Darwin nor anyone else has come up with a mechanism that produces significant levels of new variety required to move from bacteria to people. Physicists don't have to pretend that Einstein's Theory of Relativity is true—they can demonstrate the proofs in experiments. Darwinists can't, they must just work as if their theory is true.

ABOUT THE AUTHOR

Dr Jerry Bergman has the rare distinction of having nine degrees (from Medical College of Ohio, Wayne State University in Detroit, The University of Toledo, and Bowling Green State University). Apart from three undergraduate degrees, these include two Ph.D.'s (one in human biology), and five Master's degrees, in areas such as sociology, counselling and psychology, biochemistry, biomedical sciences and public health. He has taught biology, genetics, chemistry, biochemistry, anthropology, geology, and microbiology at Northwest State College in Ohio for over 31 years. He has also taught at the Medical College of Ohio (where he was a research associate in the department of experimental pathology), as well as having spent six years teaching at the University of Toledo, and seven years teaching at Bowling Green State University.

Dr Bergman has over 800 publications in 12 languages and 30 books and monographs to his name. He has published a college textbook on evaluation (Houghton Mifflin Co., Boston), and has contributed to dozens of other textbooks. He has also been a consultant for over 20 science textbooks, mostly biology and biochemistry. In creationist and ID circles, Dr Bergman is well-known for his 480-page exposé of the academic persecution of evolution dissenters, *Slaughter of the Dissidents: The shocking truth about killing the careers of Darwin doubters* (2008). Volume II, titled *Silencing the Darwin Sceptics,* was recently released. His other books include *The Darwin Effect: Its influence on Nazism, Eugenics, Racism, Communism, Capitalism & Sexism* (2014), and *How Darwinism Corrodes Morality: Darwinism, immorality, abortion and the sexual revolution* (2017).

A frequent featured guest on radio and television programs, Dr Bergman has presented over one hundred scientific papers at professional and community meetings in the United States, Canada, and Europe. He also has over ten years' experience at various mental health/psychology clinics as a licensed professional clinical counsellor, and undertook three years full-time corrections research for a large county circuit court in Michigan and inside the world's largest walled prison, Jackson Prison (SPSM). Dr Bergman has served as a consultant for CBS News, ABC News, *Reader's Digest,* Amnesty International, several government agencies, and for two Nobel Prize winners, including the inventor of the transistor. He has past or current memberships in over two dozen professional associations, and in the past decade has consulted or has testified as an expert witness or consultant in almost one hundred court cases. For further details, see creation.com/dr-jerry-bergman.

OTHER RESOURCES

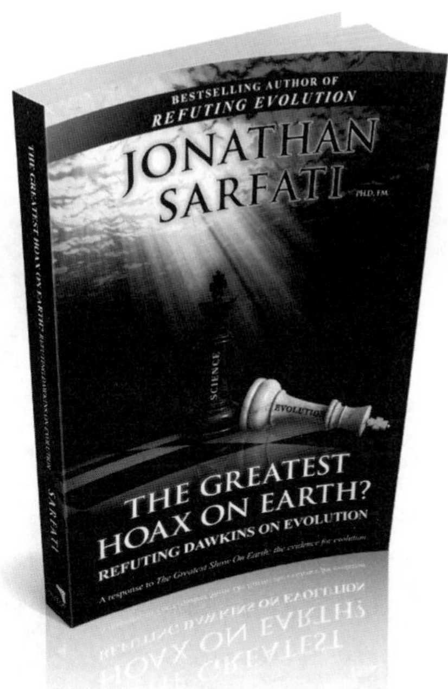

The Greatest Hoax on Earth?

Dr Jonathan Sarfati (336pgs)

Richard Dawkin's book, *The Greatest Show on Earth: the evidence for evolution* is presented as the definitive evidence for evolution/long ages. Scientist, logician, chessmaster and author, Dr Jonathan Sarfati, relentlessly demolishes Dawkin's claims point-by-point, showing biblical creation makes more sense of the evidence.

creation.com/s/10-2-555

OTHER RESOURCES

The Genesis Account

Dr Jonathan Sarfati (800pgs)

A long-awaited in-depth commentary on the crucial Genesis 1–11 chapters explaining how the Hebrew text, the rest of the Bible, and science support Creation in 6 ordinary days about 6,000 years ago and a global Flood.

creation.com/s/10-2-606

OTHER RESOURCES

Evolution's Achilles' Heels

By Nine Ph.D. scientists (272pgs)

Evolution's Achilles' Heels directly demolishes the very pillars of the belief system that underpins our now-secular culture—evolutionary naturalism. It's coupled with the Biblical command to reach the lost with the Bible's Good News. In a nutshell, it's a comprehensive outreach tool like no other.

creation.com/s/10-2-640

OTHER RESOURCES

Evolutionists Say the Oddest Things

Edited by Lita Cosner (179pgs)

Most scientists proclaim loudly that evolution has been thoroughly proved. But if you take a close look at their statements, they reveal that there are glaring holes and inconsistencies. *Evolutionists Say the Oddest Things* collects some of their most devastating admissions into one book. You'll be surprised at what evolutionists say ... when they think creationists aren't listening!

creation.com/s/10-2-608

OTHER RESOURCES

How Noah's Flood Shaped Our Earth

Michael J Oard & John K Reed (200pgs)

This book will give you a new appreciation for the power and impact of Noah's Flood—a pivotal event in the history of our planet. It was the biblical Flood, not millions of years, that deposited thousands of metres of folded, bent, and twisted rock strata all over the earth, and the billions of fossils contained therein.

creation.com/s/10-2-647

OTHER RESOURCES

Busting Myths

Edited by Dr Jonathan Sarfati & Gary Bates (230pgs)

"No real scientist believes in biblical creation?" The 30 Ph.D. scientists interviewed in this book disagree! See why specialists in astronomy, biology, chemistry, genetics, geology, and physics affirm that science supports a straightforward reading of Genesis, and why they believe that evolution contradicts both science and Scripture. They stand in the long tradition of the biblical creationist founders of most branches of modern science, which historically and logically grew from a Christian world view.

creation.com/s/10-2-605